I

Controllers for Electric Motors

By Henry Duvall James
Consulting Engineer

and Lewis Edwin Markle
Design Engineer
Westinghouse Electric Corporation

Second Edition

Here is a book to help you in getting maximum power and use from electric motors. It guides you in selecting the right controllers for specific load requirements—shows you how to maintain this equipment in successful operation—and brings you up to date on modern control apparatus.

This manual familiarizes you with popular commercial controllers. It shows the best methods for motor acceleration, speed control, mechanical and dynamic braking, regeneration, etc. Special sections discuss protective devices, installation, maintenance, inspection— and future control developments.

Recent advances in control engineering are fully discussed in this Second Edition. Dynamo electric amplifiers are described at greater length, and their types, functions, and applications are clearly explained.

Here is new material on the magnetic amplifier, magnetic clutches, the eddy-current brake, crane control, d-c control. Five different systems for controlling a-c motors are explained and illustrated, including the latest type using saturated-core reactors. Helpful information on remote and supervisory control has been added to the book.

CONTROLLERS FOR ELECTRIC MOTORS

CONTROLLERS FOR
ELECTRIC MOTORS

A Treatise on the Modern Motor Controller
with Typical Applications to the Industries

BY

Henry Duvall James, B.S., M.E.

Consulting Engineer, Pittsburgh, Pa.; Fellow, American Institute of Electrical Engineers; Past President, Engineers' Society of Western Pennsylvania

AND

Lewis Edwin Markle, B.S.

Design Engineer, Westinghouse Electric Corp.; Member, American Institute of Electrical Engineers

Second Edition

McGRAW-HILL BOOK COMPANY, INC.

NEW YORK   TORONTO   LONDON

1952

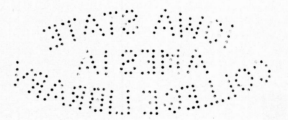

THE MAPLE PRESS COMPANY, YORK, PA.

PREFACE TO THE SECOND EDITION

This book has been written for engineers responsible for the selection of control equipment and for the men who maintain this equipment in successful operation. The engineering student will also find much to help him here; it should assist him to apply the theory he has studied in engineering courses. Sufficient material on controllers is presented to give the reader a working knowledge of design, operation, and types available on the market. The book begins with the elementary problems of control and carries through to the latest types of controllers. It avoids involved mathematics.

The second edition includes the new developments in control engineering. The magnetic amplifier will make a profound change in motor control as it becomes familiar and the details of its application are worked out. We have tried to show many possibilities for its use. The operation of the magnetic amplifier is explained in Chap. 13, and some of its applications are described.

Dynamo electric amplifiers are now more fully described. Their types and functions are given in detail, and additional applications are shown in diagram form in Chap. 12.

Magnetic clutches are now being used with synchronous motors to obtain speed changes in the load. These clutches, described in Chap. 7, also have other applications: they can be used with magnetic amplifiers to maintain constant speed of the driven device; the eddy-current brake (Chap. 8) for lowering a load is another special application.

Chapter 8, on crane control, has been entirely rewritten, and recent d-c control is described in detail. Five different systems for controlling a-c crane motors are described and illustrated, including the most recent type using saturated-core reactors.

Remote and supervisory control has been added to Chap. 22.

Material on some of the older types of control has been retained, as the control designer or maintenance man may be responsible for some of this equipment, such as the lock-out contactor (Chap. 6) and the speed control (Chap. 15).

We have received material assistance in making the book representative of American control practice from the following companies:

Allen-Bradley Company
Allis-Chalmers Mfg. Co.

General Electric Company
Monitor Controller Company

v

Clark Controller Company
Cutler-Hammer, Inc.
Electric Controller
  and Manufacturing Company
Electric Machinery
  Manufacturing Company

Square D Company
Vickers Incorporated
Westinghouse Electric
  Corporation
Ward Leonard Electric
  Company

The authors wish to acknowledge the generous response of the above manufacturers and others to our request for diagrams, illustrations, and engineering information.

HENRY DUVALL JAMES
LEWIS EDWIN MARKLE

May, 1952

PREFACE TO THE FIRST EDITION

The object of this book is to bring together in one volume sufficient material on controllers to give technical students, operating engineers, and purchasers and users of electrical apparatus a good general idea of their design and operation.

The types and methods of control described are illustrative of those in general use. No attempt has been made to represent all types of commercial equipment. Special control systems, such as those applied to elevators, steel mills, and paper mills, have not been included, since a detailed knowledge of the performance problem is necessary for an understanding of them. The information given here can always be supplemented by exact data covering the particular design under consideration.

Some elementary chapters have been included for the benefit of readers who have had little experience with control apparatus. Most of the diagrams are of an elementary nature. When it is necessary to repair or adjust a controller, a diagram and instructions should be obtained from its maker.

Among the subjects discussed is the electron tube, which has given engineers a new tool, first as a master switch to initiate control action, then as a converter to operate a d-c motor from a-c power and to control the motor voltage, as explained in Chap. 21. So far such control is available only for small motors, but larger control seems practical at a later time.

Magnetic contactors are presented in Chap. 4. The deion principle for rupturing a-c arcs is explained, and its application is shown. The interlock details and the flexible shunt, which is now mounted to give long life, are also discussed.

The time-limit method of acceleration, which also gives forced acceleration, is now popular and is discussed in Chap. 6. It requires double overload protection—one element or device to permit short-time overloads but to protect against overheating, the other to open the circuit immediately if an excessive overload occurs. Some relays now combine these features (see Chap. 23). Magnetic time-delay acceleration and new types of dashpots for timing are both used. Some systems also include current limit. Another method makes use of the time required to charge or discharge a condenser. The tendency is to reduce the number of coils and interlocks as much as possible.

The development of plugging is covered in Chap. 9.   Various relay schemes are now available.

The motor-generator control of motor voltage is discussed in Chap. 11.   The combination of a series generator with a series motor and means for adjusting the generator-field strength have made variable-voltage control available for small motors.

The development of the Regulex, the amplidyne, and the Rototrol has provided new tools for regulating motor speed.   These are described in Chap. 12.

Most squirrel-cage induction motors are started at full voltage, which has been made possible by larger power systems.   Reduced-voltage starting, using series resistors, is simpler than the autotransformer starters but takes more current from the line.   This question is analyzed in Chap. 19.

Synchronized motors have a desirable influence on the power factor, and their control is simplified and made more rugged (see Chap. 20). New types of time-delay overload relays, which more nearly represent the time of heating the motor, are illustrated in Chap. 23 and include some types mounted in the motor itself.

Recommendations for maintenance of control equipment are given in Chap. 24.

The authors wish to express their appreciation for the assistance received from engineers associated with them and to thank the various manufacturers who so kindly furnished material for the illustrations.

HENRY DUVALL JAMES
LEWIS EDWIN MARKLE

PITTSBURGH, PA.
April, 1945

CONTENTS

PREFACE TO THE SECOND EDITION. v

PREFACE TO THE FIRST EDITION. vii

1. FUNCTION AND TYPES OF CONTROL. 1

Functions not incorporated in the motor design—Current limit during acceleration with elementary diagrams—Reversing the motor—Speed regulation by armature control, by field control, by change of supply voltage —To protect from overload, from voltage failure, from injury to persons— To stop the motor—Manual and automatic acceleration. Types—Faceplate controllers, drum, cam, magnetic, liquid types—Advantages and limitations of each type.

2. HOW TO READ CONTROLLER DIAGRAMS. 14

A sign language to express control functions—Elementary diagrams of face-plate controllers, drum and magnetic—Contactor control—Elementary diagrams explained step by step—Use of symbols—How to follow wiring connections—Use of heavy and thin lines to show wires—Simple diagram enlarged to show additional functions—Drum development explained— Resistor connections shown—Use of a sequence table and scheme of main connections shown in connection with a magnetic contactor controller.

3. HOW TO MAKE CONTROLLER DIAGRAMS 25

Types of diagrams defined and application shown—Typical diagrams explained—Making a drum controller diagram, given in detail—Terminal markings shown and tabulated—Symbols shown and explained—Procedure in making a diagram given—Detail suggestions and precautions recommended—Two coils in parallel—Resistor or condenser used with a coil— What parts should be grouped together.

4 MAGNETIC CONTACTORS 38

Functions: durability, current carrying, arc rupturing, why used—Contacts, material, pressure, mass and radiation, surface—Types: butt, sliding, rolling —Advantages and limitations of types—Action in closing the contacts—Air or oil-immersed contacts—Shading coils on a-c magnets—Arc-rupturing factors—Magnetic blowout operation in arc rupturing—Types of blowout— Deion principle of arc rupturing—Contactors illustrated and design details given—Rating of contactors—Operating coils—Handling short circuits and voltage requirements.

5. STARTING CHARACTERISTICS OF MOTORS WITH DIFFERENT METHODS OF CONTROL. 57

Usual method of testing the starting of d-c motors in error—Oscillograph tests illustrated and discussed—Motor impedance reducing current peaks— Starting load effect on power demand—Friction and inertia loads—Number of starting steps required—Field effect on starting torque—Manual or automatic acceleration—Dynamic braking with field control—Line impedance influence on starting—How to calculate starting peaks—Comparison of calculated and test peak values—Suggestions for future investigations.

6. METHODS OF ACCELERATING MOTORS. 69

Starting resistor methods of acceleration—Counter emf—Current limit with series relays or lock-out contactors—Time delay—Secondary frequency of a-c motors—Combining several methods—Type of load effect on method of acceleration—Methods of acceleration explained in detail—Advantages and limitations given—Applications suggested—Time-limit methods: dashpot, magnetic or mechanical drag, geared motor, racheting device, escapement gearing, magnetic induction—Methods shown in detail—Electron tubes used to measure the secondary frequency and current to control acceleration— Use of tubes for time delay—Selection of method influenced by application, first cost, voltage regulation, power supply and preference of purchaser— Magnetic amplifier control for d-c and a-c motors.

7. METHODS OF SPEED CONTROL. 100

Varying- and adjustable-speed motors—Armature series resistor—Performance curves for shunt, series-, and compound-wound motors—Speeds with changing load—Armature series and shunt resistor—Performance curve— Adjustable speed with shunt-field control and with variable-voltage control —A-c motors with secondary resistor and with primary resistor—Performance curve—Speed change with load—Effect of change in line voltage—Starting torque—Torque changes as the voltage squared—Changing the number of poles—Cascade operation—Single-phase secondary performance—Operation at half speed—Constant speed control using magnetic amplifiers—speed control with magnetic clutch—New type of magnetic clutch.

8. CONTROL FOR CRANES, HOISTS, AND OTHER SPECIAL APPLICATIONS. 121

Special control required for various applications—Crane control with series d-c motor—Methods for obtaining dynamic braking used by different makers—Complete analysis of one type with diagrams and performance curves—Crane control with a-c motors—"Plugging"—"Counter-torque" system—Dynamic breaking with d-c excitation—Braking with unbalanced primary—Counter-torque lowering using a saturated-core reactor—Eddy-current brake and magnetic clutch for lowering loads—Pump controllers— Pressure regulators—Float switches—Elevator pump control—Machine-tool controllers with and without dynamic brake—Mine locomotive with storage-battery control—Printing-press control with auxiliary motor for make-up speed—Water rheostat design calculations—Steel-mill master switches.

9. MECHANICAL AND DYNAMIC BRAKING 155

Friction brakes—Magnet release, spring applied—Types of magnets, series, shunt, compound—Heating in magnet coils—Brake shoes, how lined— Brake wheel, diameter and width—Limiting speed—Heat storage—Curve showing the relation of wheel diameter to torque—Adjustment for wear— Mechanical parts—Dynamic braking—Speed limitations—Heating of motor —Field adjustment—Absence of mechanical wear—Plugging the motor to stop it—Effect with different field windings—Energy required to stop— Special control requirements—Applications.

10. REGENERATION 167

Power returned to the line—Similar to dynamic braking—Generated voltage exceeds line voltage—Maintaining speed or reducing it—Examples of regeneration—Field control with and without battery—Series field control—Use of compound fields—Limiting conditions—Voltage control—Motor generator system—Use of a booster—Combining motor generator and booster—Speed range—Sudden changes in line voltage—Regeneration with a-c motors—Fields of application—Stand-by losses.

11. VOLTAGE CONTROL FOR DIRECT-CURRENT MOTORS. 175

Multivoltage system—Three-wire system—Motor-generator system now used with constant-speed driving motor—Source of power usually alternating current—Constant-voltage d-c exciter—Generator field reversed to reverse working motor—Simplified control scheme shown—Regeneration obtained—Flywheel used for power storage—Slip controlled by a liquid regulator operated by a torque motor—Method for calculating size of flywheel—Curves of power input when starting set—Load-time curve of typical hoisting set—Multiple operation of machines in series—Field limiting control—Overload protection—Series exciter—Reducing generator field to zero flux—Regulation by controlling exciter magnetism—Control amplification by Amplidyne, Regulex, Rototrol—Wheatstone-bridge system for Rototrol control—Series-wound motor generator.

12. AMPLIFIERS USED FOR MOTOR CONTROL 191

Methods of regulation by means of amplifiers—Outline of different types of amplifiers for motor control—The electronic amplifier—The dynamo electric amplifier—The magnetic amplifier—Details of the Amplidyne, Regulux, Rototrol—Wheatstone-bridge system for Rototrol—Applications to elevators and skip hoists—Blooming mills—Arc furnace—Calender drive—Voltage control—Speed control—Power-factor control.

13. MAGNETIC AMPLIFIERS. 206

Description of the magnetic amplifier—How it works—Elementary diagrams of its use—Methods of accelerating its response—Different types of core—Inherent advantages—Theater dimmer—Variable-voltage control—Speed control—Load control—Blooming mill—Arc furnace—Skip hoist—Sectional paper machine—Clutch control for speed regulation—The transductor type of magnetic amplifier and some of its applications—Copper oxide and selenium rectifiers used in the above applications.

14. SERIES-PARALLEL CONTROL AND THE ELECTROPNEUMATIC CONTACTOR . . . 221

System of control—Application, usually railway—Why used—Advantages—Limitations—Methods of transition, open-circuit, shunt, bridging diagrams for each system—Speed-torque curves—Where used—Advantages and limitations of each system—Electropneumatic control—Contactor details—Historical background—Space requirements—Weight reduction—Switch group shown.

15. ADJUSTABLE-SPEED ALTERNATING-CURRENT MOTORS OF THE WOUND-ROTOR TYPE. 235

Analogy with d-c adjustable-speed sets—D-c constant-torque and constant-horsepower sets shown—Speed of a-c motor adjusted by external voltage applied to the secondary windings—Vector diagrams of secondary-voltage distribution—Operation above and below synchronism—Constant horsepower with rotary control—Constant torque with rotary control—Constant torque with commutator machine—Constant horsepower with commutator machines—Constant horsepower with frequency change—Constant torque with frequency changes—Power-input curves—Curve showing growth of electric drive for main rolls in steel mills.

16. RESISTORS 250

Definition of resistor—Cast-iron grid most common type—High-resistance units require other types—Method of mounting grids—Edge-wound ribbon resistors—Mounting similar to grids wire-wound resistors—Vetrohm, an embedded wire resistor—Round, flat tube, and plate types—Rebohm resistor, a channel-shaped metal strip—Compressor type, graphite disks pressed together—Rating for different service requirements—Spacing of grids in frame for radiation and heat absorption—Resistor classification table— Speed-regulation formula—Table for proportioning resistor steps—Limiting temperature—Time-radiation curves—Bradley unit-compression resistor— Arrangement of resistor frames in tiers—Ventilation very important

17. MANUAL CONTROLLERS. 271

Definition of manual controller—Drum controllers and master switches— Drum fingers—Drum cylinder—Star wheel—Action of drum against the finger—Finger adjustment—Magnet blowout—Lubrication of contacts— Cam controller—Action of contactor—Arrangement of cams and contactors —Methods of mounting—Face plate—Dinky controller—Compression type —Comparison of types—Comparison with magnetic-contactor controllers— Arc rupturing—Ventilation—Method of rating—Mechanical limitations.

18. DIRECT-CURRENT MAGNETIC-CONTACTOR CONTROLLERS. 281

Arrangement very flexible—Resistor steps—Nonreversing and reversing controllers—Enclosing cabinets—Field resistor, rheostats—Typical diagram —Summary—Wide range of application—Types of master switches—Methods of operation—Protective means—Overload relays; three methods of connection.

19. ALTERNATING-CURRENT CONTROLLERS 296

Control of wound-secondary induction motors—Use of resistors in the secondary circuit—Similarity to d-c motors with external resistance in armature circuit—Same secondary with different primary voltages—Methods of short-circuiting the secondary resistor steps—Operation with unbalanced secondary resistance—Single phase in secondary when starting—Liquid controller— Heating of motor with unbalanced secondary—Starters for squirrel-cage induction motors—Full-voltage starters—Power companies limit inrush current at starting—Reduced-voltage starting by an autotransformer or primary resistor—Advantage and limitations—Selection of the starting voltage—Distribution of current in the autotransformer when starting— Open-circuit and closed-circuit transition from starting to line voltage— Various methods of obtaining closed-circuit transition—Danger of open-circuit transition—Starting torque limits starting voltage—Underwriters' test requirements for autotransformer starters—Use of starters on voltage or frequencies other than the ones for which they were designed—Use of the power-transformer impedence to limit the motor current when starting.

20. SYNCHRONOUS-MOTOR CONTROL 326

Motor similar to the generator in design—Desirable because of its power-factor correction—Methods of starting—Damper winding on field poles make starting same as in squirrel-cage induction motor—Starting and pull-in torques control initial power demand when started—Torque when motor is synchronized—Control of d-c field when starting—Most advantageous position of poles when motor is synchronized—Time-delay acceleration—Use of polarized field frequence relay to synchronize—Speed-and-time method of starting—Slip-cycle impedance method of starting—Resynchronizing and pull-out protection—Reduced-voltage starters—Part winding starters—Emergency stop.

21. ELECTRON-TUBE CONTROL 340

Operation and functions of tubes—Tube acts like a switch—Elementary diagrams—Grid control—Three important tube functions—Conversion from alternating current to direct current—Adjusting delivered voltage—Limiting the current input—Use of two power tubes to give more uniform d-c power—Tubes compensate for the voltage drop in the motor armature, regulate the speed or load, regulate the field strength—Various industrial uses—Problems to be met, heating, commutation, frequency, speed range, effect of heating on speed regulation—Other uses for tubes.

22. REMOTE AND SUPERVISORY CONTROL. 357

The Rotary type using a revolving resistor for sending and a motor with rotating field for receiving—Selsyn system—Sending and recording equipment—Remote control of the rudder of a ship—Supervisory control—Use of two telephone wires—"Carrier-current" transmission over a high-voltage system—Dispatching and receiving panels—Type of relay used—Use of radio impulses—Remote control of motors—Water level—Gate valves—Static pressure—Temperature, etc.

23. PROTECTIVE DEVICES. 367

More common protective devices—Overload protection: fuses, circuit breakers, relays—Types of relays—Methods for resetting—Methods for obtaining time delay in starting: dashpots, heating bimetal strips, melting an alloy, inductive heating of a thermal element, use of invar—Curves showing the tripping time with various overloads—Selection of relay to suit the load requirements—Combined time delay on overloads and immediate trip on short-circuit—Low-voltage release and protection—Phase-failure protection—Phase-reversal protection—Shunt-field protection—Table of protective devices.

24. NATIONAL CODES, INSTALLATION, AND MAINTENANCE 396

Two important codes—Fire protection—National Board of Fire Underwriters, their rules and laboratories—Safety to persons: a qualified person, operator, other persons—Types of injury hazard listed—Protection by enclosure, isolation, guards—Methods of isolation—Grounding—Disconnecting means—Working space—Location of controller, resistor—Field maintenance—Care of contacts, magnet coils—Adjustment of air gap for a-c magnets—Overhauling and replacements—Painting—Records of operation—Details of maintenance.

25. PAST AND FUTURE CONTROL DEVELOPMENTS 415

New developments from Second World War—Electron-tube and Magnetic-amplifier control—Variable frequency—Hydraulic gear—Adjustable speed from a synchronous-motor drive—The use of telephone devices and practice —Wiring principles used in telephone and telegraph practice for remote control—Radio signals—Improved details—Greater simplification—Pioneers needed.

INDEX. 419

CHAPTER 1

FUNCTION AND TYPES OF CONTROL

THE FUNCTION OF CONTROL

The expanding field of motor control includes any device that controls the operation of an electric motor. The motor generator used for an individual motor or group of motors controlling a single process, such as a sectional paper mill, is part of the control system. The power may be regulated by electronic tubes or by mechanical transmission automatically controlled. A quick response to a changed condition may be obtained by a magnetic amplifier or by special exciters such as an Amplidyne, a Rototrol, or a Regulex. The operation may be initiated from a distance by signals transmitted over a pair of wires, and the response indicated back to the operating station in the same manner. Many different signals can be sent and received over the same pair of wires. Microwaves may be used instead of wires to send and receive these signals.

It is the duty of the control engineer to understand the requirements of the motor application, which include the initiation of its operation, its speed control, its safe operation, and many other functions.

The electrical controller and its motor should be treated as a single application unit. When a single machine is operated by two or more motors, the controller should be designed to take care of the required functions not incorporated in the motor design and to maintain correct relative speed between motors.

The proper understanding of an electric controller requires that it be considered as a part of the motor; the controller should be designed to take care of the functions not incorporated in the motor design, in order to enable the latter to operate under the specified conditions of load. Every motor has certain inherent characteristics that enable it to adapt itself to some of the conditions encountered in practice. In many cases, however, the motor would be very expensive and also very inefficient if it were given the necessary characteristics to prevent its being injured or to prevent injury to the load during the cycle of operation. The functions usually supplied by the controller are as follows:

To Limit the Current during the Acceleration of the Motor. The ohmic resistance of a motor is very low, so that, when it is connected to the line while it is at rest, a very large current would be drawn from

1

the line if external resistance were not used to limit this current.   As the motor accelerates, it develops a counter emf, which reduces the voltage available for causing a current to flow; hence the current is reduced. The current at any instant can be calculated by subtracting the counter emf from the line voltage and dividing the result by the ohmic resistance in circuit (see Fig. 1-1).   It is evident from the above that, as the motor increases in speed, the line current decreases (see Fig. 1-2) and

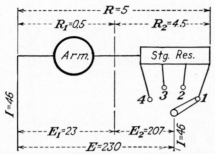

FIG. 1-1. Voltage across the armature terminals when the armature is at rest and the circuit has been closed.

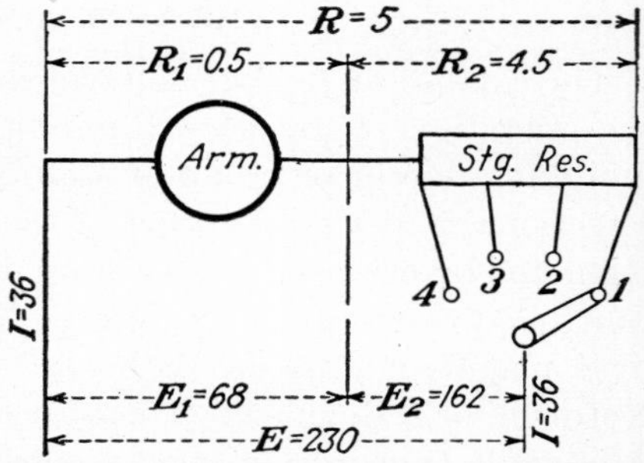

FIG. 1-2. The motor has now accelerated until the torque is balanced by the load.

the starting resistance may be reduced (see Figs. 1-3 and 1-4), until the motor is finally connected to the line without any external resistance. The short circuiting of this starting resistance can be done in several different ways.

Some d-c motors are designed to be accelerated from rest, without the use of external starting resistance; these motors are, however, for use in particular applications.   The squirrel-cage induction motor can also be started by connecting it directly to the line.

The motor armature is stationary when it is first connected to the line, and the current = volts ÷ ohms.   The ohmage in the armature is very low, assume 0.5 ohm; the total ohmage should be equal to volts ÷ amperes. Assume an emf of 230 volts and a current of 46 amp, $^{230}/_{46}$ = 5 ohms. Then $5 - 0.5 = 4.5$ ohms external resistance.   When the controller arm is on position 1 in Fig. 1-1, the current will be 46 amp.

When the motor armature revolves, it generates a counter emf (voltage).   When this counter voltage is 50, the current will be

$$\frac{230 - 50}{5} = 36 \text{ amp}$$

which is assumed as full load (Fig. 1-2) $36 \times 0.5 = 18$ volts drop through the armature resistance.   Now move the controller to point 2 in Fig. 1-3 giving an external resistance of 3.5 ohms.   The current now is

$\dfrac{230 - 50}{3.5 + 0.5} = \dfrac{180}{4} = 45$ amp. This increased current will cause the motor to speed up until the countervoltage reduces the current to 36 amp. The voltage drop in the external resistance is $3.5 \times 36 = 126$ volts. $230 - 126 = 104$ volts across the armature. The controller is then moved to point 3 and then point 4, thereby bringing the motor up to full speed.

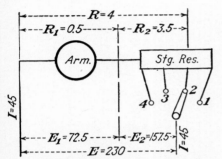 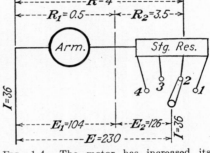

FIG. 1-3. The controller is now moved to the second resistance step, and the motor again accelerates.

FIG. 1-4. The motor has increased its speed until the torque is again balanced by the load.

To Limit the Torque during Acceleration. The torque of a motor is proportional to the current multiplied by the field strength. It is often desirable to start a motor with a gradually increasing torque; this can easily be done with a shunt motor by starting it with zero field strength. The shunt field of the motor is connected to the line at the same time as the armature. Since it takes an appreciable time for the field to build up to full strength, the torque will increase gradually and give an easy start. In this way a shunt motor can be started with twice full-load current, or even greater current, and not cause a shock or jar to the motor or to the apparatus to which the motor is connected. A series or compound motor, started in the same way, will build up its torque much faster. The induction motor also builds up its torque rapidly. No motor, however, will build up its strength instantly, so that it is not likely that any type of motor will give a hard shock to the machinery if it is started with zero field strength.

To Change the Direction of Rotation of the Motor. In many classes of service the motor is required to reverse its direction of rotation repeatedly. It is a well-known fact that the d-c motor can be reversed in rotation by reversing the current through the armature and keeping the field in the same direction. The induction motor can be reversed by reversing one of the phases, and this is usually done by interchanging any two leads on a three-phase motor or interchanging the two leads in one phase of a two-phase motor. Where the motor operates continuously in one direction, these connections can be adjusted at the time of installing the motor, but where the reversal of rotation occurs frequently, some substantial form of reversing switch should be included in the controller.

FIG. 1-5.   Crane protective panel showing overload relays with a time element to delay the relays from opening the circuit.

To Limit the Load of the Motor. This is usually done by means of fuses or a circuit breaker for manual control. Where the main-line switches are operated by magnets, an overload relay is used to deenergize the magnet and allow the switch to open. All overload devices should be provided with some form of time-element attachment. This will allow the motor to take a short peak load of a few seconds' duration without disconnecting itself from the line, which is very desirable, as such short-time peaks occur during acceleration and often during the normal operation of the motor.

Sometimes an overload relay is provided for inserting the starting resistance in the motor circuit in case of overload. This arrangement is required in special cases where it is undesirable to have the motor torque entirely cease. Such relays are sometimes called "jamming relays."

To Disconnect the Motor upon Failure of Voltage. The voltage supply sometimes fails, and a serious injury might result upon the reestablishment of voltage if the motor were left connected to the line without the starting resistance. Manually operated starters and controllers are provided with a latch, held in place by a shunt magnet. This latch retains the controller in the running position. Upon the failure of line voltage, the catch is released and the controller is mechanically returned to the starting, or Off, position.

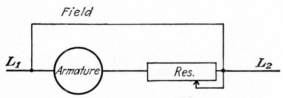

Fig. 1-6.   Direct-current motor with armature resistor.

Magnetic contactor control automatically returns to the Off position upon the failure of line voltage, as the magnets are deenergized under such conditions. The controller can be connected so that it will automatically start the motor again upon the return of voltage to the line, in which case the circuit or device is known as "low-voltage release." Where it is necessary for the operator to perform some function, such as pushing a button after the failure of voltage, the circuit or device is known as "low-voltage protection." The latter is the one usually required, as an operator may be working on the machinery and there is danger of its being started automatically and injuring him upon the return of voltage.

To Regulate the Speed of Rotation. Frequently a motor is connected to a load requiring different operating speeds. This speed change can be effected in several different ways, the most common of which are as follows:

Armature Control. Armature control (see Fig. 1-6) consists in putting resistance in series with the motor. Direct-current motors have this resistance in the armature circuit, and the voltage across the motor brushes is less than the line voltage, owing to the drop through this external resistance. Wound-secondary induction motors are controlled in a similar way, by connecting the resistance in the secondary circuit (see Fig. 1-7). The drop in speed is in this case a little more complicated to calculate; the reduction in speed is proportional, however, to the voltage drop through resistance. Motors controlled in this way are called "variable-speed motors." The speed at which the motor operates depends directly upon the torque required by the driven load. A change in torque causes a corresponding change in current, and the drop through the external resistance is equal to the current multiplied by the ohms.

Changing the Field Strength. In d-c shunt and compound wound motors changing the field strength varies their speed (see Fig. 1-8). This is

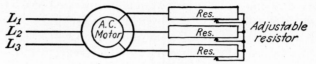

Fig. 1-7. Alternating-current motor with secondary resistor.

usually done by connecting a rheostat in series with the shunt-field winding of the motor. Such motors are called "adjustable-speed motors," since the speed remains practically constant under all conditions of loading. Commercial motors of this type are built with speed ranges as high as 4 to 1. At present no a-c motors of this class are in commercial use.

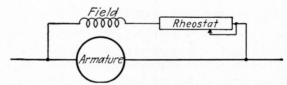

Fig. 1-8. Direct-current motor arranged for changing the field strength.

Changing the Voltage of the Supply Circuit. This also varies the speed of a motor (see Fig. 1-9). It is usually done by supplying each motor from a separate generator. This system of control is applied to elevators, mine hoists, reversing steel-mill motors, paper mills, machine tools, and many other motors (see Chap. 11).

To Start and Stop the Motor at Fixed Points in the Cycle of Operation, or at the Limit of Travel of the Load. This feature can be obtained by the use of limit switches, which are operated by the machinery to which the motor is attached. They usually interrupt only a small circuit, thereby opening magnetic contactors, which, in turn, disconnect the main motor circuit. These limit switches may be connected by gearing to the driven machinery, in which case they are called "geared" limit switches. Where the limit switches are mounted along the runway and operated by the machinery striking the switch, they are called "track," "stroke," or "hatchway" limit switches.

To Stop the Motor. The motor can be brought to rest by either friction or dynamic braking (see Chap. 9).

Friction braking is accomplished by a mechanical brake, which is usually applied by a heavy spring and released by a magnet in series with the main circuit of the motor. In this case the brake is set whenever there is no current in the motor, and consequently no special arrangement is necessary on the controller to apply the brakes. Shunt coils are also used.

Dynamic braking requires at least one additional switch on the controller. It is accomplished by disconnecting the armature from the line and short-circuiting it on itself through a resistance with full field strength, the energy stored in the rotating parts being dissipated in heating the resistance.

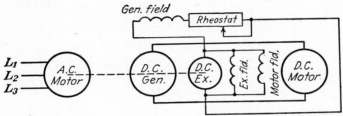

FIG. 1-9.   Method of changing the voltage of a d-c motor by changing the generator-field strength.

To Protect the Operator from Injury. It is very important to ensure the operator who uses the machinery against injury either during the starting of the motor or during the subsequent operation of the machinery. This requires the control apparatus to be properly protected, so that there is little danger of the operator's receiving a shock or being burnt by an arc in starting or during the operation of the machinery. Accidents may occur that require quick stopping of the machinery. To effect this result, safety stop devices are frequently placed around the machinery. They are operated either automatically or manually, depending upon conditions. These devices must be adapted to each particular application, but they are very important and should be carefully considered by engineers in specifying the electric drive.

THE CLASSIFICATION OF CONTROL APPARATUS

Electric controllers can be roughly divided into two general classes: manual acceleration and automatic acceleration.

Manual Acceleration. This class comprises control apparatus in which the acceleration of the motor is entirely under the control of the operator. Illustrations of this are the faceplate and drum-type controllers.

Automatic Acceleration. This class comprises control apparatus in which the acceleration of the motor is performed automatically.

These terms are usually applied to the method of acceleration. Controllers may have a combination of these two methods; for example, a magnetic contactor type of crane controller may have a master switch with five or six notches. The acceleration between notches is automatic, but the operator can determine the direction of rotation and the speed of the motor. The rate of change in speed, however, is automatic.

Controllers, including starters, may be divided into the several groups given below. These groups do not include every type that is built, but they give a good idea of present practice. The advantages and limitations listed must be interpreted in a very general manner, as they may not apply in many special cases. The magnetic contactor controller is usually automatic. The other types are generally manual; but automatic acceleration may be obtained by using an electric motor or an air cylinder to operate them.

FACEPLATE CONTROLLERS
(Fig. 2-2)

Advantages

  1. Low in price.
  2. Compact, usually with self-contained resistor.
  3. Easy to mount on wall or switchboard.
  4. Flexible in design, can be readily altered.
  5. Inexpensive, as to renewals of contacts and repairs.
  6. Low-voltage protection feature easily applied.

Limitations

  1. Design usually not well adapted to taking care of arcing. For this reason it is not good for heavy or frequent service.
  2. Design usually not rugged mechanically.
  3. A type that presents difficulties where the connections are complicated, such as a reversing control for wound-secondary motors.

DRUM CONTROLLER (CYLINDER TYPE)
(Fig. 1-10)

Advantages

  1. Low in price in small and medium sizes.
  2. Compact, but with separately mounted resistor.
  3. Entirely enclosed.   Can be made dustproof, sprayproof, or gasproof.
  4. Strong mechanically and simple to operate.
  5. Capable of having various mechanical retarding devices attached to prevent too rapid acceleration.

6. Capable of having complicated connections made; *i.e.,* forward and reverse, or power and brake, on the same drum.

Limitations

1. Modification of design difficult and expensive.
2. Frequent inspection and adjustment of contacts necessary.
3. Rapid deterioration of contacts under severe conditions.

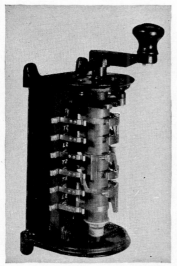

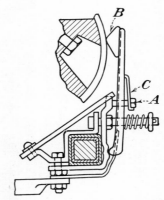

FIG. 1-10. Drum controller with cover removed.

FIG. 1-11. Drum controller, sectional view, showing the sliding contact made between the finger *B* and the drum cylinder.

4. Care of the energy of the arc sometimes difficult.
5. Limitation as to size.
6. Large sizes difficult to operate.

CAM CONTROLLERS (MANUALLY OPERATED)
(Fig. 1-12)

Advantages

1. Low in price.
2. Compact in design, but with resistor separately mounted.
3. Entirely enclosed. Can be made dustproof, sprayproof, or gasproof.
4. Strong mechanically and simple to operate. Can be provided with reciprocating as well as rotating handle.
5. Capable of having various mechanical retarding devices attached to the handle to prevent too-rapid acceleration.

6. Capable of having complicated connections made readily.

7. Capable of having new combinations made easily by changing the number of units and the shape of individual cams.

8. Rolling contacts used, which are usually free from welding.

9. Contacts, easily and cheaply renewed.

10. Entire unit can be replaced if necessary.

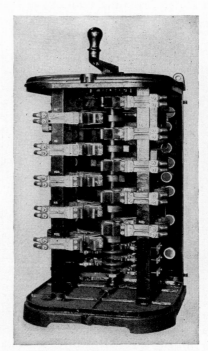

Fig. 1-12.   Cam controller with the cover removed.

11. Easy to inspect.

12. Quick closing and opening not found in drum controllers.

13. Combining the simplicity of the manual controller with the durability of magnetic control.

Limitations

1. The larger sizes require more power to operate than does a master switch.

2. On account of the enclosure the continuous capacity may be reduced and the energy of the arc must be limited.

3. There are limitations in size.

MAGNETIC CONTACTOR CONTROL
(Fig. 1-13)

Advantages

1. Long life of contacts because of the rolling action and a quick opening and closing.

2. Positive opening and closing of contacts.

FIG. 1-13. Magnetic-contactor controller with door of cabinet open.

3. Flexibility in adapting controller to various designs.

4. Can be arranged with various safety attachments.

5. More foolproof than other types.

6. Strong and rugged mechanically.

7. Automatic control can be obtained.

8. Contacts are easily and cheaply renewed.

9. Entire unit can be replaced if necessary.

10. Inspection easy.

11. A saving in copper connections, as the controller can be located close to the motor, and the master switch wherever convenient.

12. A time element in closing and opening, not found in drum controllers.

Limitations

1. More expensive than manual controllers.
2. The larger sizes occupy considerable space.
3. The wiring diagram is complicated.

Liquid Controllers
(Fig. 19-4)

Advantages

1. Large thermal capacity for starting.
2. Very gradual change of resistance.
3. Absence of arcing or other wear, as no contacts are used (except line switch).
4. The resistance can be easily adjusted by varying the amount of soda in the solution.
5. It can be readily adapted for automatic operation.

Limitations

1. Considerable floor space is required.
2. The electrodes are subject to corrosion.
3. Cooling water is required for the larger sizes.
4. The use of the liquid limits its application.

In specifying control apparatus, the following information should always be included.

1. The characteristics of the power circuit, such as voltage, frequency, number of phases, voltage regulation, should be given.

2. A brief description of the control apparatus required should be included.

3. If the motor speed is to be adjusted, the speed range should be given, the load at the maximum and minimum speed and the number of speed points.

4. The cycle of operation should be stated in detail, particularly the number of starts made by the motor per hour.

5. A description should be given of the machine that the motor drives, particularly the torque required to accelerate to full speed.

6. A description of any unusual features of the installation, such as

moisture, dust, acid fumes, limited source of power, space available for the apparatus, etc., should be noted.

7. Complete rating (nameplate reading of the motor) should be given.

All this information is necessary for the intelligent selection of both the motor and the control. In the absence of any of this information, the engineer furnishing the electrical apparatus must guess at the requirements on the basis of the best average practice. This will often take care of the situation, but exact information is very much better.

CHAPTER 2

HOW TO READ CONTROLLER DIAGRAMS

A controller diagram consists of a group of symbols joined together by lines that represent wires; the symbols represent the motor and the controller elements. It is a sign language used to express the functioning of the control system.

The symbols and terminal markings used in this book are listed on page 30. Some of these symbols are more elaborate than those used on manufacturers' diagrams because they require less imagination to understand and are, therefore, easier to read. After anyone has become experienced in reading diagrams, he can understand any reasonable symbols.

The present discussion is intended to deal, in an elementary manner, with a few simple forms of controllers, with the intention of explaining some of the fundamental principles of operation. A thorough understanding of this section will be of material assistance in the consideration of subsequent discussions of more complicated forms of controllers as they are used in various industries.

FACEPLATE CONTROLLERS

The faceplate controller is the simplest type used for starting or regulating the speed of an electric motor. Figure 2-1 illustrates the elements of this controller. While this arrangement is operative, commercial apparatus usually has additional features, which in this instance are omitted for the purpose of clearness. L_1 and L_2 represent the two power wires leading to the controller and a compound-wound motor. If the rheostat arm be moved from the Off position, shown in the diagram, to the contact R_1, current will flow from L_1 to the arm, from this to contact R_1, through the regulating resistance to R_{10}, thence through the armature and series field of the motor to L_2. The shunt field is connected from R_1 to L_2, and is energized as soon as the rheostat arm makes contact with R_1. The voltage across the armature will be equal to the line voltage minus the voltage drop through the regulating resistor. The torque of the motor will be proportional to the armature current and the field strength. When the contact is first made at R_1, the field strength is zero; it takes a short interval for the field to reach its full value, so that under ordinary conditions the torque will increase from zero to a value that will start the motor. The rotation of the armature in the motor field generates a voltage known as the counter emf which opposes the line voltage. As the motor increases in speed, the difference between the line and counter emf becomes less and the motor current decreases until a balanced condition is reached. When this balancing condition is reached, the speed of the motor may be further increased by moving the rheostat arm to contact R_2. Additional increments of speed

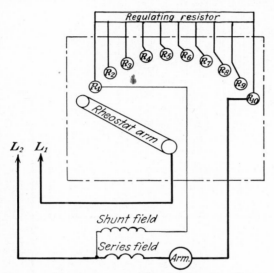

Fig. 2-1. Elementary controller with faceplate rheostat.

are obtained by additional movements of the arm to other contacts until all of the regulating resistance is eliminated from the circuit and the arm *rests* on contact R_{10}. The arm should be allowed to remain on each contact until the motor reaches its balancing speed for that step of the resistance, so that the minimum amount of current will be taken by the motor.

In bringing the motor to rest, the reverse operation of the arm is made. In passing from contact R_1 to the Off position, the connection between the motor and L_1 is interrupted, causing the motor to come to rest. The shunt field, however, will still be connected across the armature of the motor, including the regulating resistor. This connection should be used wherever possible, as it allows the field current to die down gradually as the speed of the motor decreases. The drop in voltage through the starting resistor, with only the field current flowing, is so small that it may be neglected and the field can be considered as having a voltage

equal to the counter emf of the motor.   The shunt-field winding consists of a large number of turns of fine wire.   Any change in the value of
the field current is opposed by the self-induction of this winding, so that
a change in the current should be made gradually.   If an attempt is
made to open the field circuit abruptly, the self-induction will cause a
high voltage to build up between the terminals of the field coils, which
may result in the breaking down of the insulation.

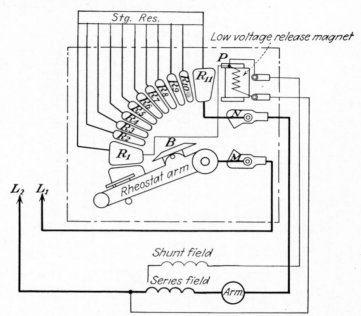

Fɪɢ. 2-2.   A commercial controller using a starting rheostat.

If the rheostat is to be used for starting purposes only, the resistor
is made of less current-carrying capacity than that needed for regulating
purposes.   It is called a "starting rheostat" or a "regulating rheostat,"
depending upon the purpose for which it is used.   The connections,
however, are the same, the difference being only in the capacity of the
resistor.   A commercial design of starting rheostat is shown in Fig. 2-2.
This rheostat differs from the one previously described in the addition of
the low-voltage release magnet.   The rheostat arm is provided with a
spring, which returns it to the Off position if the handle is released during
the starting of the motor.   After the motor has been brought up to speed
and the rheostat arm rests upon contact R_{11}, the low-voltage release
magnet holds the arm in this position.   Brush B bridges between the
terminals M and N, so that in the running position the current passes

from L_1 to terminal M, through the brush B to terminal N, thence to the armature of the motor and through the series field to L_2. This provides a circuit parallel to the one through the rheostat arm to contact R_{11}, so that the continuous flow of current will not overheat the rheostat arm and its contacts. In the running position, the rheostat arm is held firmly by the low-voltage release magnet, so that current flows from

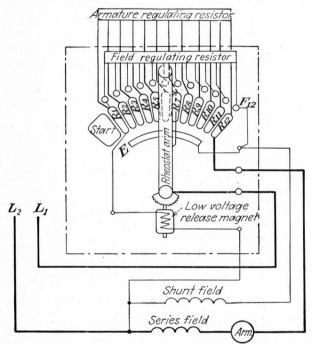

Fig. 2-3. A starting and speed-regulating rheostat having both armature and field resistors.

L_1 through the rheostat arm to point P on the magnet. One circuit then passes through the magnet winding to L_2. The other circuit is connected to the shunt field. If, for any reason, the line wires are disconnected or the voltage on the circuit fails, the low-voltage release magnet will be deenergized and the spring will return the rheostat arm to the starting position.

A controller provided with both armature- and field-regulating resistance is shown in Fig. 2-3. The motor is known as an adjustable-speed motor and can have its speed changed by adjusting its field strength. The rheostat arm is made in two parts, the under part making contact with the segments marked R_1 to R_{12} and with the contact ring E, while the top arm engages the upper row of round contacts. When starting, the two arms are held together by a latch. The bottom arm is provided with a notched segment engaging a plunger forming part of the low-voltage release magnet. The notched segment and the pawl hold the arm in any operating position after the low-voltage magnet is energized.

To start the motor, the contact arms are moved from the Off position to contact R_1. The current flows from L_1 through the arm to contact R_1, thence through the armature-regulating resistor to contact R_{12}, and then through the armature and series field to L_2. The shunt-field current flows from L_1 through the arm to the segment E, to the field windings, and thence to L_2. Connected with R_1 is a shunt circuit passing from the positive side of the line through the low-voltage release magnet to the negative side of the line. The arms are gradually moved to the right, eliminating successively each section of the armature resistor until the bottom arm makes contact with R_{12}. In this position the armature is connected directly across the line and the segment E is disconnected from the rheostat arm. The shunt-field circuit now is from the positive side of the line through the upper rheostat arm to the right-hand field contact F_{12}, thence to the field winding. This gives a motor speed corresponding to full field strength. If it is desired to increase the speed of the motor, the upper arm can be moved to the left across the field contacts to insert resistance gradually in the shunt-field circuit and thus within its range give the increased speed required, while the low-voltage release magnet holds the lower arm on contact R_{12}.

If the circuit is interrupted, the low-voltage release magnet will allow the lower arm to be carried to the Off position by means of its spring. It, in turn, picks up the upper arm, and the two are moved quickly to the Off position.

DRUM CONTROLLERS

A drum type of controller is shown in Fig. 2-4. Such a controller consists of two rows of contact fingers attached to the framework of the controller, but insulated from it so as to be electrically separated from each other. Between these rows of fingers is mounted an insulated cylinder, or drum, which is revolved by the handle. On this drum are mounted copper segments of different lengths, which engage the contact fingers. The length and location of these segments are such as to make different connections for each "notch" of the controller. Attached to the drum shaft at the top is a wheel having notches corresponding to each of the operating positions of the controller handle. A roller is forced into one of these notches by a spring whenever a set of contacts is properly engaged, thus indicating to the operator the correct running positions of the controller and preventing motion from any of these positions, due to vibration or other accidental means. Figure 2-5 shows the segments of such a drum as they would appear if rolled out flat. The two vertical rows of circles represent the stationary contact fingers. The horizontal strips represent the segments of the rotating drum, and the vertical dotted lines show the position of the segments with respect to the controller fingers at each successive position of the drum.

A slip-ring motor control arrangement with the controller connected only to the secondary circuit of the motor is shown in Fig. 2-6 with the drum rolled out, or "developed," as in Fig. 2-5. When the primary of the motor is connected to the power line, current passes through the secondary wires and thence through the resistor, completing the circuit. When the motor is at zero speed, the controller drum should be in position 1. If the cylinder of the drum is now moved from right to left, the dotted line 2 travels over to the center line of the contact fingers and the resistor section R_{11} to R_{12} is short-circuited, decreasing the resistance in part of the secondary circuit of the motor. As the speed of the motors increases, a further movement of the drum will cause the vertical line 3 to intersect the contact fingers. This will short-circuit the resistor section from R_1 to

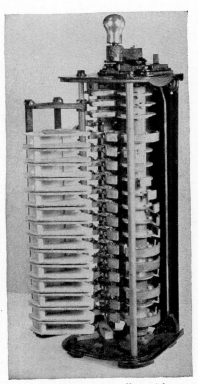

Fig. 2-4. Drum controller with cover removed and arc boxes rotated away from the contacts.

R_2. At each increase of the motor speed a further movement of the drum may be made until the vertical line 13 intersects the controller fingers. In this position all of the resistor is short-circuited and the motor is operating at full speed.

A drum-controller diagram similar to that shown in Fig. 2-6, except that it provides for reversing the direction of rotation of the motor, is given in Fig. 2-7. One motor terminal marked T_3 is connected directly to the line. The other two terminals of the motor, marked T_1 and T_2, are connected to correspondingly marked terminals of the controller. In

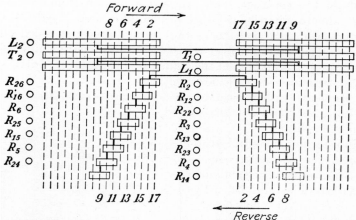

Fɪɢ. 2-5. Diagrammatic representation of a drum switch and its contact fingers rolled out flat. (See Fig. 2-7 for a complete diagram.)

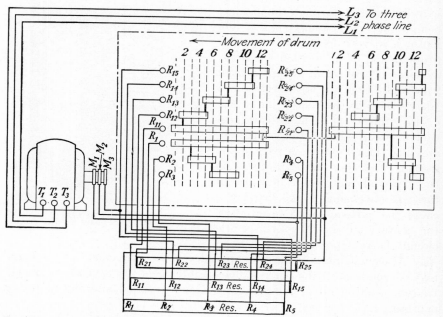

Fɪɢ. 2-6. A nonreversing controller for a three-phase wound-secondary induction motor showing the resistors and drum development.

the forward direction, the drum segments on the right-hand side of the diagram move toward the left-hand row of fingers, and the segments on the left-hand side of the diagram move toward the middle row of fingers. This will be understood if the developed diagram showing the drum contacts is replaced so as to fit on the surface of a cylinder, or drum, and the contact fingers marked on two vertical sticks of wood mounted on each side of the cylinder 180 deg apart. When the drum segments are moved

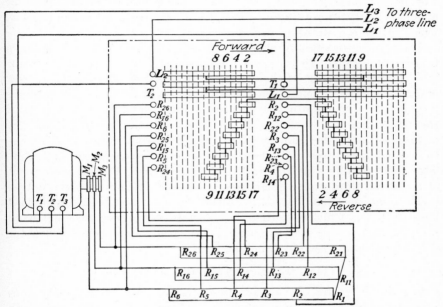

FIG. 2-7.   A reversing controller for an a-c wound-secondary induction motor.   The drum development alone is shown in Fig. 2-5.

from left to right for forward operation, the terminal T_1 of the motor is connected through finger T_1, and the second and third segments from the top, which are connected together as indicated, to L_1 power wire. Likewise, the terminal T_2 of the motor is connected to L_2 power wire.

The arrangement of the drum contacts for short-circuiting the secondary resistors differs somewhat from that shown in Fig. 2-6. The first notch in the forward direction closes the contacts to the primary of the motor T_1 to L_1 and T_2 to L_2. A drum segment is brought in contact with the finger marked R_2 on this notch, but as no other connection is made to the resistors, this contact causes no change in the secondary resistance. The motor, therefore, starts to rotate at its minimum speed with all resistance in the secondary. When the drum is moved over until the dotted line 2 intersects the central row of fingers, the one marked R_{12} is connected to the drum, short-circuiting the section of the resistor between R_2 and R_{12}. Next the dotted line marked 3 intersects the central row of fingers and R_{22} is connected to the drum, short-circuiting another section of the resistor. This sequence is continued until the dotted line 8 intersects the central line of fingers connecting R_{14} to the drum. A further movement of the drum causes the dotted line 9 in the right-hand part to intersect the left-hand row of fingers connecting resistor R_{24} to the drum. The dotted lines 10 to 15 successively intersect the left-hand row of fingers. A further rotation of the drum short-circuits all of the resistor, which brings the motor up to full speed.

The reverse direction of operation causes the drum segments to move from right to left. In this case the left-hand dotted lines are brought into contact with the left-hand row of fingers and the right-hand row of dotted lines into contact with the middle row of fingers. The primary terminal T_1 of the motor is connected to line L_2 and the terminal T_2 of the motor line L_1, when the dotted line 1 intersects the middle row of fingers. A further movement of the drum from right to left causes the dotted lines 2 to 8 to intersect successively the central row of fingers. This short-circuits a part of the starting resistors. Further movement of the drum from right to left causes the contact shown on the dotted line 9 to intersect the finger R_{24}. A further movement brings the dotted lines 10 to 15, inclusive, so that they successively intersect the left-hand row of fingers. This short-circuits all of the resistor and brings the motor up to speed in the reverse direction.

MAGNETIC-CONTACTOR CONTROL

In a simple starter of the magnetic-contactor type, the controller consists of a panel, at the top of which may be mounted a knife switch, with two fuses for overload protection, and four contactors underneath. A contactor is a switch that is held in the open position by gravity and closed by a magnet. Contactor M (Fig. 2-8) is provided with a blow-out coil, because of opening and closing the main motor circuit. Contactors $1A$, $2A$, and $3A$ are used for short-circuiting the starting resistor sections, which are mounted in the rear of the panel. This arrangement is shown diagrammatically in Fig. 2-8. At each point where the circuit is broken by two small parallel lines is a contactor. The numbers opposite these parallel lines are the same as those shown in the sequence table. The single loops represent the series coils for contactors $1A$ and $2A$. Underneath this scheme of main connections is shown a table called "Sequence of switches." This table has four vertical rows, in which circles are drawn. The first row represents the first starting position of the controller, and the last row the running position of the controller.

Where a circle is shown opposite a switch number, it indicates that that contactor is closed. This table is used as follows:

In the first vertical column, opposite M is shown a circle that indicates that the contactor M is closed. This operation connects the shunt field of the motor from M to the negative side of the line. This arrangement of shunt-field connections is the same as was previously explained. Now refer to the diagram and trace the main current from the positive side of the line through contactor M and the coil of $1A$, to R_1 of the

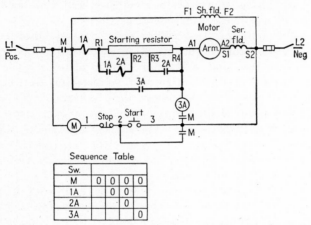

Sw.				
M	0	0	0	0
1A		0	0	
2A			0	
3A				0

Fig. 2-8. Connections of a magnetic-contactor controller with three starting steps.

resistor, through this resistor to the A_1 terminal of the motor, through the motor armature and series field, to the negative side of the line. Referring again to the table, it can be seen that in the second column contactor $1A$ also is closed, the path of the current being from the positive side of the line through M and $1A$ contactors, the coil of contactor $2A$, to R_2 on the resistor; from there it follows the same path as that for the first column. The third column of the table shows that contactor $2A$ is closed. The current now passes to R_2, as has been previously described, through one section of the resistor to R_3, from here to A_1 on the motor armature, and through the armature and series fields to the negative line. The fourth column of the table shows that contactors M and $3A$ are closed. The path of the current then is from the positive line through switch M to switch $3A$ to A_1, through the armature and series field to the negative line. This connects the motor directly to the line, without any external resistance, and is the full-speed position of the controller.

In the diagram, the magnetic-contactor coils are represented by circles and the contacts by two parallel lines. When the coil is energized sufficiently to attract the armature, the two parallel lines are brought together and current can flow between the terminals of the switch. Underneath contactor M are small switches. At the bottom of the diagram are two push buttons. The button marked Start is held in the open position by a spring, and the Stop button is held in the closed position by a spring. If the Start button is depressed for a moment, current flows from the positive line through the knife switch and fuse to the coil of switch M, through this coil to the terminal 1 of the Stop button, to terminal 2 and through the Start button, fuse, and knife switch, to the negative side of the line. This energizes the coil of contactor M and closes the main contact. This coil is now connected from terminal 1 through the Stop button to terminal 3 on the interlock underneath this switch to the negative side of the line, which makes the circuit to the coil M independent of the Start button, so that this button may now be released. The current now passes from the positive side of the line through the contactor M and through the coil of contactor $1A$ to R_1, through the starting resistor to R_4, thence to A_1 on the motor, through the armature and series field of the motor to the negative side of the line. As the motor increases in speed, the current through the coil of $1A$ decreases until this contactor closes.

This contactor operates on what is known as the "lock-out" principle; *i.e.*, it closes when its current is below a set value and above another much lower value. When $1A$ closes, it short-circuits one section of the starting resistor from the terminal R_1 through the contact on $1A$ to the coil of $2A$ to R_2 on the resistor. This again increases the current of the motor and prevents $2A$ from closing until the current has decreased to a fixed value. When $2A$ closes, it short-circuits the section of the resistor between R_3 and R_4. This leaves the resistor section between R_3 and R_4 in series with the motor. The coil of contactor $3A$ is in shunt across the armature of the motor through the interlock on contactor M. The circuit is from A_1 through the coil of $3A$, the interlock underneath M to the negative line. Since the A_2 terminal of the motor armature is connected to the negative side of the line, the voltage across this coil is equal to the counter emf of the motor. When the speed of the motor reaches the proper value, contactor $3A$ closes, connecting the A_1 terminal of the motor directly to L_1 through the contact on M.

To stop the motor, push the button marked Stop, thus opening the circuit to the operating coil of contactor M. This opens contactor M and disconnects the motor from the positive line.

CHAPTER 3

HOW TO MAKE CONTROLLER DIAGRAMS

Skill and experience are required to make a clear, readable diagram. This is particularly true of the more complicated diagrams of automatic controllers. For the making of such diagrams, experience has revealed a number of features that should be considered, most of them based on existing practice that has developed with the art. A definite plan and method of procedure should be worked out for each diagram.

In order to classify the different types of diagrams the National Electrical Manufacturers Association adopted the following definitions.

Controller Wiring Diagram. A diagram showing the electrical connections between the parts comprising the controller and indicating the external connections.

External Controller Wiring Diagram. A diagram showing the electrical connections between the controller terminals and outside points, such as connections from the line to the motor and to auxiliary devices.

Controller Construction Diagram. A diagram indicating the physical arrangement of parts, such as wiring, buses, resistor units, etc. Example: A diagram showing the arrangement of grids and terminals in a grid-type resistor.

Elementary Controller Diagram. A diagram using symbols and an elementary plan of connections to illustrate, in simple form, the motor circuits and the scheme of control.

Control Sequence Table. A tabulation of the connections which are made for each successive position of the controller.

Several of these diagrams are illustrated in order to make the definitions more easily understood. It is desirable to have a definite name for each kind of diagram, in order that engineers may better understand each other in discussing questions. In adopting these definitions the Electrical Manufacturers considered all of the names commonly used for these different diagrams and formulated names and definitions which seemed the most logical to describe particular diagrams. We shall now proceed to make some diagrams.

The diagrams for manual controllers, such as drum controllers and faceplate control, are the simplest. Typical diagrams are shown in Figs. 2-1, 2-2, and 3-1 to 3-4. Often the complete diagram can be made up without first making an elementary controller diagram.

Diagrams for automatic control using magnet contactors can best be

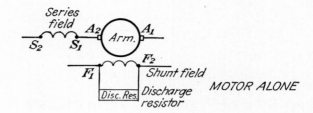

MOTOR ALONE

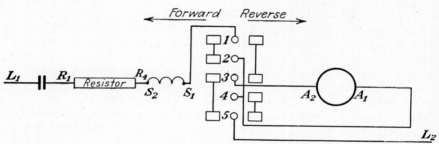

Motor is now connected to power through a starting
resistor with switches to short circuit the resistor

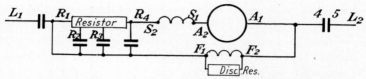

A reversing switch has been added and
the shunt field omitted for convenience

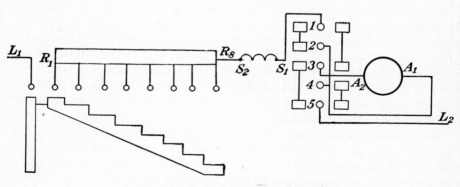

An accelerating switch is added

FIG. 3-1. Steps in the development of the diagram shown in Fig. 3-2.

made up by first working out the elementary diagrams in the following order, using the symbols shown in Fig. 3-5.

1. Make an elementary controller diagram (definition 4, Fig. 3-6).
2. Make a control sequence table (definition 6, Fig. 3-7).
3. Make the control circuit line diagram (definition 5, Fig. 3-8).
4. Make the complete controller wiring diagram (definition 1, Fig. 3-9).

If the controller is complicated, it may be desirable to make an external wiring diagram (definition 2). If the controller is for a large motor, where

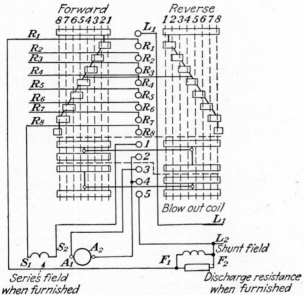

FIG. 3-2. Diagram of a reversing drumcont roller with magnetic blowout for a d-c motor.

a heavy bus structure is necessary for carrying the current, it may be necessary to make a controller construction diagram.

DESIGNATIONS

All contactors, relays, coils, interlocks, etc., should be marked. Use American Standard Z 32.3, "Graphic Symbols for Electric Power and Control."

Line or main contactors for various uses are marked as follows: M, $1M$, $2M$, etc., for line or main power contactors; $1F$ and $2F$ for forward; $1R$ and $2R$ for reverse; $1U$ and $2U$ for up; $1D$ and $2D$ for down; $1H$ and $2H$ for hoist; $1L$ and $2L$ for lower. Contactors for other specific operations or motions should be marked with similar appropriate designations.

Accelerating contactors are marked 1*A*, 2*A*, 3*A*, etc., in the order of closing.

Dynamic braking contactors are marked *DB*.

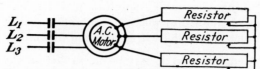

The motor primary is connected to the power through a 3 pole switch.
An adjustable resistor is connected to the secondary

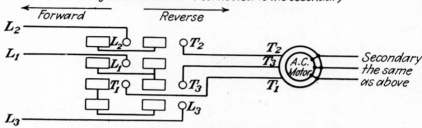

A reversing switch is added to the motor primary

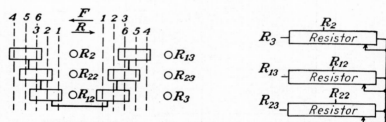

A secondary switch is added- the resistor terminals are connected
to the switch fingers having the same marks

2nd. notch R_{12}-R_{22} are connected together
3d.   „ R_{12}-R_{22}-R_{2} „   „   „
4th.   „ R_{13}-R_{22}-R_{2} „   „   „
5th.   „ R_{13}-R_{23}-R_{2} „   „   „
6th.   „ R_{13}-R_{23}-R_{3} „   „   „
The 1st. notch is reserved for closing the reverse switch·

Fig. 3-3.   Steps in the development of the diagram shown in Fig. 3-4.

Relays are marked as follows: overload, *OL*; under voltage, *UV*; brake relay, *BR*; field relay, *FR*; timing relay, *TR*. Suitable markings for relays of various kinds and any other devices, normally required can be selected from Fig. 3-5.

Other apparatus: circuit breaker, *CB*; master switch, *MS*; limit switch, *LS*

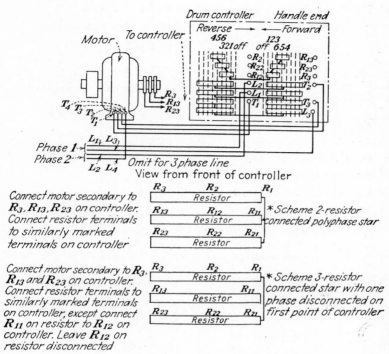

Connect motor secondary to
R_3, R_{13}, R_{23} on controller.
Connect resistor terminals
to similarly marked
terminals on controller

*Scheme 2-resistor
connected polyphase star

Connect motor secondary to R_3,
R_{13} and R_{23} on controller.
Connect resistor terminals to
similarly marked terminals
on controller, except connect
R_{11} on resistor to R_{12} on
controller. Leave R_{12} on
resistor disconnected

*Scheme 3-resistor
connected star with one
phase disconnected on
first point of controller

Part	Direct current	Alternating current
Line.	L_1-L_2	L_1-L_2-L_3, etc.
Brush on commutator.	A_1-A_2	A_1-A_2-A_3, etc.
Stator.		T_1-T_2-T_3, etc.
Series field.	S_1-S_2	
Brush on slip ring (rotor).		M_1-M_2-M_3, etc.
Shunt field.	F_1-F_2	F_1-F_2
Commutating field.	C_1-C_2	
Braking resistance.	B_1-B_2-B_3	B_1-B_2-B_3, etc.
Armature resistance.	R_1-R_2-R_3	R_1-R_2-R_3, etc.
Shunt-field resistance.	V_1-V_2-V_3	V_1-V_2-V_3, etc.
Transformer, high voltage.		H_1-H_2-H_3, etc.
Transformer, low voltage.		X_1-X_2-X_3, etc.
Two-phase line.		{ Phase 1 Mark L_1-L_3 { Phase 2 Mark L_2-L_4
Two-phase stator.		{ Phase 1 Mark T_1-T_3 { Phase 2 Mark T_2-T_4

Fig. 3-4. Diagram of a reversing drum controller for a three-phase wound-secondary induction motor.

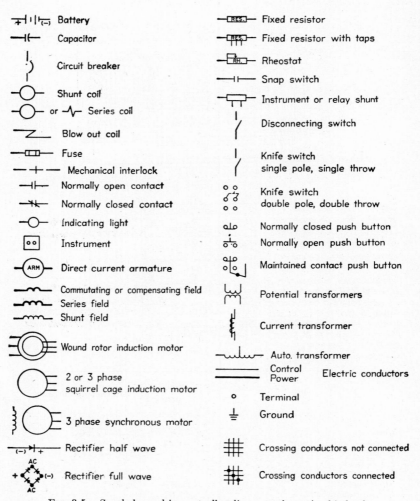

FIG. 3-5. Symbols used in controller diagrams shown in this book.

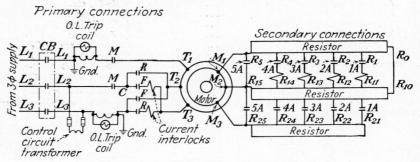

FIG. 3-6. An elementary controller diagram.

Control sequence table													
Cont.	Hoist						Off	Lower					
	6	5	4	3	2	1		1	2	3	4	5	6
F	O	O	O	O	O	O							
R								O	O	O	O	O	O
F	O	O	O	O	O	O							
R								O	O	O	O	O	O
M	O	O	O	O	O	O		O	O	O	O	O	O
M	O	O	O	O	O	O		O	O	O	O	O	O
1A	O	O	O	O	O				O	O	O	O	O
2A	O	O	O	O						O	O	O	O
3A	O	O	O								O	O	O
4A	O	O										O	O
5A	O												O

FIG. 3-7. A control sequence table.

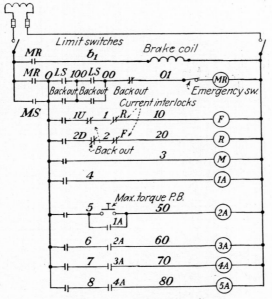

FIG. 3-8. A control-circuit line diagram.

Knife switch, symbol from Fig. 3-5 followed by the number and by *Sw.*

When more than one panel appears on the same diagram, add a dash and the panel number after the regular marking of relays, contacts, interlocks, etc.

Instrument transformers should be marked Current Transformer or

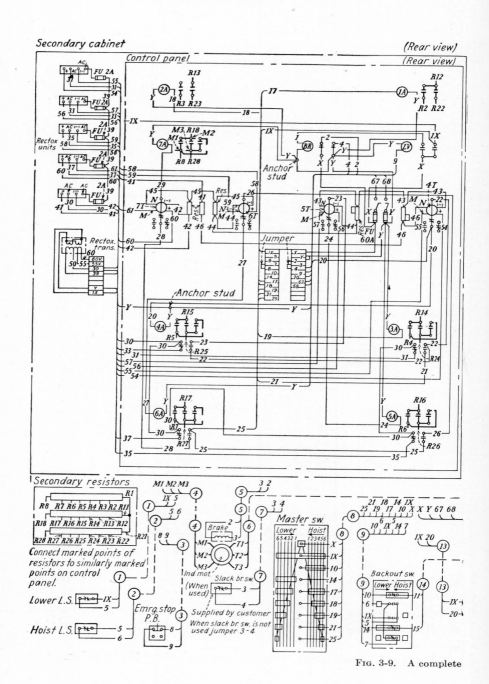

FIG. 3-9.   A complete

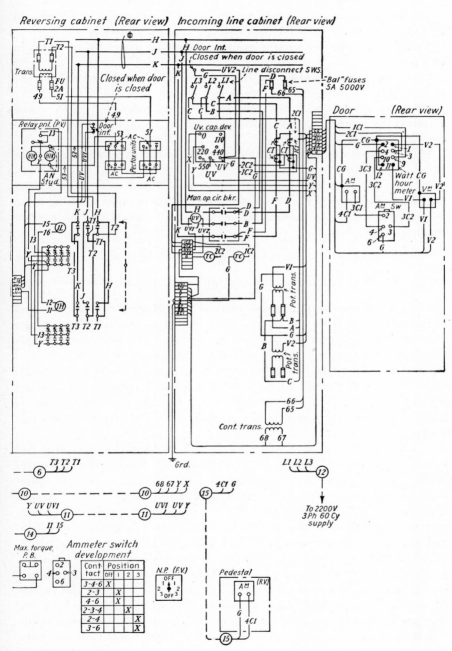

controller wiring diagram.

Potential Transformer.   Transformers supplying control circuits should be marked Control-circuit Transformer.

Terminals.   The terminal markings shown on page 30 are used in this book.

The connection between the fused knife switch and fuse should not be marked.   Terminals of meters should not be marked.

When two points with standard marking are connected to the same terminal (as S_2 and R_4), give both markings at the point where the connection is made.

Mark pilot-motor terminals the same as for the main motor, but use small letters a_1-a_2, f_1-f_2, s_1-s_2.

When more than one motor or when motors and generators having the same marking are shown on one diagram, the regular marking must be preceded by a letter indicating the machine, to avoid confusion when making connections.

Examples: For generator, GA_1-GA_2, etc.   For motor, MA_1-MA_2, etc.   For exciter, EA_1-EA_2, etc.
Resistor marking on diagrams must agree with marking on the resistance drawing.

Autotransformer terminals are marked 1, 2, 3, etc.   To avoid errors in making connections the transformers should be marked Transformer C, Transformer D, and Transformer E.   On the controller, the terminals to which transformer C is connected are usually marked $1C$, $2C$, etc., these terminals being connected to taps 1, 2, etc., on transformer C. The terminals to which transformers D and E are connected are usually marked $1D$, $2D$, etc., and $1E$, $2E$, etc.   For three phase, terminals marked 1 are usually connected together, either permanently or while starting.

In addition to using standard symbols and markings for apparatus and terminals, it is also desirable to mark the control lines so that they can easily be traced, especially on complete diagrams; otherwise, it is sometimes very difficult to trace the connections and to understand the operation of a complicated diagram.   The most satisfactory and most easily understood method of designation is that of numbering the wires decimally, as is shown schematically in Fig. 3-10 and in actual diagram in Fig. 3-9.   The energy supply lines for the control are marked $+$ and $-$ for direct current, and x and y for alternating current.   Where the supply line goes through a relay or a limit switch before reaching the master controller, it is numbered 0.   Where two or more of these are in series, they are considered as a unit and no markings are placed between them. When they are in parallel, or in series with taps taken off between them, these are numbered 0, 00, 100, 101, etc.

The fingers of the master switch, or the contacts of control push buttons, etc., and the lines leading therefrom are numbered 1, 2, 3, etc., odd numbers giving forward and even numbers giving reverse rotation on a reversing controller. Each line is given the same number at both ends and, if it is long, at convenient intermediate points, to make it easier to trace. When a circuit goes through a coil, an interlock, or other equipment, the number is changed, being multiplied by 10 at the first break and increased by one at each additional break, as is shown in Fig. 3-10, until it reaches the other terminal—or y. Where a line branches, the branches are numbered, when possible, in the order of normal operation. Where a line taps onto one previously numbered, it takes the

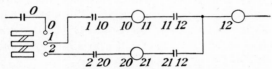

FIG. 3-10. An elementary controller diagram showing how intermediate points of branch circuits are marked.

number first assigned, as is shown in Fig. 3-10. By this system, any line with a number starting with 2—for example, 20, 21, or 24—originates on master-controller finger 2. This is a great convenience in studying the diagram.

Each separate piece of apparatus should be enclosed in a rectangle made up of a broken line, as shown in Fig. 3-9. This indicates what part of the diagram applies to each piece of apparatus. It also shows where the wires pass from one piece of apparatus to another.

Small resistors mounted directly on the panel should be shown in their relative positions. This is particularly true of small resistor tubes connected in series with magnet coils.

The parts of a motor or a generator, such as the armature, field coils, and brake coils, should be shown grouped together. Where motors, generators, and exciters are coupled together, they should be so indicated on the diagram.

When a control-circuit switch is divided from the main-circuit knife switch, it should be connected outside the main knife switch, so that the control connections can be tested without starting the motor.

It is customary to group the control-circuit terminals close together, usually near the bottom of the panel. This is very convenient in making the connections to the master switches and other auxiliary apparatus. In the smaller controllers the main-line connections are often grouped together, at either the top or the bottom of the panel. For the larger controllers the lugs for external connections are located on different parts of the panel, in order to reduce the number of joints in the circuit.

When a knife switch and fuse are used, connect the switch to the line in such a way that the fuse will be dead when the switch is open. This is done by connecting the fuse to the hinge terminals of the switch and the line to the other terminals. Single-throw switches should open in the direction of gravity to prevent the switch from accidentally closing. Do not place a knife switch above the main contactor, as the arc from the contactor may burn the operator's hand.

Do not use fuses in the main feeders to a two- or three-phase motor. If only one fuse opens when the motor is running, it will operate single phase and overload part of the windings, which may injure them. If the fuse opens when the motor is at rest, it will not start when the circuit is closed and will burn out part of the winding. Use a three-pole circuit breaker or contactor with overload relay to afford overload protection. Use three coils if the line is grounded.

The connection of two or more d-c controllers coils of different size in parallel causes sluggish opening of the contactors, owing to the discharge between the coils. This is particularly true in the case of large contactors or where coils of different sizes are in parallel. It is advisable to separate coil circuits in all cases.

If a resistor is connected in parallel with a coil, it gives slow opening of the contactor; the lower the resistance, the slower the action. If a resistor is connected in series with a coil and the coil design is so modified that the resultant flux is the same as before, the speed of closing is increased; the greater the resistance, the greater the effect.

If a condenser is connected in parallel with a contactor coil, it may cause the contactor to open more quickly. If there is considerable residual magnetism, the condenser may increase the time of opening, rather than decrease it. A condenser should be used with considerable care where the time of opening is an important factor.

The two paragraphs above apply to d-c control, as it is not good practice to use resistors or condensers in connection with a-c control equipment. The use of a resistor or a condenser is ordinarily for the purpose of reducing the arcing on a control contact in series with d-c coils. It may, however, be used to advantage in some cases in timing the operation, in order to obtain a desired sequence.

Where one side of a circuit is grounded, the master switch should be connected to the opposite side of the line. It is desirable to connect the master switch to the same side of the line as the motor armature of a d-c motor, in order that the elementary diagram and the control-line diagram may show both the armature and the master switch on the left-hand side. When two or more panels are controlled from one master switch, special care must be taken to avoid "sneak" circuits. That is, after circuits have been established and checked to see that they will produce the desired operation, an extra check should be made to ensure that no additional, unintended operation is possible. Cam-type master switches have each contactor separately insulated. Where it is practicable, use a separate cam contactor for each control panel. Where a drum-type master switch is used, it may be necessary to provide separately insulated sections of the drum for each panel.

It is desirable to provide only one control knife switch and fuse for the entire equipment. Where the control circuit to each panel is not insulated through the master switch, all overload relays and the low-voltage protective relay should have their contacts connected in series.

Where a tryout switch is provided on the control panel, it should be electrically interlocked with the master switch in such a way that when the tryout switch is used the master switch will be inoperative.

An easy way to check a diagram is to mark the control circuits having the same polarity with a blue pencil and to mark the circuits of the opposite polarity with a red pencil. Each shunt coil should now have a blue line to one terminal and a red line to the other terminal. If both terminals are the same color, the controller will not operate. If either terminal does not have a colored connection, there is an open circuit somewhere. If the controller is complicated, yellow and green pencils can be used to show intermediate steps. The lines on each side of a contact should be the same color because they will be the same potential when the contact is closed.

The illustrations of diagrams shown in this article are intended to represent general methods of making diagrams. Other symbols and terminal markings may be found better adapted for various designs of apparatus.

CHAPTER 4

MAGNETIC CONTACTORS

The detail design of controllers should be left to the manufacturer who guarantees their operation and satisfactory service. The application engineer must select the proper type and size of controller for each particular drive, and he is therefore interested in knowing how variation in design may affect the performance of a controller.

The capacity of a controller to carry current with a given rise in temperature may often be of much less importance than the durability of the contacts under repeated arc rupturing and the design of bearings to withstand wear in dirty places. A knife switch will carry current but will not last long if it is used for rupturing current. Current-carrying ability may be impaired by long periods of operation without opening and closing and the consequent scouring action on the contact surfaces.

When the controller is used infrequently and for short intervals of time, a controller smaller than normal can be selected for the motor. An application of this kind would be a crane in a powerhouse used only for repair work. For frequent operation, such as occurs with motors driving reversing tables in steel mills, the controller should be more than usually liberal. The continuous-current capacity has little to do with either of these applications. If the motor drives a condenser pump in a powerhouse, continuous-current capacity is the most important consideration.

THE FUNCTIONS OF A CONTACTOR

The essential requirements of a contactor are current carrying and arc rupturing. Means for operating and closing the contacts, while necessary, are of secondary importance to these two principal functions. Whether the contact is operated by hand, by a magnet, or by an air cylinder, it is important that it carry the motor current without injury and that it be able to interrupt repeatedly any ordinary overloads that may occur. In addition, the mechanical parts must be rugged and able to stand the wear caused by repeated operation.

FACTORS OF CONTACT DESIGN

Current Carrying. 1. *Material for Manufacture.* Hard-drawn or forged copper has given the best results.

38

2. *The Pressure between Contacts.* Other things being equal, the heavier the pressure, the more current the contact will carry. There are, of course, limits to this pressure, but the carrying capacity can be materially enhanced with an increase of pressure.

3. *The Mass of the Contact.* The greater the mass, the more heat is carried away from the contact surfaces and distributed through the adjacent material.

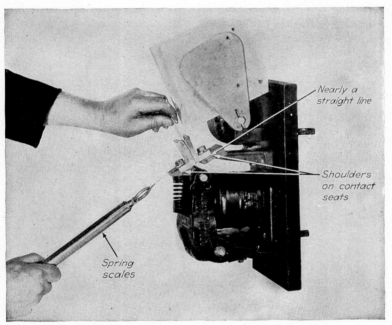

FIG. 4-1. Method of testing contact pressure.

4. *Radiation.* This factor determines the amount of energy that can be dissipated with a given temperature rise. With considerable mass in the contact, there is a greater radiating surface available for dissipating the heat.

5. *The Surface of the Contact.* The surface should be clean and free from the oxide scale that forms when the arcing takes place in the air. This oxide is a nonconductor and interferes with the passage of current. Arcing under oil usually causes a carbon deposit, which is a conductor, although it may not be as good a conductor as the original material. Usually the design of the contactor will give a small amount of wiping action, which cleans the contact surfaces when the contacts are being closed. This sliding or wiping action wears away the contacts and should be limited to a very small motion.

Types of Contacts.   Contacts are usually of three general types:

1. *The Butt Contact.*   An example of this is the laminated copper brush used in large circuit breakers.

2. *Sliding Contact.*   An example of this is the drum controller that uses fingers sliding on a cylindrical surface.

3. *Rolling Contact.*   This form of contact is the more reliable and most satisfactory now in use.   Contact is made at the tip and rolls down the surface to the heel (see Fig. 4-2).

Usually the movable contact member is attached to the armature of the magnet and mounted on an auxiliary pivoted member designated as

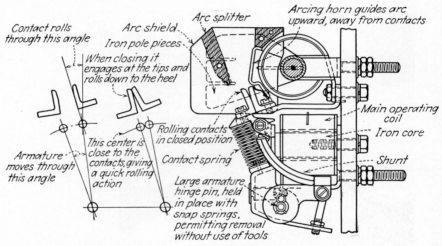

FIG. 4-2.   Action of rolling contacts.

the "contact support."   The pivot of this contact support approaches the stationary contact through the arc of a circle, and the movable contact is tilted forward so that its tip comes into contact with the stationary contact tip.   The further movement of the magnet armature causes the movable contact to roll against the stationary contact until the heels or bottom parts of the contacts are in engagement.   An important part of the design is the relation between the pin around which the contact support rotates and the position of the contacts.   The action of the contacts against each other cannot be a true rolling action, as the contact-support hinge pin rotates through a circle and, owing to this rotating action, its center moves up and down.   The rolling action, therefore, is combined with a small amount of sliding action.   The least amount of sliding is obtained when the moving contact center is located so that it moves an equal distance on either side of the line drawn from the heel of the contact to the armature hinge pin. Even with this arrangement of centers, there is always sufficient sliding action to keep the contact clean. Excessive sliding action causes additional mechanical wear on the contacts and in this way reduces their life. An endurance run on contactors having different amounts of sliding action makes the results of this wearing away of the contacts very evident.

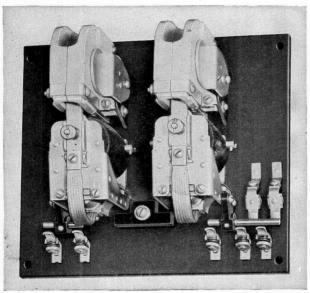

FIG. 4-3. Two single-pole magnetic contactors manufactured by the Square D Company showing electrical interlocks and a mechanical interlock between the contactors which prevent both from closing at the same time. They are useful as a reversing switch.

Excessive sliding action is disadvantageous from another point of view, as well. If the surfaces of the contacts become rough, they have a tendency to lock together and prevent the sliding action. While this locking together is not altogether positive, it has been found sufficient, in cases where the sliding action is excessive, to prevent the armature of the magnet from closing.

When a magnetic contactor is closed, the contacts strike together with considerable force and there is a slight rebound. When the contact rebounds, it draws a small arc, which softens the surface of the contacts at the point where they touched. If these contacts are permitted to come together at the same point after the rebound, there will be a tendency for them to weld or freeze, owing to the softened metal parts coming into contact. This reestablishment of contact at the same point is prevented by the closing movement of the magnet armature. During the period of rebound the armature has traveled closer to the magnet core, and the center carrying the contact support is in a new position, so that contact is reestablished at another place.

The closer the center of the contact support is to the contact, the greater is the lever action exerted by the closing means and, therefore, the greater is the ease with which a welded contact may be broken apart. This is of particular value in connection with manually actuated contactors, as these are more likely to be welded, owing to improper operation. If the contact is closed by a cam or a lever, the operator can exert a very powerful force to break open any ordinary weld.

The advantages of the rolling contact can be summarized as follows:

1. The current is carried at the heel of the contactor. This is kept clean by a slight sliding motion during the closing period. The contact at this point is under the maximum spring pressure.

2. The arcing takes place at the tip of the contact, as this is the last part of the contact to separate.

3. The rolling action minimizes the bounce upon closing.

4. When the contacts are properly operated, they will not weld.

5. The absence of any considerable sliding action prevents the contact from sticking if the surfaces become roughened.

6. Heavier pressures can be maintained between the contact surfaces than where sliding contacts are used. The pressure is limited to about 10 lb per lin in, for sliding contacts, on account of the cutting action.

Use of Oil-immersed Contacts. Oil-immersed contacts do not last nearly so long as do air-break contacts for the same service. This shortening of contact life is due to the intensely hot arc's vaporizing some of the oil, which burns the contacts and prolongs the arcing time.

Controllers for 2,200-volt and higher voltage service often have oil-immersed contacts, because these are very compact and cost less (see Fig. 19-14). One purpose in using oil-immersed contacts is to protect them from corrosive atmosphere or inflammable dust and entirely to enclose the live parts in order to shield persons from contact with live parts or the flash of the arc. Manual starters for 2,200-volt squirrel-cage motors are usually enclosed and have oil-immersed contacts (see Fig. 19-20). This makes a universal-purpose starter for general application.

When a-c magnets are used to close contacts, it is necessary to put a short-circuited turn, called a "shading coil," around part of the pole face to cause a lag in the magnetic flux in the shaded portion. This eliminates "chatter" at the pole face when the magnetism in the core passes through zero. When the armature is in the open position and the coil is energized, there is a heavy rush of current, known as the "closing current." When the armature is closed against the magnet core, the current is about 10 per cent of the initial value. This is called the "holding current." The closing current is due to the increased ampere turns required to give the reactive voltage necessary for balancing the line volts. The resistance drop is small and nearly 90 deg out of phase with the reactive volts. Large a-c contactors now use d-c coils receiving power from a small rectifier. This reduces the amperes required for the control circuit and eliminates all magnet noise.

Factors of Contact Design as to Arc Rupturing. The design of contacts to rupture current depends upon the following items:

1. The shape of the contacts.
2. The size of the contacts.
3. The material from which the contacts are made.
4. The separation of the contacts when opening.
5. The speed of opening.
6. The strength and distribution of the magnetic blowout field.
7. The design and size of the arc box and the arcing horns.
8. The material from which the arc box is made.

All these items have their effect on the maximum rupturing capacity of the contacts and the durability of the contacts and the arc box under severe service. The greater the energy handled, the larger must be the arc-rupturing means and the more important it is to consider these various items in detail. The design engineer has at his disposal a certain amount of exact information, which is supplemented by experience and test data.

A general understanding of what takes place when an arc is ruptured can be obtained from a brief description of the action in the arc box.

The arc may be considered as consisting of a stream of positively and negatively charged gaseous particles or ions that travel rapidly from one contact to the other. This stream of rapidly moving ions constitutes the arc current between the contacts. Since it is a flexible conductor, it can easily be stretched out lengthwise or readily deflected. If a transverse magnetic field is applied to this conductor, the reaction between the conductor and the field will be similar to the action that takes place in a motor where a conductor carrying current is placed in a magnetic field. The arc conductor moves in the same direction as it would in a motor. This movement increases its length, which cools the arc gases and increases the resistance to the flow of current. The increased length makes it more and more difficult for the voltage across the arc to maintain the flow of ions, until finally the arc is ruptured. The length of the arc depends upon the amount of current flowing when the arc is established, upon the voltage between the contacts, and upon the stored energy in the circuit. The length of this arc may readily be influenced by the design of the arc box and the blowout field.

In addition to the ions that make up the flexible conductor, some stray ions accumulate in the arc box. If the distance between the contacts is small, the voltage between the contacts may cause these stray ions to reestablish the arc by forming a new flexible conductor. Oscillograph records show that sometimes the arc is reestablished two or three times before it is finally interrupted in arc boxes not suitable for the service. The reestablishment of the arc depends upon the design of the arc box and the separation of the contacts. The higher the voltage, the greater is the separation required. If two contactors are used in series, there is much less liability of the arc's reestablishing itself. The two breaks in series also assist in rupturing the arc, as they require the maintenance in series of two flexible conductors made up of ions. They also distribute the heating effect between two or more arc boxes.

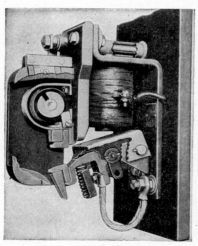

FIG. 4-4. A Westinghouse single-pole magnetic contactor for d-c power. See Fig. 4-5 for method of arc rupturing.

To rupture an arc, it is necessary to lengthen the arc path so as to increase the resistance and, therefore, to decrease the current and, at the same time, to deionize the gas and to cool the arc. The contacts should also be separated far enough to prevent a reestablishment of the arc, or two or more breaks should be used in series for this same purpose.

OPERATION OF DIFFERENT TYPES

Westinghouse Magnetic Blowout. An arc starts as the contact is broken (see Fig. 4-5). As the gap widens between the contacts, the arc is forced from the contact tips by the magnetic blowout. When the contacts are fully open, the arc has been stretched and the gas wedges keep the ends moving by the resistance of the gas in the pockets. This prevents the formation of craters. The stretching and cooling deionize the arc and extinguish it. The magnetic blowout causes the arc conductor to move outward in the same way that a conductor on a motor armature is moved in its magnetic field. As the arc is forced outward, its ends travel along the arcing horns; this lengthens the arc and increases its resistance. The arc-box sides and the air cool this stretched-out arc and extinguish it.

Electric Controller and Manufacturing Company Magnetic Contactor. In Fig. 4-7 is shown the magnetic blowout action in the contactor illustrated in Fig. 4-6. When the contacts open, the current enters at the

FIG. 4-5. Method of arc rupturing used in contactor shown in Fig. 4-4. The arc is moved from the contacts to the arc horn and shield around the blowout coil by the magnetic field which stretches and cools the arc.

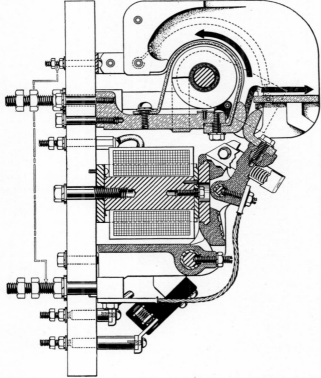

FIG. 4-6. Single-pole d-c magnetic contactor manufactured by the Electric Controller and Manufacturing Company. The action of the blowout field is shown in Fig. 4-7.

upper terminal to the blowout coil and moves thence to the stationary contact, then to its arcing horn, and through the arc to the movable-contact arcing horn.   Thence, by parallel conductors on the outside of the arc box, it passes to the lower terminal stud after the blowout field has transferred the arc from the moving contact to its arc horn. The current in the two parallel conductors outside the arc box is equal

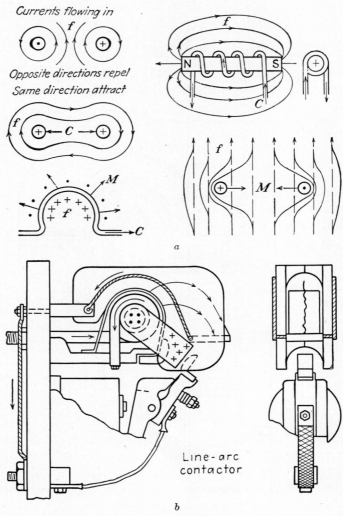

FIG. 4-7.   Action of the magnetic field in quenching the arc in contactor of Fig. 4-6. *a*, Method for keeping the arc in the center of the box by means of conductors parallel to the arc.

to the arc current and moves in an opposite direction. The two circuits repel each other and force the movable arc into the center of its arc box.

The Magnetic Blowout and the Arc Horns. The cooling and deionizing of the arc vapor and the lengthening of the arc path are usually accomplished by means of a magnetic blowout. This lengthening and cooling process may be materially assisted by arc horns and by the proper shape of the arc box.

The ions, which maintain this arc stream, are not only cooled and discharged by contact with the sides of the arc box and the surrounding air, but are cooled also by traveling along the arc horns, which increase the length of the arc under the influence of the blowout field. The projection, or throw, of the arc beyond the edge of the arc box is, therefore, decreased, and much greater energy can be broken in the same size of arc box. If the arc extends a considerable distance beyond the edge of the arc box, it ceases to be under the influence of the magnetic field and may continue to hang on for an appreciable length of time. The burning on the contacts and the arc box for any given current depends upon the length of time the arc is maintained. The further the arc must travel in order to be ruptured,

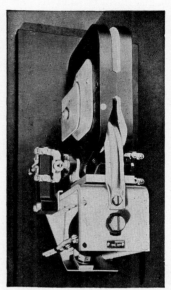

Fig. 4-8. A General Electric single-pole d-c magnetic contactor with blowout and electric interlocks. A sectional view is shown in Fig. 4-9.

the greater the time of burning. By the use of arc horns the arc is extinguished more quickly, and therefore, the amount of burning is decreased.

DESIGN DETAILS

The arc can also be quenched by blowing it through a narrow slot in the arc box. This cools the arc and deionizes the gas, which reduces its volume. It has been found that a restricted-arc-box area at the arc terminals assists in rupturing it and also reduces the burning on the arc horns.

The General Electric Company was one of the first to use the narrow arc box opening (Fig. 4-8) for their magnetic contactors. At our request, E. H. Alexander has prepared the following explanation of the principles of the restricted-arc chute:

The restricted-arc chute is a mechanism often employed on magnetic contactors to facilitate the interruption of arc currents in air. The chute usually consists of some inorganic insulating material of the ceramic variety which has good ability to withstand heat shock and has a high resistance to the erosive effect of the arc. The material should also be a poor source of electron emission at any temperatures encountered under operating conditions within its rating. It does not follow that a material which has a high resistance to the erosive effect of the arc is necessarily the best chute material. Such an arc chute is shown in Fig. 4-8.

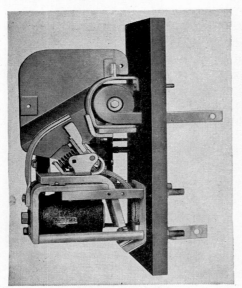 

Fig. 4-9. Sectional view of General Electric contactor shown in Fig. 4-8.

Fig. 4-10. Single-pole d-c magnetic contactor manufactured by the Clark Controller Company.

The physical relationship of a restricted-arc chute to the other component part of a large d-c contactor, is shown with one-half of the arc chute removed in Fig. 4-9.

The principle involved is one of so directing the motion of the arc plasma that its shape presents a more favorable opportunity for heat transfer to the cooler side walls of the chute. As the name implies the restricted-arc chute constricts the hot gases of the arc to a sheetlike formation; *i.e.*, the arc plasma has a high ratio of area to volume, thus presenting an optimum condition for heat transfer. Heat transfer occurs by conduction, convection, radiation, and even by the heat absorbed in vaporizing some of the arc-chute material. From the standpoint of conservation of energy, it is difficult to account for all the energy stored in the circuit being interrupted. There appears to be a considerable amount of difference between the heat appearing in the chute, contactor part, and the total heat represented by the system energy. Therefore, it appears that the action of the arc on the gases of the air may account for a considerable amount of energy absorption.

The rapid introduction of impedance into the circuit being interrupted by the contactor depends in a large measure upon the speed with which the arc can be cooled to a temperature below which ionization of the gases will not support current flow. In the design, a balance must be made between the velocity with which the arc is moved and the dimensions of the space. If it is blown too fast, the arc will reach the end of its travel on the arcing horns before the energy in the circuit is dissipated sufficiently so that the arc can go out. In this case there is

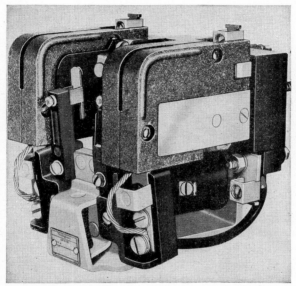

Fig. 4-11. A Westinghouse two-pole d-c contactor.

excessive burning at the ends of the horns, both on the horns and on the chute. If the slot is too narrow, too high a velocity of arc travel may be reached, which may make the arc extend to dangerous distances beyond the chute on high overcurrent. Of course, arc length (stretching) and recovery voltage phenomena both take an important place in arc extinction. The "motor action" used to propel the arc through the chute is the result of the repulsion of two fluxes, the first flux being produced by the ampere turns of the blowout coil and the second flux resulting from the magnetic field surrounding the arc current itself. The proper distribution, polarity, and the strength of the blowout coil flux are factors which must all be balanced to produce a successful design.

The deion principle can be used to rupture an a-c arc when the current passes through zero. The magnetic field moves the arc into a set of slotted metal grids (see Fig. 4-12), where the arc stream is deionized and does not reform after the current passes through zero. This principle is explained in several papers appearing in the *A.I.E.E. Journal*, February, 1929. A simple form of grid is used in commercial a-c contactors where the arc-rupturing demand is limited. The more expensive rotatory-field method is required for circuit breakers of large rupturing capacity.

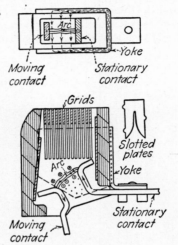

Fig. 4-12. Deion method for rupturing the a-c arc.

The Deion Arc Quencher. The deion arc quencher is used on a-c power; it confines, divides, and extinguishes the arc quickly within itself without the usual flash and the attendant scattering of flame.

The successful operation of the deion contactor depends on the principle that the thin layer of air immediately adjacent to cold cathodes will withstand about 250 volts before breaking down and, after having been subjected to an arc, deionizes rapidly and acquires the ability to withstand this voltage again very quickly. The arc space away from this thin layer of air does not deionize very rapidly. Consequently, in the deion contactor, a number of short arcs in series are utilized in order to get full benefit from the deionizing action of the cold cathodes.

As the arc is drawn between the contacts, it is forced upward by the magnetic field to the stationary end plates. After the arc transfers to the end plates, it continues to move upward into the deionizing chamber, where it is extinguished almost instantaneously. The actual amount of time required for extinction of the arc depends upon the point on the current wave at which the circuit is interrupted. The arc is frequently extinguished before it has time to move above the slotted portion of the metal plates.

As is illustrated in Fig. 4-12, these plates have a tapered slot. When a

Fig. 4-13.   General Electric three-pole a-c contactor with electrical interlock.   One arc box has been removed to show the contacts and blowout coil.

Fig. 4-14.   Cutler-Hammer three-pole a-c magnetic contactor and electrical interlocks.

number of these plates are assembled as shown, they form a V-shaped groove into which the arc is forced.   The contour of this groove is such that, as the arc moves upward, its cross section is decreased and the current density is increased with a corresponding increase in the arc voltage, *i.e.*, voltage drop across the arc.   When a sufficiently high arc voltage is attained, the arc strikes to the metal plates, forming a series of short arcs, which may move up beyond the slotted portion of the plates. The arc continues until the current passes through the zero point of the cycle, at which time each layer of air between the plates is almost instantly deionized, and acquires the ability to withstand 250 volts much faster than any practical power circuit can supply this potential.

In testing a-c contactors, a circuit in the neighborhood of 50 per cent power factor or less should be used, as this gives the most difficult con-

Fɪɢ. 4-15. Cutler-Hammer three-pole a-c contactor in cabinet. One blowout has been removed to show the contact.

ditions. It is much easier to rupture current on circuits of 100 per cent power factor, as the current passes through zero at the same time the voltage is zero and the arc is not easily reestablished. On the other hand with a low power factor there is a considerable voltage between the contacts at the instant the current passes through zero and, therefore, a reestablishment can take place more readily.

Where a large motor is started and stopped frequently, as in hoist service, it is preferable to use an air-break contactor (Fig. 4-19). An oil-immersed contactor forms carbon in the oil each time the circuit is broken; an accumulation of this carbon will ultimately interfere with the proper operation of the contactor. Each time the arc is broken, the heat is transmitted to the oil, which in turn must radiate it from the outside of the case or tank. Repeated opening and closing will very materially

OPERATING COILS

The temperature of operating coils on magnetic contactors is affected by

1. Variation of line voltage, the magnetic air gap of an a-c magnet, and variation in frequency on a-c circuits.

Fig. 4-19. Westinghouse 2,200-volt contactors to control the primary of a reversing motor. Note the mechanical interlock between the reversing contactors.

2. Variation of the air temperature, ventilation, moisture in the air, etc.

3. Variations in the load on the current-carrying parts of the contactor. Heat is readily transmitted from one part of the contactor to another, so that local heating in some other part of the contactor may materially affect the temperature of the operating coil. Sometimes the use of a small lead wire to a contactor will make considerable difference in the temperature of the contacts and the operating coil.

The rating of contactors or other control apparatus is affected by an enclosing case or cover. Any restriction in ventilation increases the temperature, and this is particularly true for control apparatus where the speed regulation of the motor is obtained through the use of resistors. Care should always be exercised in so locating heat-producing apparatus that proper ventilation will be obtained.

SHORT CIRCUITS

A severe short circuit can damage a magnetic contactor, as these contactors are not intended to replace circuit breakers; they are designed to open any operating overload or stalled motor current, but they provide only limited short-circuit protection.

The drop in voltage resulting from the short circuit may cause the magnet to release its armature and open the contacts. This severe arc may damage the controller while the circuit is being opened by other means, or the magnetic reaction of the severe current may force the contacts apart and cause them to chatter and burn. Fortunately, short circuits do not often injure controllers, because a severe short circuit seldom happens. The circuit impedance and the arc resistance limit the current so that the contactor can open the usual short circuit. When controllers are connected close to a heavy bus system, such as that of a large switchboard in a central station, the branch feeder to the controller should have special short-circuit protection. Fuses and a quick-acting circuit breaker are now available that can be used for this purpose. It is desirable to have this disconnecting means separate from the controller, so that the entire controller can be made dead when work is done on it. This is very necessary when the voltage is 2,200 volts or higher.

VOLTAGE REGULATION

A variation in line voltage beyond the guaranteed limits has a bad effect on control apparatus. A decrease in voltage may cause difficulty in the closing of contactors or the operation of other magnetic devices. An increase in voltage will cause overheating in shunt coils. If a motor is operating at a given voltage and this voltage is suddenly decreased below the counter emf of the motor, the current through the motor will be reversed and generator action will take place. A small difference of voltage is sufficient to cause a heavy flow of current if the motor is connected directly to the line without external resistance. This not only causes a jolt to the motor and the controller, but it is very bad on the drive. If gearing is used, the back lash in the gearing may cause a serious blow to the teeth. Gears have been stripped in this way. If a chain drive is used, the results are even worse. Successful operation of electric drive depends upon a reasonably steady voltage; rapid fluctuations of the voltage are particularly harmful.

CHAPTER 5

STARTING CHARACTERISTICS OF MOTORS WITH DIFFERENT METHODS OF CONTROL

The usual method of testing motors and controllers has been to use an ammeter and a voltmeter. These instruments gave good average readings, but owing to the inertia of their indicating member, only average values could be obtained. However, the improvement in the oscillograph and its general adaptation to commercial work have made possible the determination of many factors that are not shown by an ammeter. In some cases even the oscillograph has not been rapid enough to indicate excessive conditions of voltage, and a spark gap has been used. Considerable practice is required to obtain good results with an oscillograph, and experience is required in reading these results. Investigations of this kind have proved valuable, and in many cases mechanical analyses have been made, explaining in detail the phenomena observed with the oscillograph.

DIRECT-CURRENT MOTORS

The simplest form of motor and control, as well as the oldest, is the d-c shunt motor with a controller that short-circuits the armature resistance during acceleration. When this combination was first used, care was necessary in accelerating the motor to prevent excessive sparking or flashing. The starter was operated by hand and had a considerable number of steps. This was necessary in order to cut down the burning on the different steps and to introduce a time element, so that the operator, if he were careless, would not short-circuit the starting resistance too rapidly. Because of this practice, engineers have become accustomed to a considerable number of starting steps in accelerating these motors. They have based their calculations of the accelerating-current peaks on Ohm's law and have neglected a number of other factors that enter into this problem. The use of circuit breakers or overload relays without a time-element attachment has also tended toward the use of a considerable number of starting steps, in order to prevent their tripping on the overload peaks that occur.

The introduction of the magnetic contactor has provided a method of switching electric currents of considerable energy without the rapid destruction of the contact. The contactor can be used in connection with

57

automatic devices for short-circuiting the resistance during acceleration, which eliminate the personal element and prevent careless manipulation. The use of contactors for automatic acceleration immediately reduced the

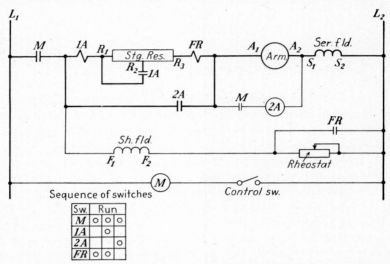

Sw.	Run		
M	o	o	o
1A		o	
2A			o
FR	o	o	

FIG. 5-1. The connections of an automatic control used in tests to analyze the starting characteristics of motors.

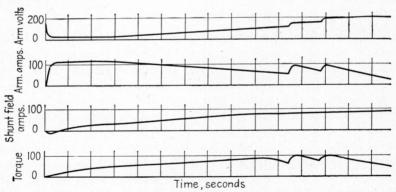

FIG. 5-2. Starting tests of a 20-hp 750-rpm d-c motor belted to a 50-kw generator with no load on the generator. External resistance 1.35 ohms plus 0.25 ohm internal resistance in the motor windings. External resistance short-circuited in two steps at 120 and 160 volts counter emf.

number of starting steps, as compared with those of the manually operated starter. A feeling still exists that several steps are needed for starting even small motors. In order to obtain some actual information, a series of tests were made with an oscillograph on a d-c motor accelerated automatically and belted to a generator of about double the motor size.

A record was made of the armature current, the armature voltage, and the field current. In a few cases a Prony brake was used for loading the motor instead of its being belted to a generator.[1] The diagram of

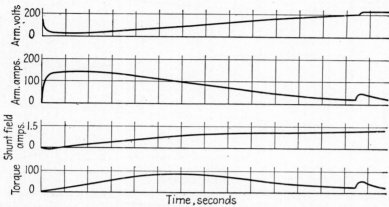

FIG. 5-3. Starting tests the same as Fig. 5-2 except that the external resistance was short-circuited in one step at 190 volts counter emf.

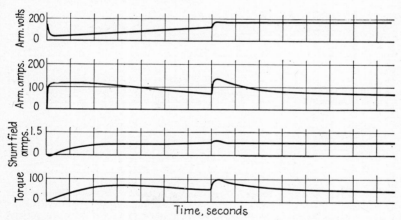

FIG. 5-4. Starting tests of a 50-hp 750-rpm d-c motor with a Prony brake load set for full-load torque at full speed with 0.725 ohm external plus 0.25 ohm internal resistance. External resistance short-circuited in one step at 125 volts counter emf.

connections is given in Fig. 5-1. Figures 5-2 to 5-9 show results of some of the tests. The internal resistance given in the captions includes the complete resistance of the controller and the motor armature circuit, also the leads between the motor and the controller. It was measured from the L_1 to the L_2 terminals of the controller with the starting resistance short-circuited. In addition, as will occur in any installation, there was

[1] The results of these tests appeared in *Proc. A.I.E.E.*, February, 1917, p. 233.

some resistance in the lead wires between the controller and the source of power.

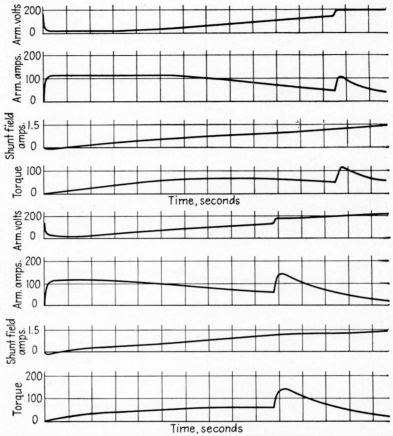

Fig. 5-5. Starting tests of a 20-hp 750-rpm motor belted to a 50-kw generator with no load on the generator. Resistance of 1.35 ohms for starting plus 0.25 ohm internal resistance. The starting resistance was short-circuited in one step at 150 volts counter emf for the upper set of curves and at 120 volts counter emf for the lower set. The adjustment for the upper curves gives equal current peaks and represents a practical controller.

The 50-kw d-c generator belted to the motor represents more inertia than usually occurs in practice. Figures 5-2 to 5-7 cover a period of about 2 sec. Figures 5-8 and 5-9 cover a period of about 4 sec.

SUMMARY OF TESTS[1]

1. It seems unnecessary, with automatic acceleration, to use more than one intermediate step in short-circuiting the armature resistor used with small motors,

[1] *Ibid.*

except where special requirements are to be met. It is practicable to use one switch with motors as large as 15-hp for general purposes and to operate this switch by counter emf, setting the switch to close at 75 per cent of normal voltage.

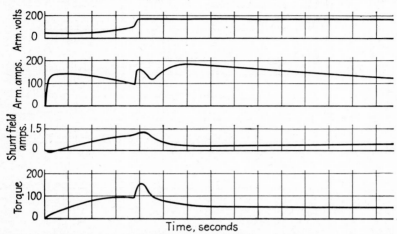

FIG. 5-6. Starting tests of a 20-hp 500- 1,500-rpm motor belted to two 50-kw generators connected to give 20-hp torque at 1,500 rpm. Resistance 0.76 ohm starting plus 0.34 ohm internal resistance. The starting resistance was short-circuited in one step when the counter emf was 100 volts. The field resistance was inserted when the starting resistance was short-circuited, the gradual rise of current being due to weakening the field.

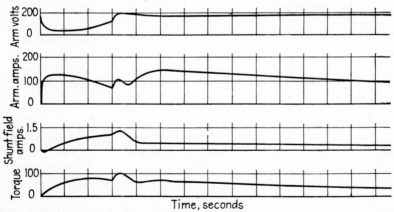

FIG. 5-7. Same data as Fig. 5-6, except that a Prony brake was used instead of the generator to give full load at 1,500 rpm. This gives a heavier starting torque and less inertia. The starting resistance was short-circuited at 120 volts counter emf.

2. If the motor field is zero or has a small value when the line switch is closed, the starting torque is also zero or has only a small value, and it will increase gradually so that the motor, or its load, will not be subjected to a heavy shock or jar when the lost motion in the drive is taken up.

3. The shunt field of small 2 to 1 adjustable-speed motors can be reduced in one

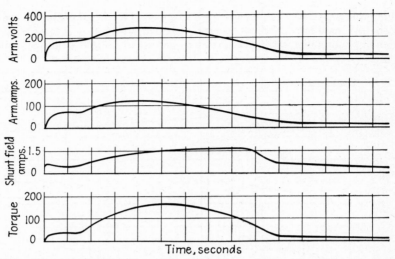

FIG. 5-8.   Effect of field variation on dynamic braking.   Made with a 15-hp 400- to 1,600-rpm motor belted to a 50-kw generator with no load on the generator.   When the motor was operating at 1,600 rpm, the armature was disconnected from the line and connected to a resistance to give dynamic braking.   At the same time the motor-field rheostat was short-circuited, strengthening the field to the 400-rpm value.   The curves show that the field built up faster than the speed decreased, so that the armature voltage at first increased and then remained practically constant for a considerable period.   A strong dynamic brake was thus maintained until the motor speed was quite low, so that it could be easily stopped by friction or a mechanical brake.

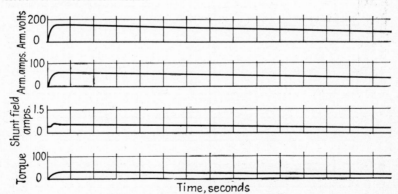

FIG. 5-9.   The same arrangement as Fig. 5-8 except that the motor field was not increased but remained at the 1,600-rpm value, showing that a decreasing torque with decreasing speed will cause considerable drift before the motor comes to rest.

step under normal load conditions without fear of undue torque or current.   This practice can be safely followed with 50-hp motors and perhaps larger.   This covers the usual range of sizes for this type of motor.   Most machine-tool motors are started light.   Under this condition, the motor can be started successfully with minimum field strength and with the field relay omitted.   This will enable the use of the same controller for constant-speed and adjustable-speed motors, supplying a separately mounted field rheostat for the latter.

4. Adjustable-speed motors can use one step of resistance for dynamic braking as the change in field strength tends to maintain the braking current constant over a considerable range of speed.

5. The time required to accelerate to 95 per cent of speed is very short. In these tests the time did not exceed 3 sec.

During the discussion of these tests, it was pointed out that the results obtained may have been materially affected by a drop in line voltage.

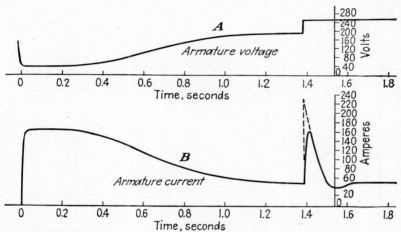

FIG. 5-10. Starting tests of a 15-hp 825-rpm motor driving a Prony brake set for full-load torque. Starting resistance 1.282 ohms plus 0.268 ohm internal resistance. The starting resistance was short-circuited in one step when the counter emf was 161.5 volts.

It was admitted that some drop in line voltage would probably occur in most installations. The effect that the use of a small number of starting steps would have if the motor and the controller were located close to the powerhouse was, however, questioned. In order to determine this point, the author had a number of tests made with the motor connected to the bus bars in the powerhouse. An oscillograph record was taken of the armature amperes, armature volts, and line voltage. The tests showed that there was practically no change in the line voltage during acceleration and that the current peaks obtained were about two-thirds of the value, as usually calculated, based upon Ohm's law. The results of these tests are shown in Figs. 5-10 and 5-11.

In calculating the starting resistance for a shunt motor, the steps are usually arranged in geometrical progression. This method is based on the assumption that each step of resistance is short-circuited when the motor current has reached a uniform minimum value. This value is that necessary to overcome the torque that the motor is required to develop during the accelerating period. During these tests, a standard 15-hp 230-volt 825-rpm shunt motor was accelerated under full load obtained by means of a Prony brake. The minimum accelerating current to overcome this torque was 50 amp. The line voltage was 258 volts, and the resistance was short-circuited in one step. Following the usual method of calculation, and assuming two equal current peaks, a calculated external resistance of 0.905 ohm would be required in series with the motor armature. This would give two equal peaks of 220 amp each. The oscillograph record of this test, shown in Fig. 5-10, was obtained with

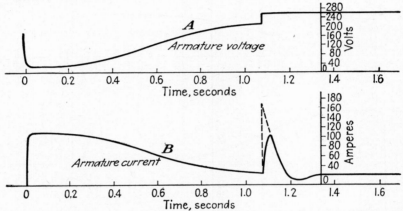

Fig. 5-11.   Same starting test as Fig. 5-10 except that the Prony brake was set for one-half full-load torque.   The starting resistance was 2.062 plus an internal resistance of 0.268 ohm.

1.282 ohms in series with the armature and shows maximum current peaks of 168 amp at start and 163 amp when the resistance was short-circuited. This short circuit occurred when the counter emf across the motor brushes was 61.5 volts. This voltage divided by 0.268 ohm, which is the internal resistance, would give a peak of 230 amp. By extending the current peak to the instant when the resistance switch closed, the curve shown by dotted lines of Fig. 5-10 gives a close check upon the calculated value of the current. The effect of the armature self-induction is shown by the difference between the dotted line and the heavy line. The starting peaks are thus shown to be about two-thirds of the calculated value, using the geometric progression method and neglecting armature reaction.

In Fig. 5-11 are shown the results of a similar test, accelerating with one-half full-load torque applied by Prony brake. The peak calculated in the usual way would require 138.6 amp, based on a minimum accelerating current of 20 amp. The actual peaks obtained were 110 and 102 amp, showing the calculated peak to be about 31 per cent in excess of the actual value.

The following mathematical analysis has been worked out for calculating the true current peak shown in Figs. 5-10 and 5-11.[1] By taking into account inductance and inertia, it is possible to calculate the true peak current when a portion of the external series resistance is short-circuited. The differential equation for the transient current is

$$L\frac{di}{dt} + M\frac{di}{dt} + Ri + K_1\int i\,dt = E^2$$

The effect of mutual inductance M is very small and can be neglected· On the other hand, the countertorque T_c will be considered and assumed constant; hence,

$$L\frac{di}{dt} + Ri + K_1\int i\,dt - K_2\int T_c\,dt = E$$

Since we are considering the case in which the motor has come up to some percentage of full-load speed and a part of the series armature resistance is short-circuited, the initial countervoltage of the motor must be added to the left-hand side of the above equation, giving

$$E_1 + L\frac{di}{dt} + Ri + R_1\int i\,dt - K_2\int T_c\,dt = E$$

The general solution of this equation takes the form

$$i = A_1 + A_2\epsilon^{\frac{-R+\sqrt{R^2-4LK_1}t}{2L}} + A_3\epsilon^{\frac{-R-\sqrt{R^2-4LK_1}t}{2L}}$$

in which A_1, A_2, and A_3 are constants of integration. The value of these in terms of known quantities when the motor is accelerating under a constant resisting torque is

$$A_1 = I = \text{the initial current}$$

$$A_2 = \frac{I(R_s - R)}{\sqrt{R^2 - 4LK_1}}$$

$$A_3 = \frac{I(R_s - R)}{\sqrt{R^2 - LK_1}}$$

where R_s = series resistance that is short-circuited

R = final resistance

---

[1] By A. A. Gazda, who made these tests.

[2] Hansen, K. L., Starting Characteristics of Direct-current Motors, Eq. (22), *Proc A.I.E.E.*, February, 1917, p. 272.

When $4LK_1$ is greater than R^2, the current oscillates around the value required for the constant torque load, and the above general solution becomes

$$i = I + \frac{2I(R_s - R)}{\sqrt{4LK_1 - R^2}} \left(\sin \frac{\sqrt{4LK_1 - R^2}t}{2L} \right) \times \epsilon^{-\frac{Rt}{2L}}$$

The values of current represented by this equation were calculated for the period immediately following the closing of the accelerating switch, as shown in Figs. 5-10 and 5-11. These values check the oscillographic curve very closely and are shown in Table 5-1. This brings out the feasibility of calculating the actual peak current during the acceleration of the motor by means of series resistance.

TABLE 5-1. ACCELERATING CURRENT VALUES

Time,* seconds	Amperes at half-load torque (Fig. 5-10)	Amperes at full-load torque (Fig. 5-11)
0.00	20	50
0.01	76	120
0.02	104.4	153.5
0.03	112.8	166
0.04	107.5	151
0.06	83.2	129
0.08	54.2	93
0.10	33.0	56.3
0.123	20	50
0.14	16.5	45.5
0.16	15.7	45
0.18	16.9	46
0.24	20	50

* Time is calculated from the instant that the resistance short-circuiting switch makes contact.

These last tests confirm the authors' opinion that only a small number of starting steps are required in accelerating a modern d-c shunt motor under ordinary conditions. Where a compound or a series motor is used, the starting torque will build up more rapidly, particularly with the series motor, so that this may prove a limiting condition during acceleration.

A number of tests were made upon a reversing planer equipment to obtain a detailed analysis of the different parts of the operation. These curves, one set of which is shown in Fig. 5-12, proved of considerable interest and value in designing these controllers.

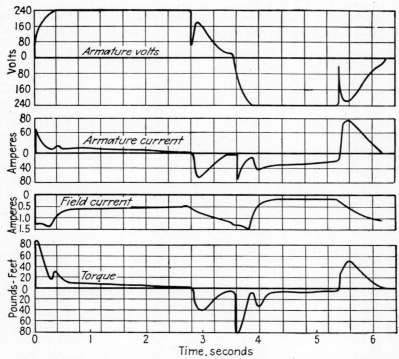

Fig. 5-12. Starting tests of a 20-hp 250- to 1,000-rpm 230-volt shunt motor operating a planer, 24-in. tool travel, 500-rpm cut, and 1,000-rpm return stroke. Beginning at the left, the motor is accelerated for the cutting stroke, then dynamic braking occurs, followed by acceleration for the return stroke. The last loop is dynamic braking from the return stroke.

ALTERNATING-CURRENT SQUIRREL-CAGE MOTORS

Under certain conditions, an excessive current may be obtained in starting a-c squirrel-cage motors.[1] These conditions are not likely to occur in the smaller sized motors commonly used. The increasing use, however, of large-sized motors of this type, particularly with two and four poles, has made it necessary to consider these phenomena and has shown the importance of analyzing the motor and controller as a unit.

Several years ago, a series of breakdowns in the insulation of a wound secondary motor occurred, which were due to the inductive effect between the windings when the secondary circuit was opened before the primary winding was disconnected from the line. Oscillograph tests at first did not disclose this difficulty, but the use of the spark gap showed that approximately five times normal voltage might be obtained in the second-

[1] Hellmund, R. E., Transient Conditions in Asynchronous Induction Machines, *Proc. A.I.E.E.*, February, 1917, p. 205.

ary circuit under these conditions.   Prior to that time, it was the general belief that an a-c motor had very little inductive effect of this kind.

FUTURE INVESTIGATIONS

The writer believes that there is an opportunity for considerable valuable work to be done along this line by universities and technical schools. Most of their laboratories are equipped with oscillographs and other means for this kind of investigation.   The work is very interesting and instructive; in the foregoing description only the more important phenomena have been discussed.   An analysis of the curves shows that the armature voltage is approximately equal to the line voltage at the instant of closing the circuit.   The shunt-field amperage starts at zero and at first has a negative value, probably because of the reactive effect of the armature current.   The peak values of the armature current show a round-off caused by the reactive effect of the circuit.   This can be varied by changing the mechanical inertia of the parts or by changing the inductance of the complete circuit.   The shunt field is assumed to follow the field current quite closely, although it undoubtedly does not reach the instantaneous values shown by the curve of field amperage.   Further investigation in this line would be interesting.

CHAPTER 6

METHODS OF ACCELERATING MOTORS

In starting a motor from rest and bringing it up to full speed from constant-voltage power, resistance is inserted in the armature circuit of a d-c motor or the rotor circuit of an induction motor to limit the current (see Chap. 1). This resistance may be short-circuited gradually by a manually operated controller, or the resistance may be short-circuited in steps automatically as the speed of the motor increases. There are several methods of short-circuiting this resistance automatically, as follows:

1. The counter emf, or speed-limit, method.
2. The current-limit method—series relay—lock-out switch.
3. The time-limit method—dashpots, forced-acceleration—gearing—magnetic inductive delay.
4. Resistance in the primary circuit of a squirrel-cage motor.
5. Secondary frequency for induction motors.

More than one of these methods may be used in a single controller.

In considering methods of acceleration, the time required to close a magnetic contactor or relay should be considered. Relays are small and close quickly, but a large contactor will take several tenths of a second to close; when three or four accelerating contactors are used, they will introduce an appreciable time lag in a total accelerating time of 3 sec. When a section of starting resistance is short-circuited, the inductance of the armature circuit retards the increase of current while the motor is increasing its speed, so that the current peak is reduced (Chap. 5).

The current peaks during acceleration should be kept uniform in order to give a smooth performance. Magnetic amplifiers (Figs. 6-40 and 6-41) assist in overcoming the friction and course adjustment of the accelerating contactors by amplifying the response of the accelerating means.

Each current peak causes a change in the rate of acceleration which should be kept uniform for some applications such as passenger elevators. In 1917 the author used an impedance coil in the armature circuit to round off the top of these current peaks in an elevator application and materially improved the smoothness of acceleration.

Figure 6-43 shows an impedance starter that can be combined with an accelerating resistor to smooth out the accelerating torque. Combining

69

the starters illustrated in Figs. 6-40 and 6-43 will give still smoother acceleration.

Motors usually accelerate under a light load, and the speeding up of the motor armature represents more than half of the work done. Fans, centrifugal pumps, and compressors do not pick up their load until nearly full speed is reached; the inertia of their rotating element is added to that of the motor armature. Machines usually have some friction load to be added. Slow-speed motors are easier to start than the high-speed ones. A centrifugal machine has a large inertia load because of its high speed and may require from 1 to 2 min to accelerate. The time required to accelerate and the work done during this period influences the selection of the method used to obtain automatic starting.

This chapter explains the fundamental principles of the methods more commonly used for automatic acceleration of a motor. They apply to the d-c motor, and most of them can be used with a-c motors.

THE COUNTER EMF, OR SPEED-LIMIT, METHOD

This method has been applied to d-c motors only and is commonly used with shunt, or standard compound-wound, motors. When a motor is started from rest and accelerated to full speed, the voltage across the rotor terminals increases as the speed of the motor increases. If the coil of a magnetic contactor is connected across the motor brushes, the current in this coil will increase as the speed of the motor increases. By the adjustment of the air gap in the magnet, the contactor can be made to close at a fixed voltage across the motor brushes. The closing of the contactor can be made to short-circuit a section of the armature resistance. By the adjustments of several contactors to close at different armature voltages, the series steps of the starting resistance can be short-circuited and the motor be brought up to full speed.

A simple diagram with one step of armature resistance and one magnetic contactor for short-circuiting this resistance is shown in Fig. 6-1. Several steps of starting resistance could, of course, be used with a contactor for short-circuiting each section.

The closing of switch M, which is operated by a push button, connects the motor to the line in series with the starting resistor. One end of the operating coil of this switch is connected to the negative side of the line, and the other end is connected through the push button to the positive side of the line. The coil of switch $1A$ is connected across the brushes of the motor armature and will close the switch when the counter emf of the motor reaches a predetermined value. The closing of this short-circuits the starting resistor R_1R_2 and places the motor directly across the line in the regular operating position.

With the elementary arrangement shown, if switch M is opened by pushing the stop button, switch $1A$ will not open immediately, as it will be held in by the counter emf of the motor. In most commercial switches a counter emf of 25 per cent of the full-speed value will hold the contactor closed. Under this condition, when the motor speed has been reduced to one-fourth full speed, and with contactor $1A$ still in the closed position, the Start button can be pushed, thus closing line switch M, with the result that the motor will be connected directly across the line, without any starting resistance, and may cause a severe jar to the motor and the

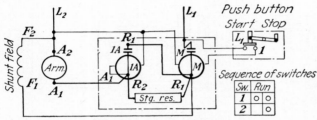

Fig. 6-1. Connections for the counter emf method of accelerating a motor.

machinery that is driven by the motor. In order to avoid such a possibility, in commercial controllers an interlock is usually provided on switch M, which opens the current of the coil on switch $1A$ whenever switch M is opened.

The advantages of this method of acceleration consist in its simplicity, since the switch does not need an auxiliary relay or any other accelerating devices.

Limitations arise where there is a considerable variation in the line voltage. An increase in line voltage will cause the contactor to close sooner than it should, and a drop in line voltage sometimes prevents the contactor from closing. These, however, are extreme cases. With a reasonable system of power distribution, especially if the power circuit is used for lights, the variation of voltage will be small and no trouble should be experienced. Another disadvantage may be caused by a change of adjustment, resulting from a change in temperature in the operating coil of the contactor. In a properly designed contactor, however, changes in the coil temperature will not cause trouble.

Where several contactors are to be installed, it is often necessary to furnish different coils, in order that adjustments can be made over the wide range of voltage necessary for the operation during acceleration. Interlocks are used for dropping out all but the last switch, in order to protect the low-voltage coils from overheating.

A modification of the connection shown in Fig. 6-1 is often used, in order to keep all the coils alike and to eliminate the interlock on the last switch. This arrangement is shown in Fig. 6-2. The operating coils of all contactors have one side connected to the motor brush farthest away from the starting resistor. The other sides of the operating coils are connected to the taps on the starting resistor, the coil on switch $1A$ being connected to R_2 on the resistor. The voltage on this coil is equal to the line voltage, less the drop in voltage through the first section of the resistor, making a combined counter emf and current-limit method of acceleration. As the speed of the motor increases, the counter emf

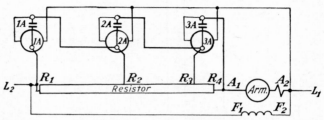

Fig. 6-2. Connections, without the line switch, showing three contactors for accelerating the motor by using the counter emf method.

causes a decrease in the armature current. This reduces the drop through the first section of the starting resistance. The voltage on the operating coil of switch $1A$ is gradually increased until this switch closes. Switch $2A$ has its operating coil connected to R_3 on the starting resistor. The voltage on this coil is increased by the closure of switch $1A$. The increase in current, however, at this instant, causes a considerable drop in the second section of the starting resistance. As this current gradually decreases with the increased speed of the motor, switch $2A$ closes. The operating coil of switch $3A$ is connected across the motor armature, the switch closing when the counter emf of the motor is nearly equal to the line voltage.

THE SERIES-RELAY, OR CURRENT-LIMIT, METHOD

There are a number of different schemes for using a series relay to control the acceleration of a motor. The principle involved in all these schemes is a relay having a series winding that holds the relay contacts in the open position when the current exceeds a predetermined value. When the current is reduced sufficiently, the relay armature drops and completes the circuit to the shunt coil of a magnetic contactor. This method of acceleration can be used for either a-c or d-c motors. The arrangement most common in industrial applications consists of a series relay for each magnetic contactor. The relay contacts are held open mechanically until the electric circuit is closed with the maximum resistance in series. The relay armature is then released mechanically but will not drop until the current is reduced to the value for which the relay is set. The dropping of the armature completes the circuit for the operating coil of a magnetic contactor, which short-circuits a section of the starting resistance.

A simple form of this control is shown in Fig. 6-3. Switch M is controlled by a push button in the same way as in Fig. 6-1. This contactor is provided with a series relay mounted directly beneath the switch, whose contacts are connected to the positive line and, through the operating coil of switch $1A$, to the negative line. When the relay armature is released, these contacts are connected together, thus causing switch $1A$

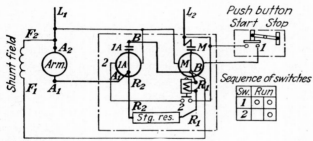

FIG. 6-3. Simplified diagram of connections. A series relay used to regulate the acceleration of the motor.

to close. When switch M is open, the contacts of the relay are held in the open position by a spring. When switch M closes, it releases this spring by mechanical means, so that the contacts may close. The current, however, in the series coil holds the armature in the upper, or open, position until the current has been reduced to a predetermined value. The armature then drops and its contacts are closed. This will not occur until after the motor has approached full speed, so that, when switch $1A$ closes and short-circuits the starting resistor, the increase in current will be limited. Several sections of armature resistance may be used with switches for short-circuiting each section, each switch being controlled by a series relay mounted on the preceding switch in the manner described.

The advantages of this method of acceleration are these:

1. The short-circuiting of the starting resistor depends directly upon the motor current.

2. This method is not affected by variation in line voltage, provided that there is sufficient voltage to close the magnetic contactors.

3. The adjustments for closing are not affected by the heating of the coil.

4. This method limits the load under which the motor will start. If

the load is too great to allow the motor to accelerate sufficiently to reduce the current to the predetermined value, the relay will not drop and close its contacts, and therefore the starting resistance will not be short-circuited.

The limitations of this method are the following:

1. This method may result in too rapid an acceleration of the motor under light loads.

2. Additional apparatus is required, *viz.*, a relay for each resistance contactor.

3. The motor may fail to start under overload. This was given as an advantage, but in some cases it may be a disadvantage, depending upon the application.

SERIES LOCK-OUT CONTACTORS

The series lock-out contactor, when used for accelerating a motor, depends on the value of the armature current in the same way as the series-relay method of acceleration. The contactor is designed so that it is held in the open position when the current through the operating coil or coils is in excess of a fixed value. When the current decreases to the value for which the contactor is set, it closes. There are two general types of these contactors, one using a single coil and the other a double coil. Some contactors depend for their operation on the saturation of the magnetic circuit, while others are designed for circuits not saturated.

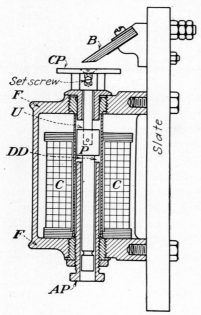

FIG. 6-4. Lock-out contactor of the solenoid type with a series coil.

The motor-armature current may pass through the operating coil, or the operating coil may be connected across a shunt in this circuit. A very convenient form of shunt is the starting resistor.

Single-coil Contactors with Saturated Iron Circuit. This type of lockout contactor is the one most easily understood. The following are several examples of this design.

A lock-out contactor of the coil-and-plunger type is illustrated in Fig. 6-4. The operation of this contactor can be understood by referring to

Figs. 6-5 and 6-6. The flux passing through the air gap *U* tends to lift the plunger *P*, which closes the contacts. This upward movement of plunger *P* is retarded by the magnetic flux in the air gap *D*. Part of the flux passing through *P* enters the narrow portion of the plunger, and part passes through the air gap *D*. The iron in the lower portion of plunger *P* becomes saturated at high current values, forcing a part of the flux through the air gap *D*. As the current through the coil *C* decreases, the total magnetic flux is less. The larger part of this flux passes through

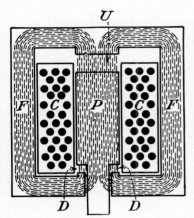

FIG. 6-5. Section of lock-out contactor magnet, solenoid type, showing distribution of flux on overload.

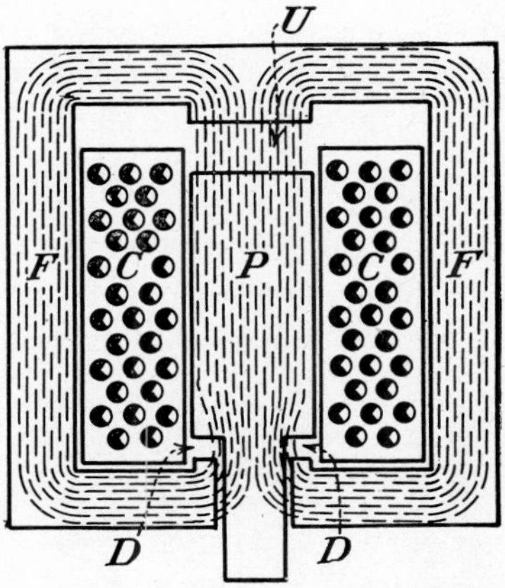

FIG. 6-6. Section of lock-out contactor magnet, solenoid type, showing distribution of flux at time of closing.

the narrow portion of the plunger *P*, and less through the air gap *D*. When the current in the coil drops to the proper value, the flux through the air gap *D* is no longer able to prevent the upward movement of the plunger, which in turn closes the contacts.

The contactor shown in Fig. 6-4 has its air gap *D* located at the end of the sleeve near the bottom of the operating coil. This air gap can be adjusted up or down by means of the threaded hollow plug *AP*. The greater the air gap, the higher the current value at which the contacts are closed.

A clapper type of lock-out contactor is shown in Fig. 6-7. The flux or magnetism in the iron is caused by current flowing through the operating coil. This flux passes through the air gap to the armature of the contactor. Part of this flux passes from the armature through the armature bracket to the magnet yoke and thence to the magnet core. Another part of the flux passes from the armature through the tailpiece to the magnet yoke. The flux through the tailpiece exerts a pull, which pre-

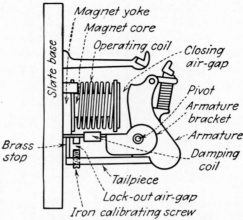

FIG. 6-7.   Clapper type of a series lock-out magnetic contactor.

vents the contactor from closing.   The magnetic path through the armature bracket has a small cross section, so that, when the current flowing

FIG. 6-8. Two-coil magnetic contactor
manufactured by the Monitor Controller
Company.   The closing coil is shunt wound,
and the lock-out coil on the bottom is
series wound.

through the operating coil exceeds
a certain value, the bracket becomes saturated and the balance
of the flux passes through the tailpiece, holding the contactor open.
As the current decreases, the flux
in the saturated armature bracket
remains constant, but the flux
through the tailpiece decreases until it is not sufficient to hold the
contactor open.   The switch can
be adjusted to close at a predetermined current value by changing the hold-out air gap between
the tailpiece and the magnet yoke.
This air gap is adjusted by means
of a calibrating screw.   The greater
the air gap at this point, the higher
is the current value at which the
switch will close.   When the circuit
is first completed through the operating coil, there is danger of the
switch's closing before the flux in
the tailpiece is sufficient to lock it open.   This tendency is overcome by
placing a heavy copper damping coil around a portion of the armature

bracket. When the operating coil is energized, this coil forces the flux to build up in the tailpiece in advance of the armature bracket.

THE TIME-LIMIT METHOD

The accelerating resistor is short-circuited under the control of a time-limit device. The contactors controlling the resistor may have the time delay incorporated as an integral part of them (see Figs. 6-11 to 6-13)

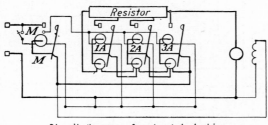

Circuit diagram of series interlocking
No coil interlocks necessary

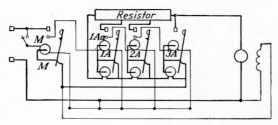

Circuit diagram of shunt interlocking

Fig. 6-9. The application of the contactors (Fig. 6-8) used for automatic acceleration. When *M* is closed the upper, or closing, coil of 1*A* is connected across the line and the lower, or lock-out, coil is in series with the motor. When the armature current decreases to a fixed value, the top coil closes 1*A* and its interlock 1*Aa* connects the top coil of 2*A* across the line. When the current is reduced to the fixed value, 3*A* closes. The starting resistor is now short-circuited.

or their magnetic circuit may be controlled by time-delay relays (see Figs. 6-16 and 6-18) or a master switch (see Fig. 6-19) may be used. Many different devices are used for this method of acceleration. Some of the more common time-delay methods are the following:

1. An oil or an air dashpot.
2. A magnetic or a mechanical drag instead of a dashpot.
3. A motor-operated timer.
4. A ratcheting device with reciprocal drive.

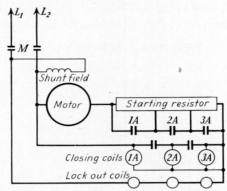

FIG. 6-10.   Contactor of Fig. 6-8, with a simplified arrangement of circuits.   Control similar to Fig. 6-9.

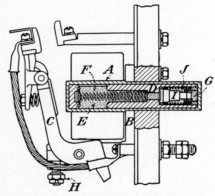

FIG. 6-11.   The Clark Controller Company's Vari-time magnetic contactor with a dashpot in the magnet core.

When the coil is energized, a flux is set up through the hollow brass cylinder A, steel frame B, and steel armature C; but since the brass core is nonmagnetic, insufficient flux is produced to cause the armature to close the main contacts.   However, because of the well-known property of a solenoid to pull its core to its magnetic center, a pull is exerted by the coil on the steel plunger D, tending to pull it forward into the center of the coil. This motion forward, however, is opposed by liquid E, trapped between the core and the front end of the hollow brass tube A.   Hence, before the core can move forward to the center, this liquid has to pass through orifice G into the rear of the cylinder.   This action controls the time required for the steel plunger D to move into the coil center, and this provides a time delay for closing the contactor.   The time can be varied by adjusting stud H.   This contactor is used for accelerating motors.

5. An escapement device controlled by a pendulum or a balance wheel, like a clock or a watch.

6. A magnetic inductive delay—usually the time required to collapse a magnetic field.

Dashpot devices are the oldest of these and are easy to understand, but experience and skill are required for designing them.   The friction

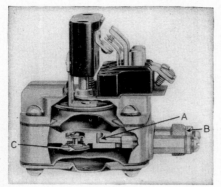

FIG. 6-12. Square D pneumatic time-delay unit.

At the start of the timing period, the operating block is held down by an external force, such as a lever attached to a magnetic contactor (Fig. 6-13). The block is mounted on a flexible diaphragm which forms the top surface of the upper air chamber. When the external force is released, spring pressure starts the block moving upward, and at the end of its upward travel, the electrical contacts close. The rate of motion of the block depends upon the rate of air flow into the upper chamber, through a restricted orifice at A. The size of the orifice (and, therefore, the length of the timing period) is controlled by a needle valve, which may be moved in or out by turning the adjusting member B.

When the timing mechanism is reset, the check valve C is forced open, allowing air to flow back instantaneously from the upper chamber to the lower chamber. Valve C then recloses, so that the restricted orifice is the only passageway for the air during the timing period.

The timer is independent of atmospheric pressure or temperature, because the lower air chamber is open to outside air through a filter. A constant operating force is supplied by the spring on the contact block, thus making the timer also independent of voltage variations.

FIG. 6-13. Square D magnetic contactor with the pneumatic timer shown in Fig. 6-12.

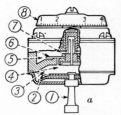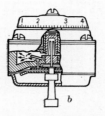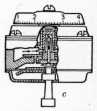

Fig. 6-14. Westinghouse pneumatic time-delay relay. (*a*) Static position. No force applied to pin. (*b*) Force applied to pin pushes air into upper air chamber. (*c*) Force removed from pin. Air from upper chamber escapes into lower chamber. Spring assists in returning pin to static position.

When the actuating pin (1), attached to the rubber diaphragm (2), is raised by action of the magnet frame, air in the lower air chamber (3) is forced through the air passage (4) into the upper air chamber (5).

Timing is initiated when the force on the actuating pin is removed. The diaphragm then tends to move downward because of the action of a spring (not shown) and air returning to the lower air chamber through a constricted air passage (7).

As the actuating pin moves down, the outer end of the operating lever (not shown) moves up, thereby actuating the contacts on the snap switch at the proper time.

The over-all timing period is determined by the position of the valve nut in the orifice and the air-passage space between the valve nut. Variation in the size of the air passage is obtained by rotating the large dial located on top of the assembly. Turning the dial (8) clockwise reduces the air passage and increases the time delay.

Fig. 6-15. Monitor Controller Company's time-limit starter using a gear train for the time delay element. If the starter is for a d-c motor, the line switch is the contactor on the left side of the panel. At the right of the panel is the overload relay. In the center is the accelerator, actuated by a solenoid magnet, that first closes the top contacts in succession to short-circuit steps in the starting resistor. The bottom contact provides the final short circuit. The gear train provides a definite time for starting.

may vary as a result of dirt and temperature, and the viscosity of oil, if it is used, is affected by temperature. In some of the designs that are now used, these limitations are largely overcome. When a separate timing device is used for each step of resistance and fast acceleration is desired, accurate timing is not very important. Often the accelerating time must not be less than a fixed value, but may exceed it to take care of variation caused by temperature, etc. There must always be enough

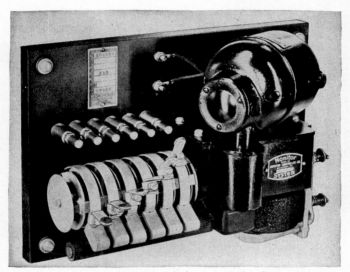

FIG. 6-16. Monitor work-cycle timer mounted on a panel. One unit may contain any desired number of contacts; this one has six.

A motor operates a shaft, through gearing, that moves the rotating contacts into engagement with the stationary contacts. The rotating contacts are connected to the shaft by friction members, which engage them when the magnet is energized. After the moving contact engages its stationary contact, the friction member slips and permits the other contacts to be moved up. The disconnecting of the magnet permits the rotating contacts to drop back to the starting position.

force to overcome the friction and the viscosity of the oil. The dashpots may require cleaning and adjustment from time to time. The application is usually made to controllers that require short periods of acceleration. Figure 6-11 shows a steel-mill contactor using an oil dashpot.

A magnetic drag is often a geared device coupled to a disk rotating through a magnetic field. A fan or a pump drag can be used in the same way. The actuating means may be a motor, a spring, or a weight. The device, which is usually applied in the form of a relay, is used where a long time delay is required.

The pilot motor-operated timer (see Figs. 6-16 to 6-20) usually depends upon its gear ratio for the timing. The coil of a series relay can be put

FIG. 6-17.   FIG. 6-18.

FIG. 6-17. Westinghouse cam controller for regulating the speed of a wound secondary-induction motor 12 to 20 steps 600 to 1,000 amp.   The operating mechanism (see Fig. 6-18) is located in the top of the controller.   The contactors and cams are shown in Fig. 6-19. Operating mechanism for controller shown in Fig. 6-17.

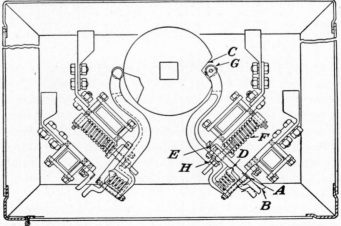

FIG. 6-19.   Contactors and cams for controller shown in Fig. 6-17.

into the main motor circuit and its contacts arranged to open the pilot-motor circuit and arrest its movement if a current limit is reached. The pilot motor drives a drum shaft or a camshaft to establish contacts that

FIG. 6-20. Westinghouse camshaft accelerator driven by a pilot motor on the back of the panel. Handwheel for manual acceleration.

short-circuit the accelerating resistor either directly or as a relay to close a magnetic contactor. Master switches often are of the drum type. When heavy currents are switched, the cam type is best.

These timers are well suited for long periods of acceleration. They are simple and rugged in design and are easy to understand. A quick reset can be obtained by revolving the shaft one notch farther in the same direction of rotation to return to the starting position automatically when the line contactor is opened, or a magnetic reset can be used (see Fig. 6-16). This type of control can be used for both a-c and d-c motors.

The ratcheting and escapement devices fall into the same class. They consist of gearing and an actuating means. The ratcheting device has a

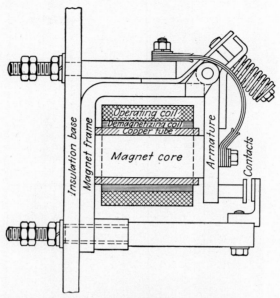

Fig. 6-21. Elementary sketch of magnetic-timing relay showing the copper tube for increasing the time of armature release and demagnetizing coil to reduce the time. Either or both can be omitted. Time can be reduced by increasing the air gap.

reciprocating drive actuating a pawl in a ratchet wheel. The escapement device is a simple and rugged set of gears similar to a clock or a watch movement, the timing controlled by a pendulum or by a balance wheel. These methods are applied to small starters and relays. Accurate timing can be obtained with the pendulum arrangement for long periods of time. It closely resembles a motor-driven clock.

The magnetic inductive delay has a variety of interesting possibilities. It is based upon the principle that time is required for magnetic flux in an iron circuit to die out. The time can be lengthened by putting a copper tube around the magnet core. This becomes a short-circuited secondary and opposes any change of flux in the iron (see Fig. 6-21). The time can be adjusted by changing the thickness of this tube. Similar results are obtained by short-circuiting the magnet coil. Resistance added to the coil circuit shortens the time. A second method is to change the air gap in the iron circuit. A small change has a large time effect. A third method is to use a small demagnetizing coil. A fourth method is to shunt the coil with a condenser or a resistor.

One type of relay has spring-closed contacts opened by a magnet (see Fig. 6-21). Upon starting, the magnet is energized to open the contacts, which are closed when the magnetic flux in the core decreases to the release value. Figure 6-21 will illustrate a single- or double-coil switch or relay.

FIG. 6-22. The General Electric Company's magnetic-time-delay relay.

In the time-current accelerating relay shown in Fig. 6-23, when a current passes through the series coil, the magnetic flux building up in the core and the frame induces a current in the aluminum tube, causing it to jump and open the circuit to a succeeding accelerating contactor coil. When the series current and the flux cease to build up, the aluminum tube starts to sink, but does this more slowly if the series-coil current remains large. For light starting loads the aluminum tube falls more rapidly. At the bottom of its stroke it bridges the stationary contacts to bring in the next accelerating contactor. The maximum time setting (2.75 sec) with stalled motor current flowing in the series coil is obtained with the core screwed up into the frame flush with a locknut. Screwing the core down shortens the time interval for a given coil current. This relay, with some modifications, is used to prevent the plugging contactor from closing until the counter emf of the motor is reduced. It is connected across the plugging step of resistance.

An interesting application of the relay shown in Figs. 6-24 and 6-25 is a group of motors that cannot be started together after a voltage failure

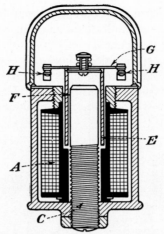

FIG. 6-23. Electric Controller and Manufacturing Company time-current accelerating relay. *A*, series coil; *C*, adjusting core; *E*, aluminum tube; *F*, core; *G*, movable contact; *H*, stationary contacts.

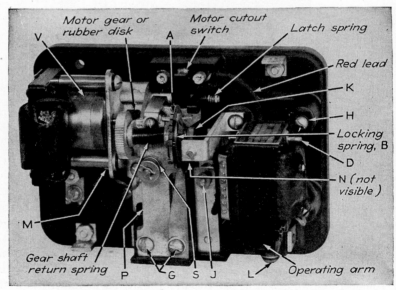

FIG. 6-24. General Electric Company's definite time-delay relay.

caused by lack of power, such as motors on an irrigation service line. A relay added to each motor control can be adjusted to start the motors at intervals. The General Electric Company's time-delay relay (Fig. 6-24) is driven by a synchronous motor suitable for use on alternating current only. When the relay is energized, the solenoid engages the motor with the contact-operating mechanism; a tap on the solenoid provides the correct voltage for the motor. After the predetermined time interval has elapsed, the normally open contact *TC* closes, the normally closed contact

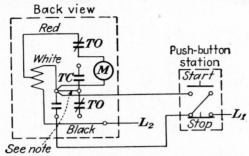

Fɪɢ. 6-25. Diagram for relay shown in Fig. 6-24.

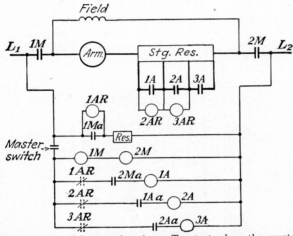

Fɪɢ. 6-26. Magnetic-time-delay acceleration. To start, close the master switch which closes $1M$, $1Ma$, $2M$, $2Ma$. When the magnetism in $1AR$ is nearly zero, $1A$ and $1Aa$ close and short coil $2AR$, which permits $2A$ and $2Aa$ to close and to short coil $3AR$. This permits $3A$ to close. Magnets $1AR$, $2AR$, and $3AR$ can be attached to the tailpiece of a contactor (see Fig. 6-28) and $1Aa$ and $2Aa$ can be interlock contacts or the magnets can be parts of separate relays (see Fig. 6-23) having contacts in series with coils $1A$, $2A$, and $3A$ shown in dotted lines. The collapse of flux in $1AR$, $2AR$, and $3AR$ can be controlled by the air gap or by damping means.

TO opens (see Fig. 6-25), and the motor cutout switch disconnects the motor. The contacts remain in the timed-out position until the relay is deenergized, at which time the solenoid drops out and the contacts are reset instantly to their original position.

An interlock contact *J* (Fig. 6-24) is provided to establish a holding circuit when the relay is energized from a momentary-contact push

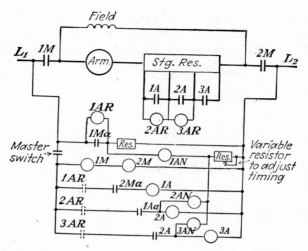

FIG. 6-27. Magnetic-time-delay acceleration with neutral-coil adjustments. Operation is the same as Fig. 6-26 with neutralizing coils added to 1AR, 2AR, and 3AR to adjust the timing.

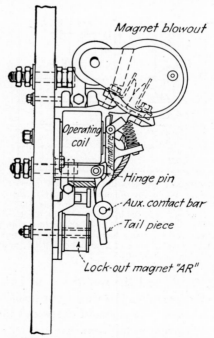

FIG. 6-28. Cutler-Hammer contactor with lock-out magnet under tailpiece. Contacts are in the closed position.

button, as shown in Fig. 6-25. This contact, which is normally open, closes when the solenoid is energized.

The time setting may be adjusted by releasing the locking spring B and turning the calibrating dial A until the locking spring is dropped into the slot marked with the desired time. The dial is calibrated either in seconds or in minutes, depending on the maximum time obtainable.

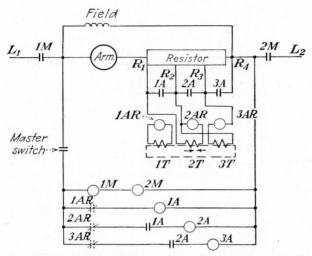

Fig. 6-29. Magnetic-time-delay acceleration using a transformer to energize the lock-out magnets.

To start, close the master switch. This closes $1M$ and $2M$ and energizes $1A$. Transformer $2T$ now predominates over $3T$, as R_1-R_2 is greater than R_2-R_3, giving $2T$ more voltage than $3T$. Current is induced in $1T$ during the rise of flux. When the flux becomes constant, $1AR$ releases the contactor (Fig. 6-28) and $1A$ closes. This short-circuits $2T$, $3T$, reverses the flux, and causes current to flow in $2AR$. When the flux becomes constant, $2AR$ releases and $2A$ closes. This short-circuits $3T$, and the flux collapses, sending current through $3AR$. When the flux is gone, $3AR$ releases and $3A$ closes.

Coils $1AR$, $2AR$, and $3AR$ can be on relays (Fig. 6-21) and hold open contacts in series with $1A$, $2A$, and $3A$ shown by the dotted lines instead of holding the contactors (Fig. 6-28) open. The timing can be adjusted the same as for Fig. 6-26.

Another type consists of a normally open switch, closed by a magnet and having a lock-out magnet attached to its tailpiece, to lock the switch open until the flux in the tail magnet dies out (see Fig. 6-28). The operation of the controllers using these three types of switches is explained in the captions under the diagrams.

The magnetic-delay method is free from friction, temperature, dirt, and moisture; its timing remains constant if the air gap does not change. One size and design of relay can be used for controlling different sizes of contactors, which makes a good manufacturing and stocking arrangement. Standard contactors can be used.

This method of control is used for a-c motors by rectifying the control-circuit current.

Two pole contactors are required to short-circuit the resistance in the secondary of a slip-ring motor.

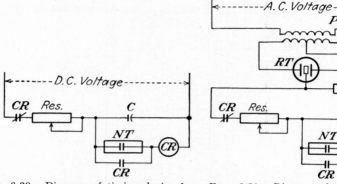

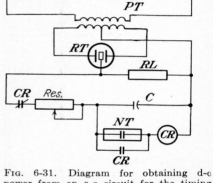

FIG. 6-30.   Diagram of timing device for relay *CR*, using a neon tube *NT*, a condenser *C*, and relay contacts *CR*.

FIG. 6-31.   Diagram for obtaining d-c power from an a-c circuit for the timing device in Fig. 6-30.

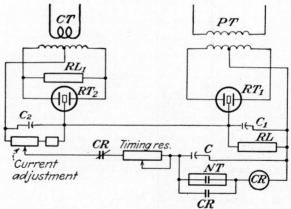

FIG. 6-32.   Diagram for obtaining current in addition to time control of relay *CR* shown in Fig. 6-31.   This gives the time-current acceleration of Electric Controller and Manufacturing Company Neo-time-current starters for a-c motors (Fig. 6-36).

Figure 6-30, taken from H. L. Wilcox's paper before the A.I. & S.E. on Dec. 4, 1939, shows how a condenser *C* and a neon discharge tube *NT* can be used to time a relay with coil *CR*.   When the voltage on the condenser reaches the ignition voltage of the neon discharge tube *NT*, the condenser discharges through the tube and the coil, which causes the relay to "pick

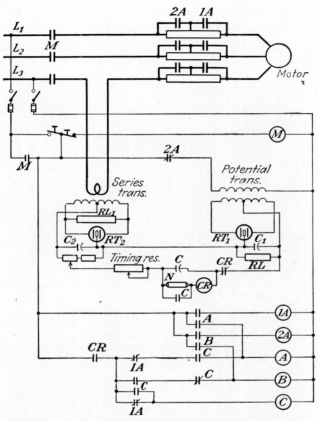

FIG. 6-33. Neo-time-current acceleration for a three-step starter for squirrel-cage motor. The first operation of the *CR*, or timing relay, closes relay *C*, which holds itself closed as long as *CR* is closed and which, when operating, opens the circuit to relay *B* and closes the circuit to relay *A*, causing *A* to operate, which in turn holds itself closed and closes the first accelerating contactor 1*A*. If the timing relay *CR* should remain closed, even after 1*A* operates, it is impossible to close relay *B*, because *C* is still held in its closed position. Therefore, only one step of acceleration can come in on the operation of *CR*, and in order to get the succeeding steps of acceleration closed, *CR* has to drop out, which will occur after the condenser has discharged. When *CR* drops out, the charging circuit to the condenser is again established and relay *C* drops open. When the condenser has again become charged, it causes *CR* to operate for the second time, and this time *CR* will close relay *B* through the contacts of 1*A* and *C*. *B* will then hold itself closed and close accelerating contactor 2*A*, completing acceleration of the motor. Closure of contactor 2*A* opens the circuit to the timing transformer and prevents further operation of the timer while the motor is running.

up," opening the charging circuit and closing a discharge circuit for the condenser around the tube and through the coil. The relay remains closed until the condenser voltage reaches the "drop-out" voltage of the relay. The relay then closes RCa and opens RC, and the cycle is repeated. Other contacts can be added to the relay to actuate contactors when the relay is either Up or Down. When used with a-c power, the d-c power

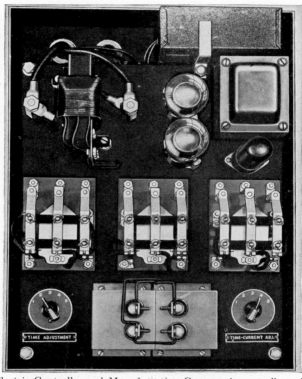

FIG. 6-34. Electric Controller and Manufacturing Company's controller using condenser timing and current limit. This is the master element for the controller shown in Fig. 6-35. This device is in the enclosed cabinet at the top of the controller.

required for operating the relay can be obtained from a rectifier of the tube type (see Fig. 6-31) or of the copper oxide or selenium type. The relay CR can be combined with a potential transformer PT and a current transformer CT (see Fig. 6-32), to give time-current acceleration of a-c motors. The current transformer opposes the voltage of the potential transformer, to increase the time required to operate the relay CR.

In the diagram shown in Fig. 6-32, PT is a potential transformer supplying voltage for the rectifier tube RT_1, similar in connections to the circuit shown in Fig. 6-32. *CT* is a current transformer, the primary of which can be connected in the primary circuit of the motor or other device, while the secondary supplies voltage to a second rectifier tube RT_2. The connections are so made that the rectified voltage from tube

FIG. 6-35. A complete controller using the master element shown in Fig. 6-34.

RT_2 bucks the rectified voltage from tube RT_1, and it is thus seen that, with higher currents in the primary of *CT*, the combined rectified voltage for charging the condenser will be reduced and, therefore, the time for the condenser to become charged will be increased. It is necessary in these connections to use load resistors *RL* and RL_1, also two filter condensers C_1 and C_2, which cause the two rectified voltages to remain in phase. By shifting the current adjustment tap on the resistance supplied with the CT timing element, it is possible to increase or decrease the amount of bucking effect and, therefore, to increase or decrease the amount of current effect upon the timing.

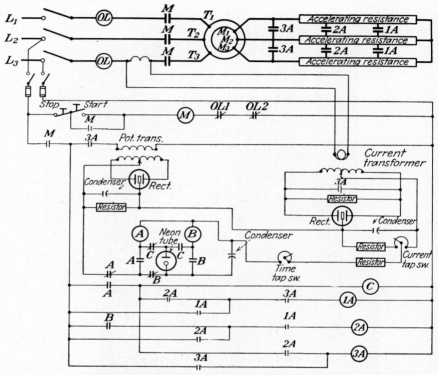

Fig. 6-36.   Diagram showing Neo-time-current acceleration for a four-step wound-rotor induction motor of the Electric Controller and Manufacturing Company.

FREQUENCY CONTROL FOR ACCELERATING
A-C WOUND-ROTOR MOTORS

When a 60-cycle a-c wound-rotor motor is accelerated, the secondary frequency decreases from 60 cycles at zero speed to 2 or 3 cycles at full speed and the voltage between phases also decreases in the same proportion. The Electric Controller and Manufacturing Company has developed a frequency-relay system responsive to this frequency and voltage change to control the short circuiting of the secondary resistor in steps, in accordance with the motor speed shown in Fig. 6-37. Use is made of the principle of resonance to hold relays open until the desired frequency is reached. Each relay coil has a condenser in series with it, and both are in parallel with part of an adjustable resistor, as is shown in the diagram. The condensors are given different capacities to make

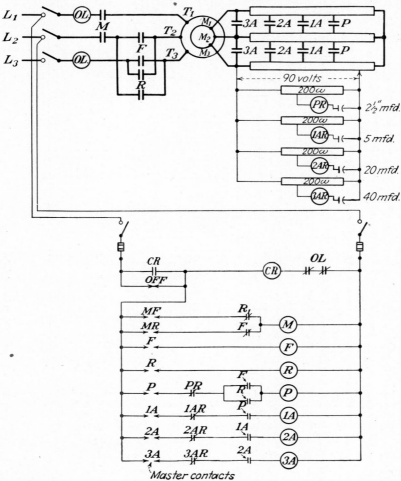

Fɪɢ. 6-37. Diagram of a-c controller using frequency relays to obtain automatic acceleration.

the relays drop out at 63 cycles for plugging, 44, 22, and 6 cycles for acceleration. Figure 6-38 shows the current curve of each relay and its drop-out point.

Both the diagram and the curve are taken from the paper by H. L. Wilcox, previously referred to. This paper describes many details of the control. The relay inductance is different at open and at closed gap, so that the relay "drops out" at a higher current than it "picks up." Should the load on the motor increase above normal, the secondary current will increase, the relay will pick up, and the secondary resistance will be increased. From Fig. 6-39, showing the speed-torque curve of a wound-secondary motor, it will be seen that for each step of resistance added, the motor speed is reduced; this usually reduced the load. The

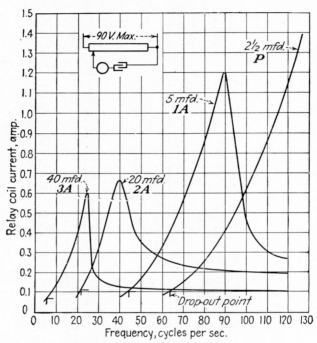

FIG. 6-38. The drop-out points of relays when the frequency decreases during acceleration of a wound-rotor induction motor (Fig. 6-37). These points are at 63, 44, 22, and 6 cycles.

motor will be automatically accelerated to full speed again when the load returns to normal. The curves also show that the resistor should not be reduced faster than the motor accelerates, as this will reduce the torque and the motor may "pull out." When the load has a flywheel, these relays can be used to "step back" on the resistor to let the flywheel take part of the load and keep the current peaks down.

MAGNETIC-AMPLIFIER CONTROL FOR ACCELERATING D-C AND A-C MOTORS

The magnetic amplifier is explained in Chap. 13. It is a saturated-core transformer which is worked close to the saturating point of the iron so that the control winding can make a large change in saturation with

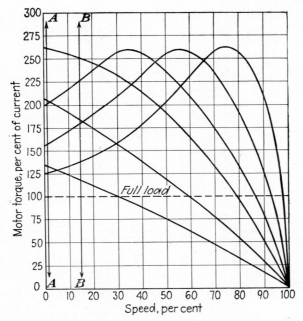

Fig. 6-39. Speed-torque curves of a wound-rotor induction motor. Each curve has a different amount of resistance in the secondary circuit. The last curve to the right has no external resistance, and the secondary windings are short-circuited.

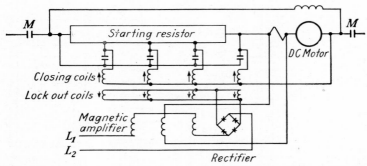

Fig. 6-40. Direct-current starter of the magnetic-amplifier type (Chap. 13). The contactors short-circuiting the starting resistor have two coils opposing each other. The "closing" coils are connected to taps on the starting resistor so that their coils receive an increasing voltage as the motor accelerates. The "lock-out" coils receive a voltage through the magnetic amplifier which is proportional to the load. This arrangement closes the starting contactors in steps as the motor accelerates.

very little current change.   This control winding is connected across the interpole windings of a d-c motor (Fig. 6-40) or across the terminals of a series transformer in the primary of an a-c motor (Fig. 6-41).   This

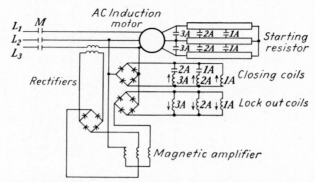

FIG. 6-41.   Magnetic-amplifier starter for wound-secondary a-c motor (see Chap. 13).
    Two-pole contactors 1*A*, 2*A*, and 3*A* are provided to short-circuit the starting resistor in steps as the motor accelerates.
    Each contactor has two coils on its magnet; one coil closes the contact, and the other coil prevents closure as indicated by the arrows.   These "lock-out" coils are energized through the magnetic amplifier and a rectifier.
    The control coil of the amplifier receives power from a series transformer in proportion to the motor current.   When *M* is closed, the motor current is high and the lock-out coils will prevent 1*A* from closing.   When this current decreases, owing to an increase in motor speed, 1*A* closes, reducing the secondary resistance and energizing the closing coil of 2*A*. Contactor 2*A* closes when the increase in motor speed reduces its current and the current in its lock-out coil.   Contactor 3*A* closes when the motor reaches full speed and short-circuits all the starting resistor.

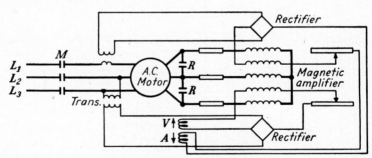

FIG. 6-42. Magnetic-amplifier control for wound secondary-induction motor. The amplifier is connected in the secondary circuit and provides some of the impedance during starting.

current is converted to d-c power through a static rectifier (page 220). (The diagonal squares are rectifiers.)   A small increase in current in the control winding makes a large reduction in the impedance and a corresponding increase in the rectified current in the lock-out windings of the resistor contactors.   These windings oppose the closing coil windings and prevent the contactor from closing until the motor current decreases to a fixed value.

This system of control is new and will probably be found useful for larger size motors where accurate accelerating load limits are more necessary. A slip regulator of this type is shown in Fig. 11-6.

CONCLUSION

The selection of the proper method of accelerating a motor depends upon the application, the voltage regulation of the power supply, the first cost, and the preference of the purchaser.

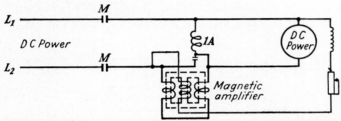

FIG. 6-43. Induction starter for d-c motor (see Chap. 13). When M is closed, the field current increases slowly and the amplifier impedance is high to limit the motor starting current. As the field current increases and the motor gains speed, the impedance is reduced. At full speed contactor $1A$ closes to short-circuit the amplifier.

Customer preference shifts from one type to another, and all types have their limitations—a circumstance that influences the situation. Often several different methods of acceleration are equally satisfactory for the same application. Usually the type having the lowest first cost is preferred in the general-application field. More expensive types are justified in special fields, as they reduce the maintenance expense and shutdown time. Time delay is preferable where the line voltage fluctuates. The increment starting required for large motors connected to network systems uses definite time-delay acceleration. The counter emf system requires the least apparatus.

The series lock-out contactor, which was once very popular in steel-mill service, is not used much at present. The popular method now is time delay.

CHAPTER 7

METHODS OF SPEED CONTROL

DIRECT-CURRENT VARYING-SPEED MOTORS

Variations in the speed of a d-c motor can be obtained by changing the voltage across the motor brushes. Usually this is accomplished by placing a resistor in series with the armature, as shown in Fig. 7-1. The

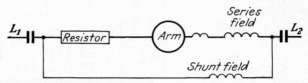

FIG. 7-1. Diagram of connections for varying the speed of d-c motors that use a resistor in series with the armature.

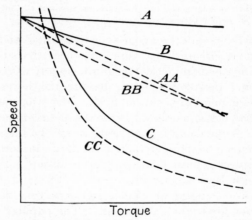

FIG. 7-2. Characteristic regulation curves of d-c motors that use the series-resistor scheme in Fig. 7-1.

drop in voltage through the resistor is equal to the resistance multiplied by the current. If the line voltage remains constant, the speed of the motor can be varied by changing either the ohmic resistance or the load. The characteristic curves for d-c shunt, compound, and series motors are shown in Fig. 7-2. Curve A is for a shunt motor. The difference in speed between full load and no load is caused by the drop in voltage due to the internal resistance of the motor. The amount of change in speed

100

is called the regulation of the motor, which may be expressed by giving the speeds at no load and at full load or as a percentage change in speed. The shunt motor is assumed to have a constant field strength; therefore, the change in speed is small. If, however, a resistor is placed in series with the armature, a curve such as AA is secured, which shows considerable reduction in speed at full load, the amount of speed reduction depending upon the resistance in series with the armature. In this case, it can readily be seen that the speed of the motor depends upon the load and will vary with different values of torque. For this reason these motors are called "varying-speed" motors.

If part of the field winding is made up of series turns, the field strength will increase with increased torque, so that the difference between no-load and full-load speed is quite marked, as is shown by curve B. If external resistance is used, a curve such as BB results. This curve can be changed by varying the amount of resistance in series with the armature. Curve C shows the regulation curve of a series motor. Theoretically, at no load, there is zero field strength and, therefore, infinite speed. Consequently, it is necessary to have a definite load on a series motor to prevent its running away, and series motors should not be used for any applications where the load is reduced to a very small value. Usually 25 per cent of full load is required to keep the speed within safe limits. If a resistor is used in series with the armature, curve CC results, which can be varied by changing the resistor.

It will be seen from these curves that the series motor is best adapted for speed regulation by the use of series resistance, the slope of its curve being much steeper than those for the shunt and the compound motor. Where the load may become very light at times, it is necessary either to make a special arrangement for energizing the series field, as will be explained later, or to use a compound motor. The curve for the compound motor will vary between that of the series and that of the shunt motor, depending upon the percentage of compounding used.

With this method of speed control, it is necessary to change the amount of armature resistance to obtain the correct speed with a changing load. This at first sight may seem to be rather complicated, but in practice the operator can move his controller lever forward or back until the desired speed is obtained.

Where it is desirable to regulate the speed of the motor within closer limits, the arrangement of resistors shown in Fig. 7-3 is used, where RA is a resistor in series with the armature and RS is a resistor in shunt with the armature. This is known as a combined armature-series and shunt-resistance control. If RS has a very low ohmic resistance, the speed of the armature can be held at a low value throughout its range

of load.   Figure 7-4 shows the various curves for this arrangement.
Curve 1 is the armature current.   Curve 2 is the line current, and curve
3 is the shunt current passing through the resistor *RS*.   Curve 4 is the
speed-current curve for the motor connected directly to the line.   It can
be seen from these curves that the motor performance is somewhat
similar to a badly regulated shunt motor.   At no load, the series field
obtains current through the resistors *RA* and *RS* so that the speed of the

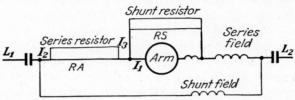

Fig. 7-3.   Diagram of connections for speed regulation that use the combined series- and
shunt-resistance control method.

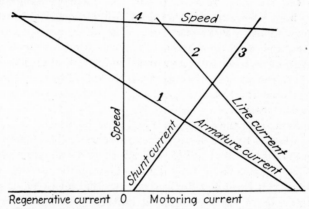

Fig. 7-4.   Characteristic curves of d-c motors that use the control scheme in Fig. 7-3

motor has a fixed value.   The speed can be changed by varying either
RA or *RS*.   Sometimes both are changed simultaneously.   In figuring
the speeds obtained with this arrangement, the circuit is rather complicated.   The problem can be simplified by drawing curves similar to the
ones shown in Fig. 7-4.   Two points in these curves can readily be determined.   The armature and line current can be found for zero load and
for zero speed.   The shunt current in resistor *RS* can be figured from
these two values.

DIRECT-CURRENT ADJUSTABLE-SPEED MOTORS

If the internal resistance of the armature is neglected and if it is
assumed that the number of conductors on the armature is fixed, the

speed of the motor will depend upon the strength of the field, provided that a constant voltage is maintained across the armature brushes. If the motor is shunt wound and a rheostat is placed in series with the field winding, the current can be changed and the motor caused to operate at different speeds. The speed of the motor will be practically constant for whatever value the rheostat is adjusted and will not vary under changing loads. For this reason, the motor is called an adjustable-speed motor. There will be a small change in speed between no load and full load, owing to the drop through the armature resistance. This change in speed, however, is usually negligible for most applications. The amount of speed range that can be obtained on a given motor depends upon the iron in the magnetic circuit. The slowest speed is obtained with the maximum field strength. This field strength, of course, reaches a limit when the iron in the magnetic circuit becomes saturated. The maximum speed is obtained with the weakest permissible field strength. This can be reduced only a limited amount, as sufficient field must remain to give stable operation of the motor. To obtain a wide speed range by field control involves considerable expense in the motor, and usually a maximum of 4 to 1 is all that is attempted commercially.

For many applications, the combination of armature resistance and field control is used. The slow speeds are often required for only short intervals of time or at reduced loads, so that the loss in armature resistance is small.

DIRECT-CURRENT MOTOR VARIABLE-VOLTAGE CONTROL SYSTEM

If a separate generator is provided for each motor, the speed of the motor may be altered by changing the field strength of the generator. This alters the voltage of the generator, and the motor has a speed corresponding to the generator voltage. The generator field may be reversed to reverse the rotation of the motor. Very slow speeds can be obtained, and the speed remains fairly constant between no load and full load. At first, this method of control was reserved for large motors of several hundred horsepower, being particularly adapted for reversing service, as for large mine hoists and reversing steel mills. Later it was successfully extended to smaller motor installations, such as elevators, reversing planers, etc. The controller is small and inexpensive, as only the field current of the generator is manipulated. It is the practice to connect the generator and motor armatures in a closed circuit provided with a single overload circuit breaker, which is opened only in cases of emergency. Electron tubes can be used instead of the motor-generator set (see Chap. 21).

Sometimes this arrangement of control is combined with a motor having a 2 to 1 speed range by field control, so that higher speeds can be obtained for certain operations. The initial cost of this combination is less than that of the constant-speed motor, as it does not add a great deal to the cost of the motor to obtain the additional increase in speed, and a smaller generator can be used than would be required if the entire speed range were obtained by varying the generator voltage.

A more detailed discussion is given in Chap. 11.

ALTERNATING-CURRENT VARYING-SPEED MOTORS

The relation between the speed and the torque of an induction motor having a wound secondary with collector rings is shown in Fig. 7-5.

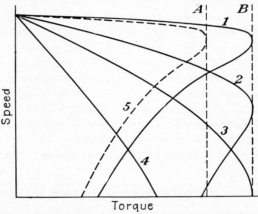

Fɪɢ. 7-5. Typical speed-torque curves of a wound-rotor induction motor. Obtained by varying the resistance of the secondary circuit.

When the collector rings are short-circuited, the speed of the motor decreases very little from no torque to the maximum torque. When this torque is exceeded, the speed of the motor drops abruptly and continues to decrease until zero speed is reached. If, however, the torque is sufficiently reduced, the motor will again increase in speed until it is very close to full speed. The curve shows that there is a maximum torque that the motor is capable of exerting and that, if this torque is exceeded, the motor will stop. This maximum torque is usually called the "pull-out torque" of the motor. The drop in speed from no load to maximum load is small and compares with that of the d-c shunt motor. This drop in speed is due to the internal resistance of the motor.

If resistance is introduced in the secondary circuit of the motor, the slope of the speed curve is increased, so that the difference in speed between no load and maximum load is considerable, as shown in curve 2. Sufficient resistance can be used to bring the speed to zero at the maximum torque, as shown in curve 3. With a still further increase in resistance of the secondary, curve 4 results. These curves are typical, and any particular curve desired can be obtained by adjusting the resistance in the secondary circuit of the motor. If a controller is arranged for varying the resistance in the secondary of the motor, the speed of the motor can be adjusted to any required value at a given torque. The speed, however, will change with the torque, and for that reason the motor is called a "varying-speed" motor.

When the motor is started from rest, it may not commence to rotate on the first notch of the controller; the operator will, therefore, move the controller handle to the second notch to reduce the resistance in the secondary. This reduction of resistance will increase the starting torque by changing the shape of the curve up to the point of maximum, as shown in curve 3. If the resistance is reduced still further, the current will increase, but the torque will decrease, as shown in curves 2 and 1. Hence, it will be seen that care must be exercised in starting these motors under heavy load, to prevent reducing the resistance in the secondary beyond the value for maximum torque.

The speed of the motor at no load is called the "synchronous" speed. When the motor is loaded, the actual speed of the motor is less than the synchronous speed. This difference in speed is called the "slip" of the motor. The curves show that this slip in speed is dependent upon the resistance in the secondary circuit.

The torque of the motor is proportional to the square of the voltage. A reduction of 10 per cent in voltage reduces the torque to 81 per cent of its maximum value, or the pull-out torque of the motor is reduced from the dotted line *B* in Fig. 7-5 to the dotted line *A*. The speed-torque curve of the motor with short-circuited secondary and 90 per cent normal voltage is shown by the dotted curve 5. Thus the output of a crane or a hoist is often seriously affected by poor voltage regulation. It may happen that, when the voltage regulation is poor, the motor will fail to start its maximum load from rest.

If the motor is provided with a high-resistance secondary, as shown in Fig. 7-6, curve 1, which is a speed-torque curve similar to curve 3 in Fig. 7-5, the speed of the motor may be regulated by reducing the primary voltage, as shown in Fig. 7-6, curves 2, 3, and 4. This method has been employed but has the disadvantage of giving reduced torques at decreased voltages. Usually the motor is required to exert as much torque at the slow speed as at the high speed; this method is, therefore, seldom used. The method in universal use at present for varying the speed of induction motors is to maintain the primary voltage constant and change the resistance in the secondary of the motor.

There are several other methods of controlling the speed of the slip-ring induction motor, some of which are applicable only to large motors. They consist in connecting the slip rings of the motor to some source of voltage supply the voltage and frequency of which can be varied. These methods of control are not in common use (see Chap. 15).

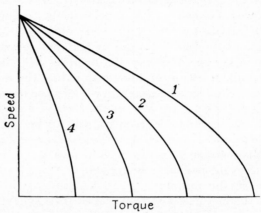

Fɪɢ. 7-6.   Typical speed-torque curves of a squirrel-cage induction motor.   Obtained by primary-voltage control.

ALTERNATING-CURRENT ADJUSTABLE-SPEED MOTOR

The best means for adjusting the speed of a-c motors is to change the number of poles in the primary.   Quite frequently, motors are built having two sets of poles, one set giving high speed and one set slow speed.

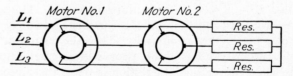

Fɪɢ. 7-7.   Cascade connection of induction motors for speed regulation.

Usually these motors are provided with squirrel-cage secondaries, but slip-ring motors also have been built of this type, particularly for elevator and hoist work.   The controller consists of a double-throw switch or its equivalent for changing the connections of the motor primary so as to give the desired number of poles.

Another method, which is equivalent to changing the number of poles, consists in connecting two motors in cascade, the secondary of the first motor being connected to the primary of the second, as shown in Fig. 7-7. Let us consider that the first motor is wound with six poles and the second motor with four poles.   These motors can be connected together, so that they have a combined speed equivalent to the sum or difference of the poles, which would be a ten-pole or a two-pole speed. Either motor can be operated separately as a six-pole or a four-pole motor. With this combination it is possible to get a speed equivalent to two, four, six, and

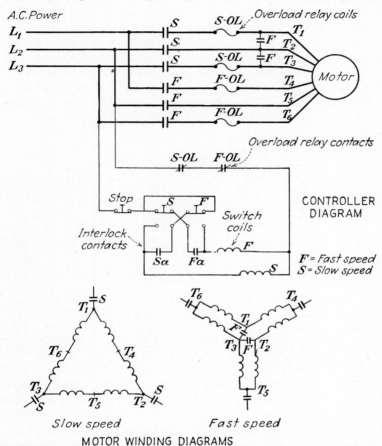

FIG. 7-8. Diagram of a two-speed single-winding squirrel-cage induction motor showing the controller contacts. *S* contacts give slow speed; *F* contacts give fast speed.

ten poles. It is necessary that both motors be mounted upon a common shaft or rigidly coupled together. Arrangements of this kind have been used in a number of cases, particularly with large motors.

A two-speed motor may have two separate windings or a single winding arranged so it can be connected to give two sets of poles in the ratio of 2 to 1. Three-speed motors usually have two windings. Other speed ratios usually require two separate windings.

Three-speed motors usually have three separate windings. Four-speed motors may have two windings, each group of two giving a 2 to 1 speed ratio. Many of the smaller machine-tool and fan motors have multispeed windings. When stepping back from a higher to a lower speed, the motor will regenerate until it reaches the slower speed. This gives a sharp reverse torque, which may be guarded against if it is undesirable, by opening the circuit until the speed is reduced. Figure 7-8 shows a schematic diagram of connections for a two-speed motor.

In a later chapter other methods of adjusting the speed are described.

A special condition of operation exists in the slip-ring type of induction motor when one phase of the secondary circuit is open. This gives

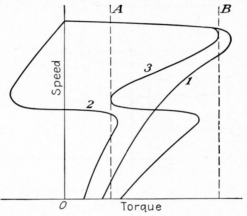

FIG. 7-9. Typical speed-torque curves of a polyphase motor that has a single-phase secondary winding.

a single-phase circuit only in the secondary, and the motor operates at approximately half speed over a considerable range of load. The explanation of this is shown in Fig. 7-9. Curve 1 represents the standard speed-torque curve set up by the primary, and curve 2 the speed-torque curve of the single-phase secondary. Curve 3 is the resultant of 1 and 2. As curve 2 passes through half speed it approaches a horizontal position; therefore, a slight change in the speed of the motor results in a considerable change in torque, which tends to maintain the speed constant at this value. If the motor is started from rest and the load is not too heavy, it will accelerate to half speed and remain approximately at this speed, unless the external torque is less than the value shown by the dotted line *A*. If the torque is less than this value, the motor will continue to accelerate on the upper part of curve 3 and approach full speed. After the motor has reached the upper part of curve 3, it will not again be brought to half speed unless the primary circuit is first opened, thus allowing the motor to drop down below half speed. However, the motor will stop if the load exceeds the dotted line B. The value shown by the dotted line A depends upon the secondary resistance of the motor and a number of other factors. This arrangement of speed control might be applicable for fans, where the torque depends largely upon the speed.

Methods of speed control for cranes and hoists are given in Chap. 8.

CONSTANT SPEED WITH RHEOSTATIC CONTROL BY MEANS OF THE MAGNETIC AMPLIFIER

It has been shown that the speed of a d-c motor can be adjusted by changing a resistor in series with the armature. Low speeds are usually obtained by adding a resistor in shunt with the armature (Fig. 7-3). When the load changes, the speed can be corrected by changing these resistors. This principle is used for crane-hoist controllers (Chap. 8).

The a-c motor with a positive load can have its speed adjusted by varying its secondary resistor. The desired speed for both the a-c and d-c motors, with positive load, can be maintained constant at reduced speeds by using a magnetic amplifier to adjust the resistor as the load changes.

The d-c motor with negative load can have its speed maintained constant by an adjustable armature shunt. In all cases the accuracy of the speed adjustment will depend upon the number of resistor steps available. This method of control is best suited to applications where exact speed adjustment is not necessary. It is not desirable for accurate speed matching. A printing press can have its "make-up" speed adjusted by using a series and shunt resistor shown in Fig. 7-3, omitting the series field. A reduction in load causes the motor to overspeed and reduces the current in the shunt resistor RS. The motor can be returned to normal speed by reducing resistor RS. An increase in load requires an increase in resistor RS in order to maintain constant motor speed. The speed adjustment can be obtained automatically with a magnetic amplifier and a rectifier (Fig. 7-10). When the load increases, this amplifier increases the motor voltage by increasing the current through the rectifier and thus reducing the current through R. A decrease in load decreases the rectified current and the current in R.

The amplifier has two control coils: coil A responsive to current and coil V responsive to motor voltage. Coil A assists coil V. When the load increases, coil A increases the flux in the amplifier, which increases the rectified current (see Chap. 13). A reduction in load decreases the rectified current. In this way the rectifier adjusts the voltage applied to the motor to compensate for the IR drop of the armature, caused by the load, and maintains normal speed.

With a decrease in the load, which decreases the rectifier current, the voltage drop in the series resistor is increased and the motor voltage is reduced and restored to normal speed.

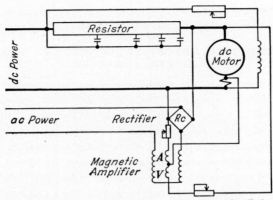

FIG. 7-10. Constant slow speed by rheostatic control. Control coil A measures load, and coil V speed. An increase in load increases the current in RC to balance the IR drop in the motor armature by an increase in voltage to the motor. A decrease in load decreases the motor voltage (see Magnetic Amplifiers, Chap. 13).

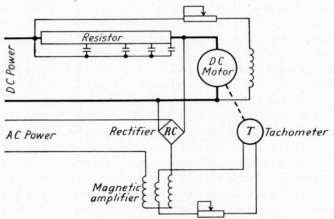

FIG. 7-11. Tachometer speed control with rectifier in shunt to armature and series resistor similar to Fig. 7-10.

Automatic speed control using a series and a shunt resistor can also be obtained by changing the strength of the motor field as shown in Fig. 7-12. This motor is shown with two shunt fields: PF, the pattern field, which is hand-adjusted for a selected speed of operation, and CF, the control field, which maintains a constant speed and is connected to the magnetic amplifier with two control coils A and V. Coil A measures the current, and coil *B* measures the armature volts. The two coils oppose each other. An increase in load decreases field *CF* so as to compensate for the increase in voltage drop through the armature and to increase the speed to normal. A decrease in load strengthens the motor field *CF* and reduces the speed to normal. Note that in each case field *CF* opposes field *PF*, which always predominates.

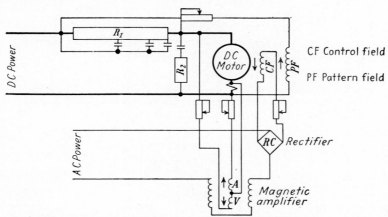

F𝐢𝐠. 7-12. Constant slow speed by field control with series and shunt resistors. When load increases, *CF* reduces motor field when load decreases, *CF* increases motor field.

If the motor has only one shunt field, the rectifier can be connected in either series or shunt with this field and controlled as shown. A larger rectifier may be required. This control method will be useful where the slow speed is below the speed obtained by field adjustment.

ADJUSTABLE-SPEED MAGNETIC CLUTCH

When a squirrel-cage induction motor is started from rest, the primary is energized and creates a rotating field which induces current to flow in its secondary windings, causing the secondary to rotate at a speed depending upon the load and the resistance of its windings. If the primary of a magnetic clutch has a set of d-c poles and is rotated by a synchronous motor, it will cause its squirrel-cage secondary to rotate in the same manner as the secondary of the induction motor. The speed of rotation of this secondary will depend upon the strength of the primary field as well as on the load and the resistance of the secondary windings. The difference in speed between the primary and secondary of the clutch is called its "slip." The heat in the secondary winding is equal to the load times the slip. This heat must be disposed of by ventilation. A commercial form of magnetic clutch is shown in Fig. 7-13.[1] A synchronous

[1] Built by the Electric Machinery Co., Minneapolis.

motor rotates the primary of this clutch, which consists of a squirrel-cage ring (Fig. 7-14). Inside it is a series of d-c magnet poles that rotate the load (Fig. 7-15). By changing the strength of the current in the d-c poles of the primary, the speed of the squirrel-cage secondary is adjusted to suit the load requirements. Smaller magnetic clutches do

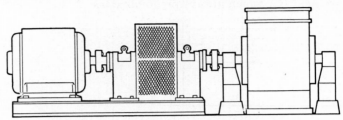

FIG. 7-13.   Fan driven by a motor through the magnet clutch.

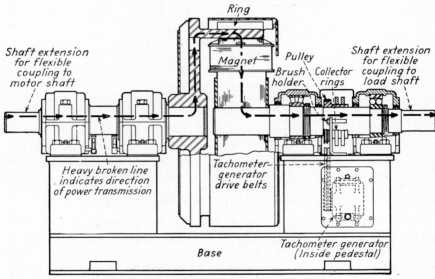

FIG. 7-14.   Cross section of magnetic clutch.

not have a secondary winding; they depend upon eddy currents generated in the rim of the secondary ring. Larger clutches can have wound secondaries with slip rings and external resistance.

This type of adjustable-speed clutch is suitable for fans or pumps where the load varies as the cube of the speed. Such a variation reduces the heat loss in the clutch compared with a load that varies directly with the speed.

The d-c power required for the clutch is about the same as that required for the excitation of the field of a similar size motor. This excitation

FIG. 7-15.   End view of clutch rotor.

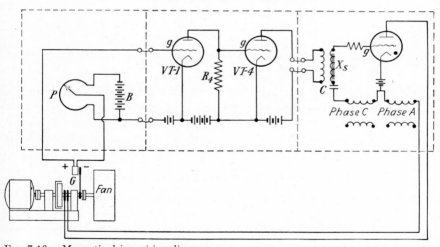

FIG. 7-16.   Magnetic-drive wiring diagram.

The output of the tachometer generator G is balanced through the potentiometer P against a portion of the fixed reference voltage from a 12-volt battery B.   Thus a certain voltage is impressed on the grid of VT-1, resulting in a definite fan speed.

Assume that the driven fan starts to speed up.   The voltage generated by G will increase in value and will make the grid g of VT-1 more positive; this increases the flow of current through the plate circuit of VT-1 and through resistor $R4$.   The resultant IR drop through $R4$ will result in making grid g of VT-4 more negative.   The output through the plate circuit of VT-4 will then decrease.   This decreases the saturation in reactor $X5$ and increases its reactance.

Increasing the reactance creates a phase shift in the reactor-condenser circuit, causing an increased angle of lag of the grid voltage behind the plate voltage.   This decreases the exciting current passed through the magnetic drive and brings the speed back to the previous point where the output of generator G balances the selected portion of the battery B.

can be controlled with electronic tubes, which permits exact speed regulation over a wide range of load by using a tachometer generator G (Fig. 7-16), with a permanent-magnetic field, belted to the output shaft of the clutch. Its armature is connected to the tube circuit shown in Fig. 7-16.

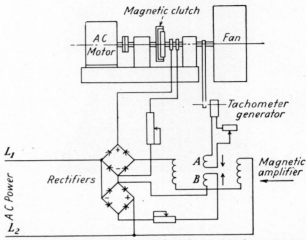

FIG. 7-17. Use of a magnetic amplifier instead of electronic tubes to control the speed of the fan in Fig. 7-13.

Other details may be added such as an "antihunt" circuit and a "snubbing" circuit, depending upon the application. A transfer switch should be provided to connect the clutch to a manual control for testing and making repairs to the automatic control. A magnetic amplifier can be substituted for the electronic tubes (see Fig. 7-17).

MAGNETIC-AMPLIFIER SPEED CONTROLLER

The magnetic amplifier can replace the tube controller in Fig. 7-16 (see Chap. 13). The tachometer generator G is connected to the control coil A of a magnetic amplifier. This coil opposes coil B to change the magnetic saturation of the amplifier; this in turn changes the magnetizing current in the clutch coil to alter the fan speed. An increase in fan speed increases coil A and reduces the magnetism of the amplifier by opposing coil B. This reduces the clutch magnetism and the fan speed because of greater "slip" in the clutch. A decrease in fan speed reduces the strength of coil A and increases the magnetism in the amplifier, which increases the clutch magnetism and the fan speed because of less slip in the clutch.

The boiler draft fan is a good illustration of the use of a magnetic clutch compared with some other methods of control. Several methods of varying the output of boiler draft fans are in use. The most common are:

1. Constant-speed motor, single- or two-speed, with
   a. Dampers.
   b. Inlet vanes.
2. Variable-speed drive, such as
   a. Steam engines or turbines.
   b. Direct-current motors.
   c. Slip-ring motor with auxiliary damper control.
   d. Slip-ring motor with liquid slip regulator.
   e. Hydraulic coupling.
   f. Magnetic drive.

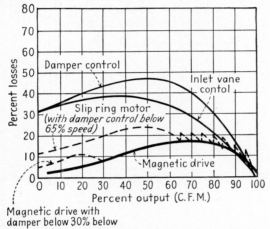

Fig. 7-18. Curves showing advantages of magnetic drive. (*Courtesy of the Electric Machinery Co. of Minneapolis.*)

Fig. 7-19. A Magneclutch used with a 5-kw motor-generator power unit.

There are advantages and some specific disadvantages to each of the above methods.

As shown in Fig. 7-18 quite substantial savings are to be made in driving power if the boiler draft fan is operated at the proper speed over the entire practicable speed range.

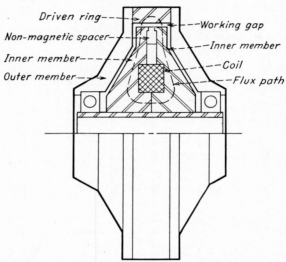

FIG. 7-20.   Simplified drawing of a Magneclutch illustrating the essential components of the magnetic circuit.

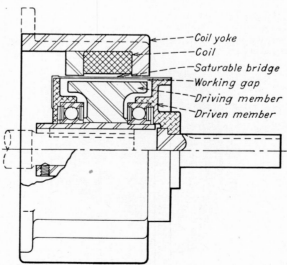

FIG. 7-21.   Simplified drawing of an external-coil, saturable-bridge Magneclutch.

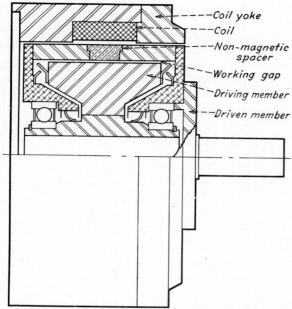

FIG. 7-22. Simplified drawing of an external-coil, nonsaturable-bridge **Magneclutch.**

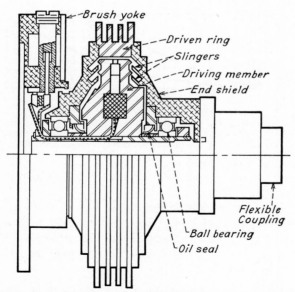

FIG. 7-23. Magneclutch with slingers to aid centrifugal acceleration in preventing magnetic-particle medium from reaching bearings.

THE MAGNECLUTCH

A new type of magnetic slip clutch has been developed by the Vickers Electric Division of the Spirey Corporation, known as the "Magneclutch." The two independent rotating members are separated by a

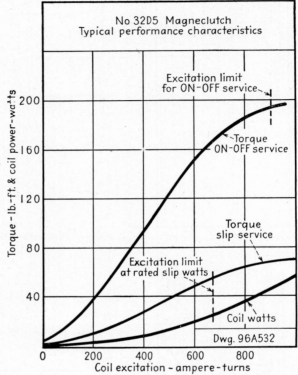

Fig. 7-24. Performance curves of a Magneclutch (Fig. 7-25). Type: internal coil. Mounting: shaft-mounted (brush yoke is flange-mounted). Weight: 135 lb. Maximum continuous-duty ratings: rotational speed, 3,600 rpm; temperature rise of coil, 85°C (40°C ambient). On-off service: torque, 195 lb-ft; d-c coil excitation, 900 turns; coil power, 45 watts; magnetic-particle medium, type 33B67. Slip service: slip dissipation, 1,000 watts; torque, 55 lb-ft; d-c coil excitation, 675 amp-turns; coil power, 25 watts; magnetic-particle medium, type 33B66.

space filled with ferromagnetic particles which transmit the torque between these members in proportion to the strength of the magnetic field, in the air gap, induced between the two rotating elements shown in Figs. 7-20 and 7-21. The Vickers Electric Company explains the operation of this clutch as follows:

The magnetic circuit of a Magneclutch may be simple, as shown in Fig. 7-20. The source of magnetomotive force is the exciting coil in the inner member.

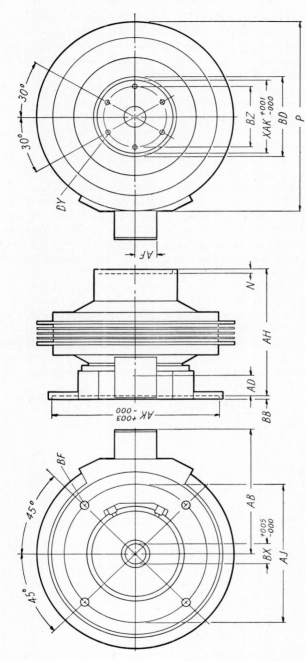

Fig. 7-25. Dimensions of a Magneclutch (Fig. 7-24). *N*, 1/8; *P*, 14%; *AB*, 9⅛; *AD*, 2; *AF*, 1⅝; *AH*, 9³⁄₁₆; *AJ*, 11; *AK*, 12½; *BB*, ³⁄₁₆; *BD*, 6¼; *BF*, 1¹⁄₁₆; *BX*, 1⅛; *BY*, ¼-20; *BZ*, 4⅝; *XAK*, 5³⁄₁₆ (all inches).

With this type of design, power is fed to the coil through slip rings (not shown). The magnetic circuit includes the two halves of the inner member, the driven ring of the outer member, and the working gap which contains the magnetic-particle medium.   The series air gap in the central portion of the inner member is kept small; consequently, the main source of reluctance is the working gap.   The non-magnetic spacer, which separates the two halves of the inner member at their peripheries, prevents a magnetic short circuit at that point.

It has been found practical to design this clutch with a stationary, external coil even though an additional air gap is introduced in the magnetic circuit between the coil structure and the rotating clutch members.   Two general forms of this type of design are the saturable and nonsaturable bridge types, illustrated in Figs. 7-21 and 7-22, respectively.

These clutches utilize a dry magnetic-particle medium, the characteristics of which depend on the type of service in which a Magneclutch is employed.   Retention of the magnetic-particle medium is assured by effective sealing means. Figure 7-23 illustrates the principle by which the labyrinth formed by slingers assists the centrifugal reaction in confining the charge to the working gap.   The success of this method can be deduced from the fact that, even in filling a clutch, particles rarely find their way below the slingers.

Magneclutches are termed "torque" clutches when they are used in applications requiring simply the connection or disconnection of a driven load.   They are termed "slip" clutches when they are operated continuously at a greater or lesser slip to obtain adjustable output torque.

The two curves of Fig. 7-24 represent the limiting torque-excitation characteristics for two types of service (torque and slip service) for the same Magneclutch Fig. 7-25 and are determined by the magnetic-particle medium employed.

CHAPTER 8

CONTROL FOR CRANES, HOISTS, AND OTHER SPECIAL APPLICATIONS

Some applications require modifications of standard control to meet their particular requirements. A few of the more common features of these special-purpose controllers are given below in the form of simplified diagrams.

CRANE CONTROL FOR D-C SERIES MOTORS

During the hoisting cycle, an armature shunt resistor is used for slow speed in connection with the series resistor.

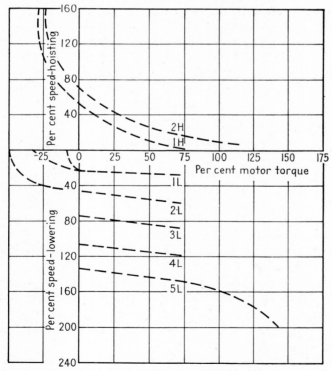

Fig. 8-1. Desirable features for a crane hoist.

A dynamic brake is used in the Off position.   During the lowering cycle the motor operates as a shunt machine.   With an overhauling load, the motor becomes a generator and the armature circuit is closed through a resistor, to absorb the power delivered by the generator.   This action is referred to in Chap. 9 under Dynamic Braking.

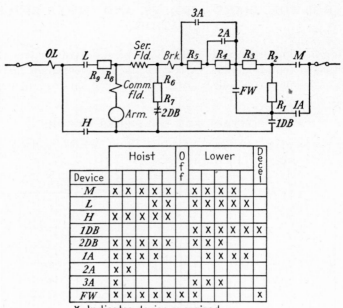

Device	Hoist					Off	Lower					Decel
M	X	X	X	X	X		X	X	X	X		
L				X	X		X	X	X	X	X	
H	X	X	X	X	X							
$1DB$							X	X	X	X	X	X
$2DB$	X	X	X	X	X		X	X	X			
$1A$	X	X	X	X			X	X	X	X		
$2A$	X	X										
$3A$	X						X	X	X			
FW	X	X	X	X	X	X	X					X

X— Indicates device energized

FIG. 8-2.   Power elementary diagram.

Figure 8-2 shows an elementary diagram and sequence table for a General Electric Company d-c crane controller.[1]   Figure 8-3 shows a diagram for each step of control.   Figures 8-5 and 8-6 are the test curves for this controller.   Figure 8-4 shows schematic diagrams used by other manufacturers for their d-c crane controllers.   These different schemes of control are being changed from time to time as more field experience is available.

For the first step in lowering, a load should have a flat speed-torque curve in order to reduce the difference in speed with light and heavy loads.   The initial torque should not exceed about 35 per cent to permit of easy "jogging."   The torque on the second lowering point should

[1] *Westinghouse Engineer*, March, 1952, describes that company's d-c crane controller.

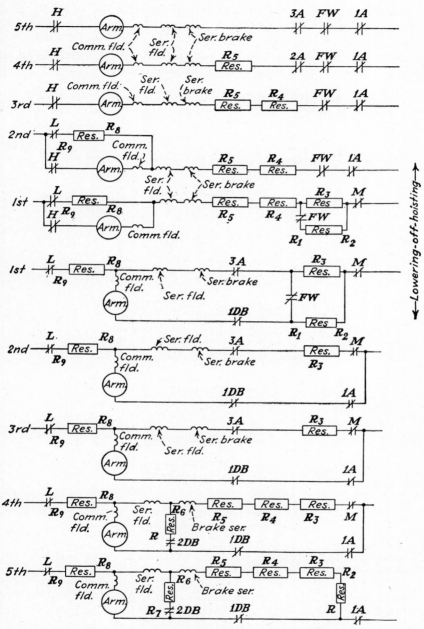

FIG. 8-3. Crane controller for d-c motor. General Electric Co.

be about 50 per cent in order to obtain rapid acceleration of a light load. The speed-torque curves for the remaining lowering speeds should be evenly spaced and should not cross each other. Typical curves are shown in Figs. 8-5 and 8-6; at 200 per cent of lowering speed the motor should develop about 140 per cent of full-load torque.

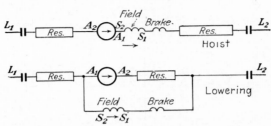

Cutler-Hammer system—Armature reversed

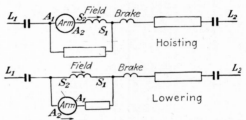

Electric Controller and Mfg. Co. system—Armature reversed

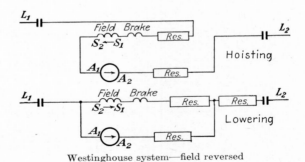

Westinghouse system—field reversed

Fig. 8-4.   The connections on the first controller notch used by other controller companies. The resistors are changed for the other controller notches to get higher speeds.   Each arrangement differs from the others in a few details.

In the first step in hoisting, enough holding torque should be provided, when the brake is released, to prevent the load from moving downward. In the second step, the rated load should be lifted.   In the remaining steps, the rated load should be accelerated up to full speed.

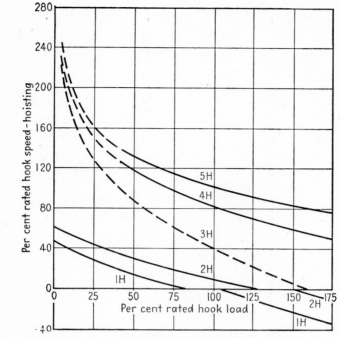

FIG. 8-5.   Test curves—hoisting.

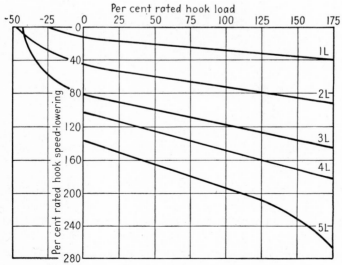

FIG. 8-6,   Test curves—lowering.

CRANE AND HOIST CONTROLLERS FOR WOUND-SECONDARY INDUCTION MOTORS

Many a-c cranes use a standard reversing controller with a "load brake" to absorb the energy when the load is lowered. This brake requires the motor to deliver some positive torque in order to lower the load so that the speed can be readily controlled. Figure 8-8 shows a

FIG. 8-7.   General Electric magnetic reversing dynamic-braking d-c control panel, 36 to 55-hp, 230-volt.   For use with series motor on crane hoist.

controller diagram suitable for this application. If the motor secondary is connected single-phase on the first controller notch, the starting torque will be about one-half of that obtained with the secondary connected three-phase. The load brake can be the conventional friction type, or an "eddy-current" brake (Fig. 8-9) can be used. The retarding force of this latter type of brake can be adjusted by changing the exciting current.

Several methods are used for obtaining a retarding torque from the motor windings during lowering. In order to make it easier to compare these different methods of control, all the diagrams and detail explanations are taken from one manufacturer (the Westinghouse Electric Corporation), who offers all types. Other manufacturers offer modifications of these types which they believe are better suited for particular applications. A detailed study should be made before selecting the controller. This book describes only the fundamentals of each method. They are as follows:

1. **"Plugging"** or **"Countertorque"** (Fig. 8-11). This consists of reversing the motor torque and cause the load to drive the motor as a generator. An ordinary reversing manual controller (Fig. 8-8) can be used, but better results are obtained with the automatic controller shown in Fig. 8-11. This method is best suited to applications requiring 50 to 100 per cent full-load lowering torque.

2. **Direct-current Dynamic Braking.** This system (Figs. 8-12 and 8-17) requires a d-c motor generator to supply power to the primary windings of the hoist motor when the load is lowered in order to convert the hoist motor into an a-c generator that will deliver power to the resistor. This system does not overheat the motor. It is well suited to large overhead cranes, gantry-type shipyard cranes, etc. Figure 8-12 shows the connections and operation of this system for cranes.

3. **Dynamic Braking with Unbalanced Primary Voltage** (Fig. 8-13). During lowering, the contactor B is closed to obtain single-phase operation of the motor so that the reverse torque of the motor can be adjusted to control the speed of the descending load. Good speed adjustment is obtained with loads up to 50 per cent of maximum. Tests made with this type of control show high current values which may overheat the motor winding. (See the paper by C. B. Resler in *Steel*, Jan. 15, 1945.) This is a modified type of "plugging control."

4. **Reactor System** (Fig. 8-14). This system controls lowering speed by regulated "counter" or "plugging" torque. The regulator coordinates the countertorque with speed, so that an increase in overhauling speed is accompanied by an increase in retarding torque.

The wound-rotor motor operates with a fixed value of rotor resistance, a value which would produce 125 per cent torque at 100 per cent slip (standstill) and 250 per cent torque at 200 per cent slip with balanced

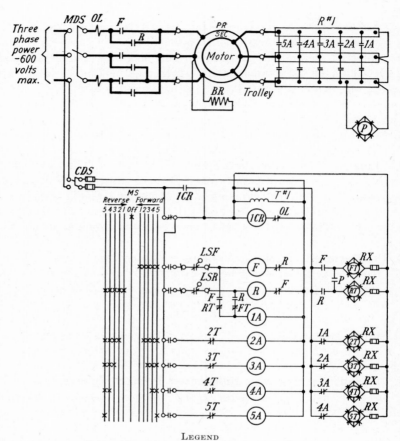

LEGEND
(Equipment shown in schematic wiring diagram)

1A	Plugging contactor	*MS*	Master switch
2A, 3A	Plugging contactors	*OL*	Magnetic overload relay
4A, 5A	Accelerating contactor	*P*	Plugging relay
BR	Motor brake—a-c magnetic	*R*	Reverse directional contactor
CDS	Control-circuit disconnect switch	*R1*	Motor secondary resistor
ICR	Undervoltage relay	*RT*	Plugging time-relay reverse
F	Forward directional contactor	*RX*	Rectox—time relays
FT	Plugging time relay forward	*2T, 3T*	Definite time accelerating relays
LSF	Shunt limit switch forward	*4T, 5T*	Definite time accelerating relays
LSR	Shunt limit switch reverse	*T1*	Rectox transformer for accelerating relays
MDS	Main circuit disconnect switch		

FIG. 8-8.

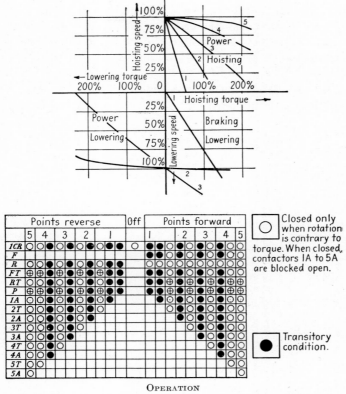

Closed only when rotation is contrary to torque. When closed, contactors IA to 5A are blocked open.

Transitory condition.

OPERATION

For Reversing—Plugging Applications. When starting from rest, the first point of the master switch closes the appropriate directional contactor and plugging contactor to place all starting resistance in the circuit. The torque obtained depends upon the resistor used. All accelerating points are controlled by automatic time-limit accelerating relays.

If the master switch is quickly reversed, the directional contactors reverse immediately, but the plugging contactor is blocked open by the plugging relays until the motor has reversed. The initial plugging torque will ordinarily be equal to the starting torque on starting from rest.

When a drift point is required, a brake relay is included to keep the brake released with the motor deenergized.

For Hoisting Applications. This control when used for hoist service with a mechanical load brake is the same as for plugging service except that the relays associated with plugging are omitted. With this arrangement the plugging contactor is utilized as an additional accelerating contactor providing one more point of acceleration for hoisting than for plugging service. This additional point permits application of low torque on the first controller point for purposes of hooking on or raising light loads.

"Plugging" control.

primary voltage applied.   With single-phase voltage applied to an induction motor, no torque will be developed at zero speed.   In this system the applied voltage is approximately balanced three phase near 200 per cent slip and is gradually converted toward single phase as the speed falls toward 100 per cent slip so that the retarding torque will vanish at zero speed.   For lowering curves 1, 2, and 3, single phase is reached at about 140 per cent slip, and for further decrease in speed, the voltage is returned toward the balanced condition, but with the opposite phase rotation (lowering torque).

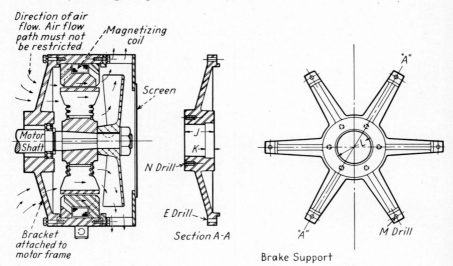

Fɪɢ. 8-9.   Crane hoist "eddy-current" brake.   A modification of the magnetic clutch is the eddy-current brake for lowering a load.   The "spider" supporting the stationary part of the brake and the coil is attached to the motor frame.   The revolving wheel and fan are mounted on the motor shaft.   The braking effect is similar to a squirrel-cage motor with its primary connected to d-c power.   The outer rim of the wheel acts like the squirrel-cage secondary of the motor.   When no squirrel-cage windings are used, the magnetic flux through the rim causes eddy currents to flow in the iron which develop a retarding torque or braking action to retard the descending load.   If necessary, squirrel-cage windings can be added.   The speed of lowering can be automatically controlled by a magnetic amplifier (see Fig. 8-10).

The applied voltage "balance" is controlled by a network of one transformer and two variable-impedance reactors.   The transformer $T4$ (Fig. 8-14) sets up what might be termed the "fourth-phase voltage $L4$," where $L1$, $L2$, $L3$ represent the voltages of a three-phase system in Fig. 8-15(a).   At 100 per cent slip the excitation of $L1$ and $L2$ is balanced and of low degree, the voltage drop across each is the same, and single-phase voltage is applied to the motor windings. Near 200 per cent slip the excitation applied to $L1$ is increased, and its impedance is reduced to about one-fiftieth of its normal value. The voltage drop across $L1$ is greatly reduced, and $T2$ [Fig. 8-15(b)] tends to take the same vector position as $L2$ to bring the applied voltage toward balance. Figure 8-15(c) shows the vector relations applying to lowering curve 4. The excitation of $L2$ is increased in order to shift $T2$ toward $L4$ sufficiently to provide a small lowering torque at 100 per cent slip.

Variable excitation for reactor $L1$ is obtained from the rotor circuit, where the voltage increases with slip. The voltage from the rotor cir-

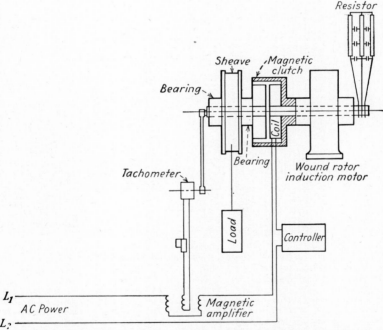

FIG. 8-10. Magnetic clutch for lowering a load at constant speed. A holding torque is provided by the magnet brake or by reversing the motor with resistance in its circuit. The magnetic clutch provides a slip speed for lowering, adjusted by the rheostat in the circuit to the tachometer generator T and the control coil of the magnetic amplifier. An increase in the speed of T increases the current passing through the magnetic amplifier to the clutch coil and retards the load. A decrease in the speed of T reduces the current in the clutch coil and increases the load speed.

cuit at 100 per cent slip is biased out by a countervoltage taken from the line, such that the reactor is affected only by that component of rotor voltage appearing above 100 per cent slip.

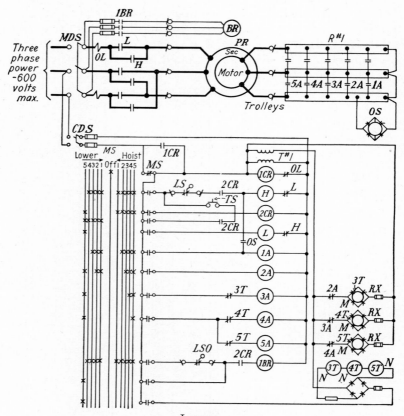

LEGEND
(Equipment shown in schematic wiring diagram)

1A, 2A	Accelerating contactors	R1	Motor secondary resistor
3A, 4A	Accelerating contactors	RX	Rectox—time relays
5A	Accelerating contactors	3T(M)	Accelerating relay main coils
BR	Motor brake-thruster type	4T(M)	Accelerating relay main coils
IBR	Brake relay	5T(M)	Accelerating relay main coil
CDS	Control-circuit disconnect switch	3T(N)	Accelerating relay neutralizing coil
1CR	Undervoltage relay		
2CR	Sequence relay	4T(N)	Accelerating relay neutralizing coil
H	Hoist directional contactor		
L	Lowering directional contactor	5T(N)	Accelerating relay neutralizing coil
LS	Hoist limit switch		
MDS	Main circuit disconnect switch	T1	Rectox transformer for accelerating relays
MS	Master switch		
OL	Magnetic overload relay	TS	Master controller thumb switch
OS	Speed limiting relay		

FIG. 8-11.   Dynamic braking

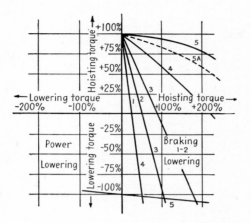

	Points lowering						Off	Points hoist					
	5		4	3	2	1		1	2	3	4	5A	5
1CR	○●●●●●●●	○○○	●○	○			○	○○○	●○	●○	●●	○	
2CR	○●●●●●●●	⊗⊗	●⊗	⊗				○○○	●○	●○	●●	○	
1BR	○●●●●●●●	⊗⊗	●⊗	⊗				○○○	●○	●○	●●	○	
H		⊗⊗	●⊗	⊗				○○○	●○	●○	●●	○	
L	○●●●●●●●												
1A		⊗⊗	●⊗	⊗				○●	○●	○●	●○		
2A	○●●●●●●	●	●⊗	⊗				●○	○●	○●	●○		
3T	○●●●●●		●⊗	⊗				○○	●○	●●	○		
3A	○●●●●							●○	●○	●●	○		
4T	○●●●							○●	○●	●○			
4A	○●●							●○	●●	○			
5T	○●							●○	●○				
5A	○							○●	○				
OS					⊘								

⊗	Closed only when master controller is moved from 5th position lowering towards "off" position, or after thumb switch has been operated on any of points 1 to 4 lowering.
⊘	Closed on overspeed only.
●	Transitory condition

OPERATION

In the hoist direction, the first point of the master switch closes the hoist directional contactor and causes the motor to exert a minimum starting torque. The hoisting torque is controlled manually through the first three points on the master switch, but if the master switch handle is moved directly to the fifth point, automatic time-limit acceleration prevails for the remaining points.

To lower, the master switch is moved to the last lowering point. When lowering on the last point, the motor will tend to run slightly above synchronous speed. To retard the load, the operator moves the master switch toward the Off position. On the fourth master-switch point, the line contactors are reversed with all secondary resistance inserted and the motor produces a slight retarding or countertorque. Increased countertorque is obtained by moving the master switch toward the Off position, the maximum value being obtained on the first point.

with reverse a-c torque.

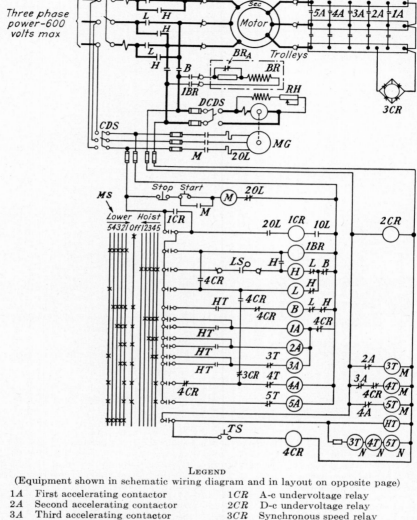

LEGEND

(Equipment shown in schematic wiring diagram and in layout on opposite page)

1A	First accelerating contactor	1CR	A-c undervoltage relay
2A	Second accelerating contactor	2CR	D-c undervoltage relay
3A	Third accelerating contactor	3CR	Synchronous speed relay
4A	Fourth accelerating contactor	4CR	Inching relay
5A	Fifth accelerating contactor	DCDS	D-c disconnect switch
B	D-c dynamic-braking contactor	H	Hoist directional contactor
BR	Motor brake	HT	Torque-holding relay
IBR	Brake relay	L	Lowering directional contactor
BRa	Brake coil protective interlock	LS	Hoist limit switch
CDS	Control-circuit disconnect switch		

FIG. 8-12.   Diagram for d-c

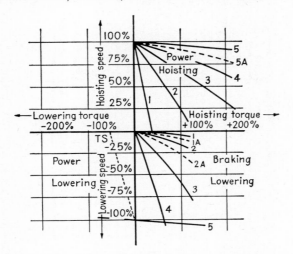

	Points lowering							Off	Points hoist					
	5	4	3	2A	2	1A	1		1	2	3	4	5A	5
M														
1CR														
2CR														
1BR														
H														
L														
B								⊗						
1A								⊗						
2A								⊗						
3T								⊗						
3A								⊗						
4T								⊗						
4A								⊗						
5T								⊗						
5A								⊗						
HT								⊗						

⊗ Closed momentarily only when master controller is returned to "off" position from the first point lower.

● Transitory condition.

M	Motor-generator set-starting contactor	*3T(N)*	Accelerating relay neutralizing coil
MDS	Main-circuit disconnect switch	*4T(M)*	Accelerating relay main coil
MG	Motor-generator set	*4T(N)*	Accelerating relay neutralizing coil
MS	Master switch		
1OL	Magnetic overload relay	*5T(M)*	Accelerating relay main coil
2OL	Thermal overload relay	*5T(N)*	Accelerating relay neutralizing coil
R1	Motor secondary resistor		
RH	Motor-generator set field rheostat	*TS*	Master controller thumb switch
3T(M)	Accelerating relay main coil		

excitation when lowering load.

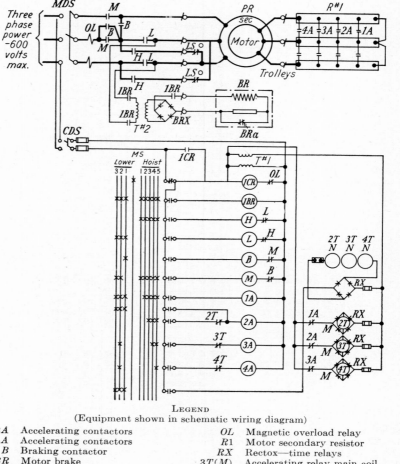

LEGEND
(Equipment shown in schematic wiring diagram)

1A, 2A	Accelerating contactors	OL	Magnetic overload relay
3A, 4A	Accelerating contactors	R1	Motor secondary resistor
B	Braking contactor	RX	Rectox—time relays
BR	Motor brake	$3T(M)$	Accelerating relay main coil
1BR	Brake relay	$2T(M)$	Accelerating relay main coil
BRX	Rectox—brake	$4T(M)$	Accelerating relay main coil
CDS	Control-circuit disconnect switch	$2T(N)$	Accelerating relay neutralizing coil
1CR	Undervoltage relay	$3T(N)$	Accelerating relay neutralizing coil
H	Hoist directional contactor		
L	Lower directional contactor	$4T(N)$	Accelerating relay neutralizing coil
LS	Hoist limit switch		
M	Line contactor	T1	Rectox transformer
MDS	Main-circuit disconnect switch	T2	Rectox transformer
MS	Master switch		

FIG. 8-13.   Dynamic braking

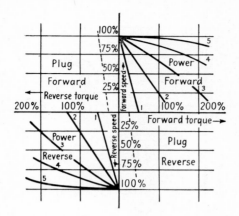

	Points lowering			Off	Points hoist				
	3	2	1		1	2	3	4	5
1CR	O O ● ● ● ● O ●			O	O ● O ● O ● O O				
1BR	O O ● ● ● ● O ●				O ● O ● O ● O O				
H					O ● O ● O ● O O				
L	O O ● ● ● ● O ●								
M	O O ● ● ● ● ●				O ● O ● O ● O O				
B	O ●								
1A	O O ● ● ● ● O ●				● O O ● O ● O O				
2T	O O ● ● ● ● O				O ● O ● O O				
2A	O O ● ● ● ● O ●				● O O ● O O				
3T	O O ● ● ● ●				O ● O O				
3A	O ● ●				● O O				
4T	O ●				O O				
4A	O				O				

● Transitory condition

OPERATION

When starting in the hoisting direction from rest, the first point of the master switch closes the hoist directional contactor and causes the motor to exert a minimum starting torque. The hoisting torque is controlled manually through the first three points on the master switch, but if the master switch handle is moved directly to the fifth point, automatic time-limit acceleration prevails through the fourth and fifth points.

On the first point lowering, the motor is connected to operate under the principle of a-c dynamic braking and exerts no electrical driving torque. Any mechanical rotation is opposed by electrical retarding torque. On the second point of the master switch, the motor exerts driving-down torque and rapidly accelerates light or heavy loads to approximately synchronous speed and power is returned to the line through the principle of regenerative braking. The third point of the master switch continues the regenerative braking but at a lesser degree, such that full load may be lowered at a higher speed not exceeding 25 per cent in excess of synchronous.

with unbalanced primary voltage.

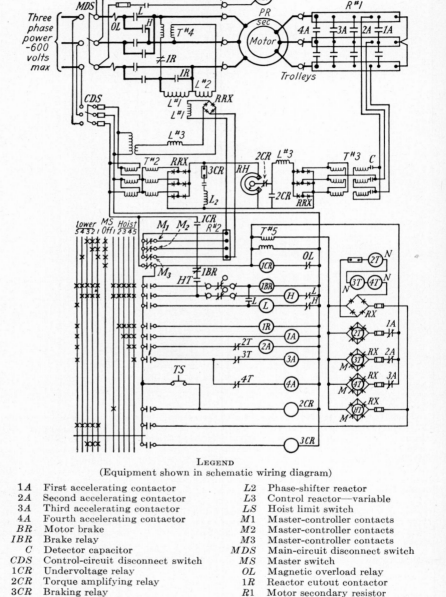

LEGEND

(Equipment shown in schematic wiring diagram)

1A	First accelerating contactor	L2	Phase-shifter reactor
2A	Second accelerating contactor	L3	Control reactor—variable
3A	Third accelerating contactor	LS	Hoist limit switch
4A	Fourth accelerating contactor	M1	Master-controller contacts
BR	Motor brake	M2	Master-controller contacts
1BR	Brake relay	M3	Master-controller contacts
C	Detector capacitor	MDS	Main-circuit disconnect switch
CDS	Control-circuit disconnect switch	MS	Master switch
1CR	Undervoltage relay	OL	Magnetic overload relay
2CR	Torque amplifying relay	1R	Reactor cutout contactor
3CR	Braking relay	R1	Motor secondary resistor
H	Hoist directional contactor	R2	Lowering speed-control resistor
HT	Torque holding relay	RH	Potentiometer—torque adjustment
L	Lowering directional contactor		ment
L1	Main reactor—variable		

FIG. 8-14.   Lowering of load by regulated

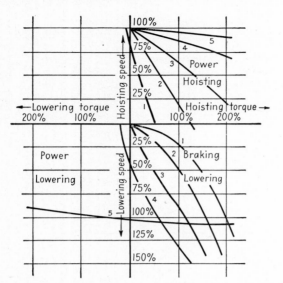

	5								4	3	2	1	Off	1	2	3			4		5		
1CR	O	●	●	●	●	●	●	●	O	O	O	O	O	O	O	●	O	●	O	●	O	●	●	O
2CR													O											
1BR	O	●	●	●	●	●	●	●	O	O	O	O		O	O	●	O	●	O	●	O	●	●	O
H									O	O	O	O	⊗	O	O	●	O	●	O	●	O	●	●	O
L	O	●	●	●	●	●	●	●																
1R	O	●	●	●	●	●	●	●							O	●	O	●	O	●	O	●	●	O
1A	O	●	●	●	●	●	●	●								●	O	●	O	●	O	●	●	O
2T	O	●	●	●	●	●	●										O	●	O	●	O	●	●	O
2A	O	●	●	●	●	●												●	O	●	O	●	●	O
3T	O	●	●	●															O	●	O	●	●	O
3A	O	●	●																			●	●	O
4T	O	●																					●	O
4A	O																							O
HT	O	●	●	●	●	●	●		O	O	O	O	⊗											
M1										O	O	O	O											
M2											O	O	O											
M3										O		O	O											
3CR											O	O	O											

 Closed momentarily only when master controller is returned to "off" position from the first point lower.

● Transitory condition.

RRX	Rectox—reactor	3T(M)	Accelerating relay main coil
RX	Rectox—time relays	3T(N)	Accelerating relay neutralizing coil
T1	Transformer—main reactor control supply	4T(M)	Accelerating relay main coil
T2	Transformer—detector bias voltage	4T(N)	Accelerating relay neutralizing coil
T3	Transformer—detector voltage	TS	Master-controller thumb switch
T4	Phase-shift transformer	T5	Rectox transformer for accelerating relays
2T(M)	Accelerating relay main coil		
2T(N)	Accelerating relay neutralizing coil		

countertorque using saturated core reactor.

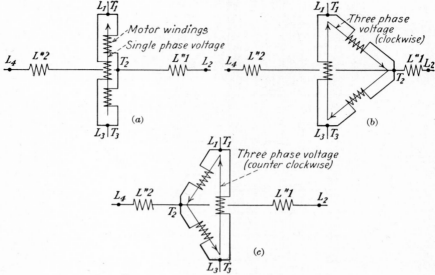

Fig. 8-15.   Vector diagram for Fig. 8-14.

Fig. 8-16.   Cutler-Hammer pressure regulator of the diaphragm type.

The diaphragm regulator consists of a metal diaphragm having pressure on one side and a weight or spring on the opposite side (see Fig. 8-16). The diaphragm is raised or lowered with variations in the water pressure. This movement of the diaphragm mechanism closes or opens the contacts of the master switch. The diaphragm regulator ordinarily does not require a relay, as the contacts are large enough to take care of the control circuit of an ordinary-sized contactor.

When a pressure regulator is used with a positive-acting pump, it should not be connected directly to the pump delivery, as the pulsations cause the regulator to open and close the contacts in rapid succession and give very poor results. Usually, the pump delivers to a pressure tank or standpipe, and the pressure regulator can be connected to the tank or standpipe. Where the pump delivery is long and it is not convenient to connect the pressure

FIG. 8-19. Cutler-Hammer float switch.

regulator in this way, special precautions should be taken to prevent the regulator from being oscillated by the pulsation in the pump delivery.

Float Switch. The master switch of the float type consists of a small contact that is opened or closed according to a difference in the level

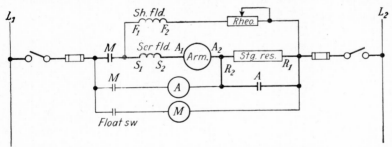

FIG. 8-20. Connections of a two-point d-c automatic-pump controller operated by a float switch.

of the water in the tank or reservoir. One form of this switch is shown in Fig. 8-18 and another in Fig. 8-19. The contacts are provided with a quick make-and-break arrangement, so that the slow movement of the float does not cause arcing. This float switch is connected to the pilot

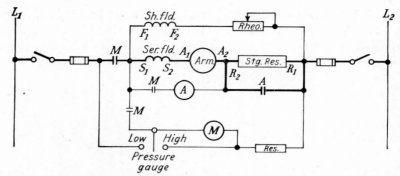

Fig. 8-21. Connections of a two-point d-c automatic-pump controller operated by a pressure gauge.

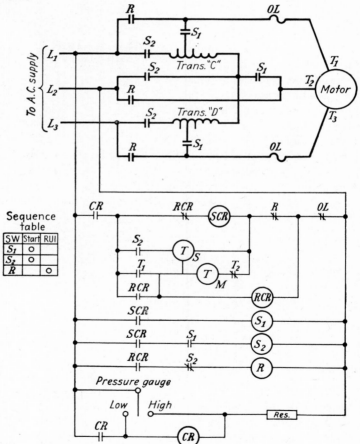

Fig. 8-22. Connections of an automatic autostarter for a squirrel-cage pump motor operated by a pressure gauge.

wiring of the controller and serves to start and stop the motor according to variation in the water level. If this float switch is used in a reservoir where large waves are likely to occur, it should be mounted in an enclosed compartment to protect it from the wash.

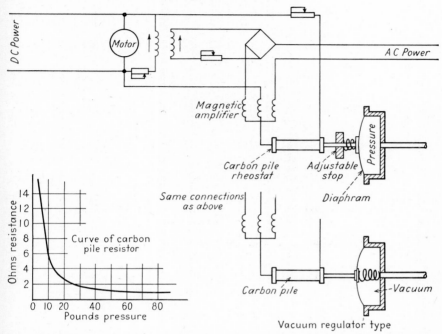

Fɪɢ. 8-23. Pressure regulator with magnetic-amplifier control (see Chap. 13). The pressure- or vacuum-responsive device changes the pressure on a carbon pile to regulate the current through the control coil of the magnetic amplifier. This changes the strength of the motor field so that its speed is altered in order to restore the pressure or vacuum to normal. The curve at the left shows the rapid change in resistance of the carbon pile between pressures of 5 to 15 lb caused by changes of pressure or vacuum in the regulator which can be adjusted by the spring.

ELEVATOR PUMPS

Elevator service is a special application. Hydraulic elevators are usually operated in banks comprising several elevators connected to a single pressure tank. The elevators discharge into an open tank, and the pump takes the water from the open tank and delivers it to the pressure tank. For large installations, several pumps are used. The pumps are controlled by pressure regulators which start and stop the pump for variations in pressure. During some portions of the day, the pump is operated at infrequent intervals, as the elevator service is light. At other times, particularly the noon hour and the closing hour in the evening, office-building elevator pumps are started and stopped frequently, some-times two or three times a minute, and this entails a considerable shock upon the system. One method of overcoming this difficulty is to slow

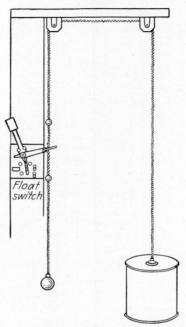

Fig. 8-24. Arrangement for operating a float switch.

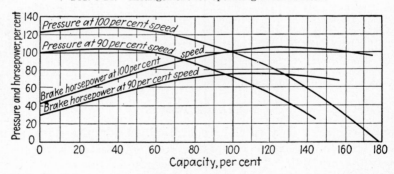

Fig. 8-25. Typical capacity and horsepower curves of a centrifugal pump showing the effect of a 10 per cent speed variation.

the pump down, rather than to stop it, when the pressure reaches a pre-determined value. If a positive-acting pump is used, considerable power may be lost by such an arrangement, as the water pumped is directly proportional to the speed of the pump. To reduce the output one-half, the pump must operate at half speed, which causes a loss in resistance equal to half the electric power delivered to the motor. If centrifugal pumps are used and designed for this service, a small change in speed

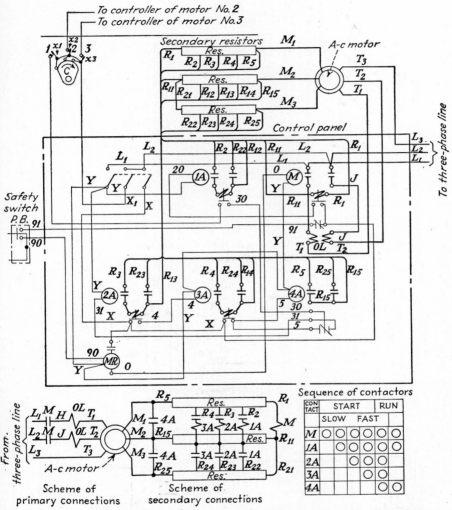

Fig. 8-26. Connections of a wound-secondary induction motor for a large elevator pump.

will make a large change in water delivery. The curves in Fig. 8-25 represent the gallons of water delivered by a typical pump with reference to the speed of the pump. This shows that a small reduction in speed makes a large difference in the output and that, therefore, by the insertion

Fig. 8-27.   Westinghouse drum controller for machine-tool service.

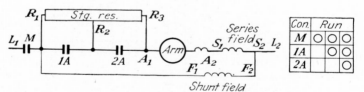

Fig. 8-28.   Connections of nonreversing machine-tool controller panel.

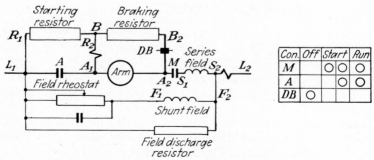

Fig. 8-29.   Connections of nonreversing machine-tool panel with a dynamic brake.

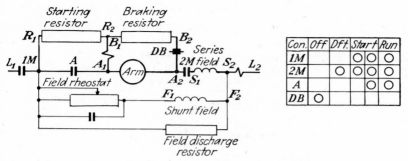

Con.	Off	Dft.	Start	Run
1M		○	○	○
2M	○	○	○	○
A			○	○
DB	○			

FIG. 8-30. Nonreversing machine-tool controller with the addition of a drift-point contactor.

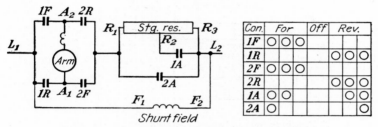

Con.	For.			Off	Rev.		
1F	○	○	○				
1R					○	○	○
2F	○	○	○				
2R					○	○	○
1A	○	○				○	○
2A	○						○

FIG. 8-31. Connections of a reversing-control panel.

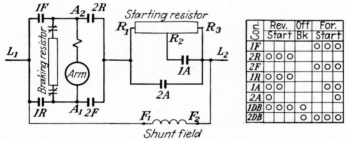

Con.	Rev.		Off	For.	
	Start	Bk			Start
1F					○ ○ ○
2R	○ ○ ○				
2F					○ ○ ○
1R	○ ○ ○				
1A	○ ○				○ ○
2A	○				○
1DB	○ ○ ○	○			
2DB		○			○ ○ ○

FIG. 8-32. Connections of a reversing-control panel with a dynamic brake.

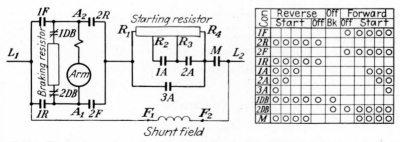

Con.	Reverse		Off	Forward	
	Start	Off Bk		Off	Start
1F					○ ○ ○ ○ ○
2R	○ ○ ○ ○ ○				
2F					○ ○ ○ ○ ○
1R	○ ○ ○ ○ ○				
1A	○ ○ ○				○ ○
2A	○ ○				○ ○
3A	○				○
1DB	○ ○ ○ ○ ○	○			
2DB		○	○		○ ○ ○ ○
M	○ ○ ○ ○				○ ○ ○ ○

FIG. 8-33. Connections of a reversing-control panel with addition of drift-point contactor.

of a small amount of resistance in the motor circuit, the output of the pump can be materially decreased with only a small loss in the resistance. Assuming a 10 per cent reduction in speed, only 10 per cent of the input of the motor will be wasted as heat in the resistance.

MACHINE TOOLS

Machine tools use either reversing or nonreversing general-purpose starters. Some have a dynamic brake for stopping and, sometimes, a

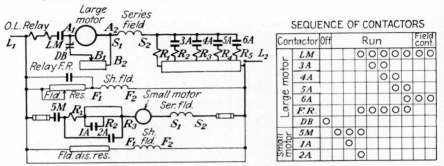

FIG. 8-34. Printing-press control for operation over a wide range of speeds.

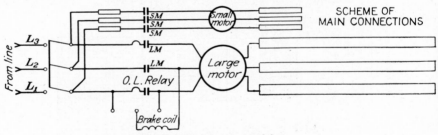

FIG. 8-35. Printing-press control for a-c motors.

drift point on the controller to keep the brake circuit open. Typical diagrams are shown in Figs. 8-28 to 8-33.

PRINTING PRESS

A printing press requires a very slow speed for make-up and for feeding the paper through the press. One method for getting this slow speed is to use a small motor for operation during the make-up period. The diagrams show a simple type of this control (see Figs. 8-34 and 8-35).

MINE LOCOMOTIVES

Mine locomotives may be operated by storage batteries. The diagram in Fig. 8-36 shows a typical control scheme for two series motors. Trucks and other vehicles operated by storage batteries use similar control. Control for single motors is much simpler.

OTHER SPECIAL CONTROL EQUIPMENT

Water Rheostats. A water rheostat of any kind is a special-purpose controller. Although it is usually not very popular, it has some very desirable features. These rheostats differ so widely in design that no

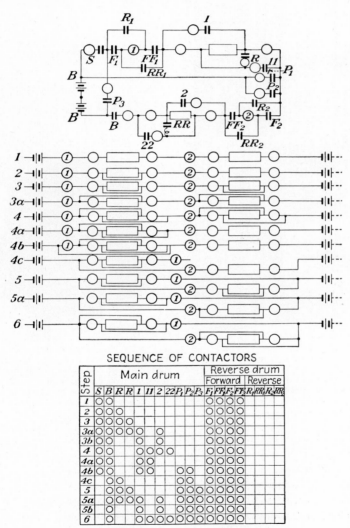

SEQUENCE OF CONTACTORS

Step	Main drum											Reverse drum							
---	---	---	---	---	---	---	---	---	---	---	---	Forward				Reverse			
	S	B	R	R	1	11	2	22	P_1	P_2	P_3	F_1	FF_1	F_2	FF_2	R	RR_1	R_2	RR_2
1	O	O										O	O	O	O				
2	O	O	O									O	O	O					
3	O	O	O	O								O	O	O					
3a	O	O	O	O	O		O					O	O	O					
3b	O	O		O		O						O	O	O					
4	O	O		O	O	O	O					O	O	O					
4a	O	O		O	O							O	O	O					
4b	O	O		O	O				O	O		O	O	O					
4c	O	O							O	O		O	O	O	O				
5	O	O	O						O	O	O	O	O	O	O				
5a	O	O	O	O		O			O	O	O	O	O	O					
5b	O			O		O			O	O		O	O	O					
6	O		O	O	O	O	O	O	O	O	O	O	O	O				

FIG. 8-36.   A two-motor storage-battery control for a locomotive.

attempt has been made to cover them extensively in this book.   Figures 11-2 to 11-4 and 19-4 to 19-6 illustrate two types.

The water rheostats will carry heavy overloads, because the heat is absorbed by vaporizing some of the water.   They are used for field testing and emergency repairs because they can be constructed quickly from

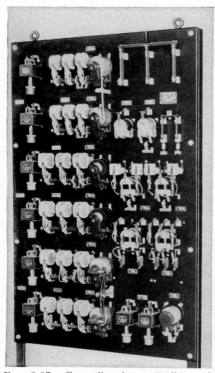

FIG. 8-37. Controller for a "roller and catch table" with roll polishing control built by The Clark Controller Company. It shows how the control for four motors, two reversing and two nonreversing, serving a single machine can be combined into one unit. The operating coils are direct current.

FIG. 8-38. General Electric dustproof reversing cam-type five-point master switch. Oblique rear view showing method of bringing control wires in through conduit entrance in bottom of switch and under wire retainer to terminal boards.

water barrels or other available tanks, using iron plates for electrodes. The following information may be useful in approximating the size of a temporary rheostat.

The current density on the plates or electrodes should not exceed 5 amp per sq in. of surface.   Higher values will cause vapor bubbles to form on the electrodes, reducing their effective area and causing steaming; then the current will fluctuate.   Provide 1-in. separation of plates for each 100 volts between plates.   The resistance will depend upon the density of the solution.

The electrolyte is made of a solution of sodium carbonate (Na_2CO_3), using as pure water as is obtainable.   Sodium carbonate is obtainable

Fig. 8-39.   General Electric treadle-operated watertight push button.

Fig. 8-40.   Track-limit switch built by the Clark Controller Company.   The contacts are double break, silver to silver.   They can be changed from normally open to normally closed, and either single or double pole can be used.   The operating arms are malleable iron, cadmium-plated, and by means of a holding bolt can be adjusted with respect to the shaft in any required position for operation.

commercially in two forms, sal soda and soda ash, the difference between these two being in the amount of water of crystallization that they contain.   Sal soda contains approximately 35 to 40 per cent of sodium carbonate (Na_2CO_3), while soda ash contains from 95 to 99 per cent of Na_2CO_3.

Add ½ to 1 lb soda ash to 100 lb water. If it is found that the current should be larger, more soda should be added. After a 3 per cent solution of sodium carbonate is obtained, further addition of this material will only slightly affect the resistance. The largest variations of resistance are obtained between 0 and 1 per cent solution.

The operating temperature of the electrolyte should not exceed 160°F. It may be necessary to provide cooling coils to keep the temperature down; 5 to 6 gal per hp hr absorbed by the electrolyte will probably be enough. The horsepower-hours can be determined from the complete load cycle by the following formula:

HP = horsepower of motor
a = full-load torque
b = starting torque
c = starting time in minutes
d = number of starts per hour
e = regulating torque or torque when running at reduced speed
f = per cent speed reduction
g = number of minutes per hour during which speed regulation is required

Then the horsepower-hours absorbed equals

$$\left(\frac{HP}{2} \times \frac{b}{a} \times \frac{c}{60} \times \frac{d}{1}\right) + \left(\frac{HP}{1} \times \frac{e}{a} \times \frac{f}{100} \times \frac{g}{100}\right)$$

Auxiliary Switches. Such auxiliary switches as overspeed switches, limit switches, friction switches, bearing thermostats, and many others which are available, are necessary for some applications. They open the control circuit usually to guard against accident. Details are to be found in commercial publications.

A number of special applications of motor drive are given in some detail in "Electric Motors in Industry," by D. R. Shoults and C. J. Rife.[1] The principal electric manufacturers have special publications covering electric power in different industries.

Control equipment is so flexible that it can be applied to any motor drive when the operating conditions are definitely known. Experience is continually improving the automatic features of these special controllers.

[1] Shoults, D. R., and C. J. Rife, "Electric Motors in Industry," Chaps. IX–XI, John Wiley & Sons, Inc., New York.

CHAPTER 9

MECHANICAL AND DYNAMIC BRAKING

The previous chapters have dealt with methods of accelerating the motor from rest to full speed. In this chapter we shall discuss means of stopping the motor, commonly called "braking." The two general methods employed are (1) friction braking and (2) dynamic braking.

FRICTION BRAKING

The Magnet Brake. The type of friction brake usually employed for electric motors is known as a "magnet brake." It consists of a friction

FIG. 9-1. Clark Controller Company's band brake. Direct-current magnet release; spring applied.

member held against the brake wheel by a spring or a weight and released by a magnet. The various commercial designs of this brake are shown in Figs. 9-1, 9-3, 9-4, and 9-6 to 9-8. The releasing magnet may be designed for either direct current or alternating current. The a-c magnets are always shunt wound. The d-c magnets may be series, shunt, or compound wound, depending on the application. Most d-c magnet brakes are wound with series coils. The heating characteristics of these

155

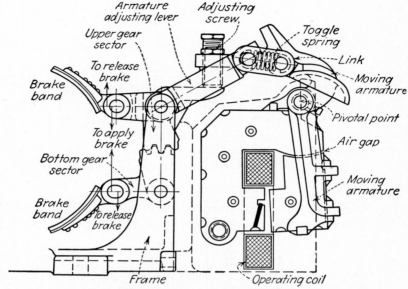

FIG. 9-2.   Alternating-current magnet for releasing the brake of Fig. 9-1.

FIG. 9-3.   Westinghouse shoe type of magnet brake.

FIG. 9-4.   Electric Controller and Manufacturing Company's d-c magnet shoe brake.

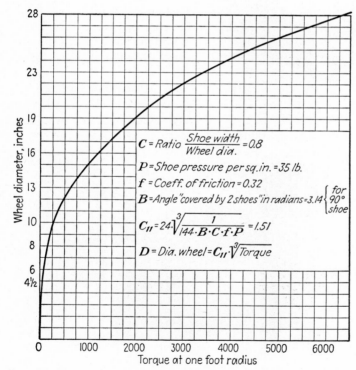

$$C = Ratio \frac{Shoe\ width}{Wheel\ dia.} = 0.8$$

$$P = Shoe\ pressure\ per\ sq.in. = 35\ lb.$$

$$f = Coeff.\ of\ friction = 0.32$$

$$B = Angle\ ''covered\ by\ 2\ shoes''in\ radians = 3.14 \begin{cases} for \\ 90° \\ shoe \end{cases}$$

$$C_{II} = 24 \sqrt[3]{\frac{1}{144 \cdot B \cdot C \cdot f \cdot P}} = 1.51$$

$$D = Dia.\ wheel = C_{II} \cdot \sqrt[3]{Torque}$$

FIG. 9-5.   The relationship between the torque and the wheel diameter.

coils should be the same as the series coils of the motor with which they are used.   The most common applications for these series-wound brakes

are cranes and hoists.   The coil is connected in series with the motor armature and releases the brake shoes as soon as current is supplied to the motor.   The shunt-wound brake is applied to elevators and a few other applications where the load on the motor varies over a wide range.

The a-c magnet brake is always provided with a shunt coil.   This coil may be connected across two of the primary circuits of a wound-secondary induction motor so that it will release whenever the motor primary is energized. This arrangement cannot be applied to squirrel-cage motors if reduced voltage is used in starting.   In this case, a separate switch is required for the brake coil.

A mathematical discussion of the stored energy of a rotating body such as a motor armature or a moving load

Fig.   9-6.   Cutler-Hammer   vertically mounted magnet brake.

such as a hoist can be found in any textbook of mechanics.[1]

Fig. 9-7.   Cutler-Hammer horizontally mounted magnet brake.

[1] A concise explanation of these formulas is given by E. M. Bouton in his article on the braking of electric motors, *Elec. J.*, May, 1918, p. 168.

The design of a magnet brake may seem to be a simple one. In practice it has been found difficult to make a brake embodying all the desirable features. A brief discussion of some of the elements entering into this design will be of interest.

The Brake Shoes. Experience has shown that the shoe type of brake is the design best adapted for general applications. The brake shoes are

Fɪɢ. 9-8. General Electric two-shoe d-c brake, approximately 16 in. high, 30 in. wide, 12 in. deep. Front view oblique from left, showing wheel. Weight: 450 lb.

provided with a lining that can be renewed from time to time. This lining should have a constant coefficient of friction over a wide range of speed and should not be affected by moisture or by a small amount of oil that might get on the brake wheel. This lining should be a good conductor of heat, and the coefficient of friction should not be seriously affected by any operating temperature. The best form of brake lining now available consists of asbestos and rubber interwoven with copper wires. This lining is usually riveted to a cast-iron shoe, the whole shoe being removable in order that the lining may be replaced.

The Brake Wheel. The diameter of the brake wheel should be kept small in order to reduce its stored energy and to keep the fiber stresses in the rim within safe limits. The stored energy represents a direct loss, as the brake must absorb this energy in addition to stopping the motor armature and load. The outer fiber stress enters as a factor in wheels of large diameter and in some cases makes it necessary to use steel wheels. The series motors with which these brakes are used are guaranteed to operate at a speed considerably above normal without mechanical injury to the armature. The brakes used with these motors must have the wheels so designed that there will be no danger of bursting when they are operating at the maximum guaranteed speed of the motor.

Another limitation in the size of the brake wheel is the distance between the motor shaft and the motor feet. When they are separately mounted, it is desirable to have the brake wheel small enough to permit mounting the brake on the same foundation level as the motor. Brakes that are attached to the motor should have their mechanical parts designed so that they will clear this foundation line.

These limitations fix the maximum diameter and weight of the brake wheel. On the other hand, the larger the diameter of the brake wheel, the greater the torque exerted with a given pull on the magnet. The torque of a brake is equal to the force exerted by the brake shoes multiplied by the radius of the wheel. Its value is usually expressed in foot-pounds, the diameter of the wheel being given in feet. The force exerted by the brake shoes is equal to the area of the shoe times the pressure per square inch permissible with a given lining. If we select a working pressure per square inch with a brake-shoe lining that will give reasonable wear and have determined the maximum diameter of wheel that can be used, we can then obtain the width of the shoe. It is found in practice that the percentage of brake-wheel surface covered by the shoe remains constant and that the width of the brake shoe may be assumed to have a definite relation to the diameter of the wheel. Assuming a definite ratio for these values and a fixed working pressure per square inch for the lining, we obtain the curve shown in Fig. 9-5 which gives the relation between the torque and the brake-wheel diameter corresponding to these design limitations.

Adjustment for Wear. As the brake lining wears down, means should be provided for adjusting the shoes so that the clearance between the brake wheel and the shoes is kept within small limits, in order that the magnet may release them. This adjustment should be so arranged that, if neglected, the brake shoes will always set firmly against the wheel and the gap between the armature and the core of the magnet will be gradually increased. If this continues without attention, in time the magnet will fail to release the brake. This condition will be apparent in the operation of the equipment and will, therefore, get attention. In no case should the design of the brake be such that the brake shoe will fail to set against the wheel.

The Magnet. Two types of magnets are available for brakes, the armature type and the plunger type. Theoretically, the plunger type is the more efficient, but the selection of the type of magnet depends upon the general design of the brake and its application.

Magnet coils can now be impregnated and treated to make them moisture resisting to a very high degree, so that an open coil is satis-factory for most installations. Where this coil is exposed directly to the weather or is intended for use on shipboard, a totally enclosed magnet should be used.

The size of the magnet is determined by the pull required to release the brake shoes with the maximum air gap in the magnetic circuit. At this point most of the ampere turns are used to overcome the reluctance in the air gap, so that the iron used for d-c magnet frames can be selected on the basis of its cost rather than on that of its magnetic properties. Care should be taken in the design of the magnetic circuit to reduce the leakage paths to a minimum and to prevent the iron core from becoming saturated, which reduces the pull.

A magnet should be large enough to release the brake shoes quickly. When it is series wound, the brake coil is usually designed to release the magnet at 40 per cent of the rated load of the motor and to hold the magnet in the closed position as low as 10 per cent of the rated load of the motor. Series windings on d-c magnets have the following several advantages:

1. They can be connected in series with the motor armature, reducing complications in wiring.

2. The coils have low inductance and, therefore, act quickly.

3. Should the series motor overspeed, it will reduce the current to a low value and allow the brake magnet to set, thus reducing the liability of a runaway.

4. In case the armature circuit of the motor should be accidentally opened, the brake will set. This is of particular advantage in lowering loads.

5. The voltage between turns is so low that an insulation breakdown seldom occurs and insulating material can be used having high heat-resisting qualities.

When a shunt winding is required for a d-c brake, it is advisable to design this winding for a relatively low voltage and use a resistance in series with it. In most cases a shunt resistance will also be required to take the discharge. The fewer the turns on a shunt coil, the more quickly it will act.

The a-c magnet presents some additional problems. The iron struc-ture must be laminated to prevent eddy-current loss, and the pole face must be provided with shading coils to reduce the noise and eliminate vibration. The a-c flux passes through zero twice every cycle; there-fore, the magnetism will also pass through zero the same number of times. In order to prevent the magnet armature from releasing each time the current passes through zero, shading coils, consisting of a copper or brass strap, are placed around a portion of each pole face. These coils cause the magnetic flux in the area surrounded by the coil to lag behind the flux in the other part of the circuit, so that there is always sufficient flux to hold the armature firmly against the pole face (Fig. 9-2).

Alternating-current brake magnets of the smaller sizes are wound single phase, but the larger sizes are sometimes wound polyphase. The current taken by the magnet with the armature gap open is considerable, and it may be desirable to use a polyphase winding to distribute the load between the phases when larger sized magnets are used.

Mechanical Parts. The brake structure supporting the magnet and the shoes is very frequently made of cast steel in order to give it the proper strength. Stresses set up on portions of this structure are quite severe and are suddenly applied, so that care must be taken in the design of the parts. When the brake magnet releases the armature, a spring or weight forces the shoes against the brake wheel. The shoes travel only a very short distance, but some of the brake levers have more travel and store up considerable energy. This kinetic energy increases the pressure of the brake shoes against the wheel and may cause the brake shoes to exert enough torque to twist off the motor shaft. In order to avoid this, the brake lever attached to the magnet armature or core is usually arranged with a lost motion, so that it can overtravel without exerting pressure against the brake shoes. Springs are preferable for applying the brake shoes, as they have little inertia. Where a weight is used, it should have a dashpot to control its action or some form of spring should be used to cushion the blow.

The size of the magnet is fixed by the pull required and the air gap through which the armature travels. In order to keep the design of these magnets down to a reasonable size, the brake shoes are given very little clearance when they are released. The magnet structure must therefore be very rigid so that there is little or no deflection in these parts; otherwise, the magnet does work in deflecting these parts before it releases the shoes, and the design is very inefficient.

DYNAMIC BRAKING

If a motor is driven by the load and its field remains excited, it will generate a voltage which, if high enough, will return energy to the line. The motor in this case becomes a generator and does work in holding the load. Such an arrangement is useful only where the motor is driven at a high speed. If it is desired to stop the motor, this generator action can be used by connecting a resistor across the motor terminals, reducing it gradually, if necessary, to bring the motor to rest. This method of stopping a motor is known as "dynamic braking." It is used very extensively for hoists and other moving loads that must be frequently stopped. The extra duty of generating the braking current increases the heating in the motor armature and must be taken into account in selecting the motor. This method does not use friction surfaces, and there are therefore no parts to wear out. It is very useful in reducing the speed of the motor to a low value, so that a friction brake is required only to stop the motor from the low speed and to hold the load stationary.

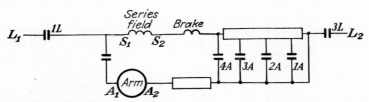

FIG. 9-9. Crane controller diagram showing dynamic-brake lowering of load with a series motor.

When a field rheostat is used to adjust the motor speed, it can be short-circuited during dynamic braking, to build up the field strength while the armature is slowing down and maintain the braking current at a higher value. This brings the motor to a slower speed before the friction brake is applied. The dynamic brake resistor across the armature, if desirable, can be provided with taps and means for short-circuiting it in steps, to maintain the braking current at a high value. The control is the reverse of acceleration.

A series motor can be connected so that it operates as a shunt generator in lowering loads on hoists and for other similar applications. Figure 9-9 shows one method of doing this. The motor is started in the down direction as a shunt motor with an armature-series resistor and a resistor in series with the field connecting it across the line. When the load overhauls, the motor becomes a shunt generator and can have its speed increased by inserting resistance in the circuit. No. 1A is first opened to increase speed; then Nos. 2A, 3A, and 4A open in succession, to give further speed increase. When there is no load on the hook, the motor again operates as a shunt motor to lower the hook. This has been more fully explained under the subject of crane control in Chap. 8.

An interesting application of dynamic braking is illustrated in Fig. 9-10, in connection with an adjustable-speed d-c motor. This motor has a 4 to 1 adjustable-speed range, and very little energy is required to stop it from the low-speed position. When it is operating at a higher speed, the motor field is connected for its maximum value at the time the dynamic-brake circuit is established. This causes the motor field to build up while the armature speed is being reduced. At first this increases the voltage of the motor terminals, causing an increased dynamic-braking torque. As the speed is further reduced, this voltage decreases rapidly. A relatively quick stop results without changing the value of the dynamic-brake resistance.

Dynamic braking should be used whenever it is necessary to stop the motor quickly. It is more economical than a friction brake and requires less attention.

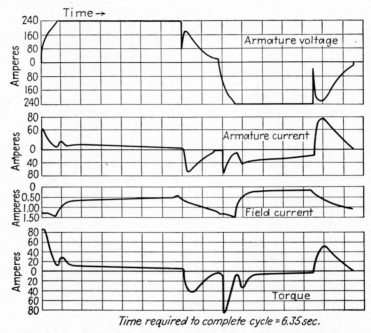

FIG. 9-10. Dynamic braking of a 4 to 1 adjustable-speed d-c motor.

Plugging. When a motor is running in one direction and is quickly reversed, the action is termed "plugging." It is usually done to stop the motor quickly. The control should be designed for this action in order to prevent damage to the motor or to driven machinery. The effect on the motor is different for d-c shunt and series motors and for a-c induction motors. The field flux of the d-c shunt motor remains substantially constant, and its counter emf is added to the line voltage when the armature connections are reversed. Additional armature resistance is added to the starting resistance to limit the current to the same value as it had at starting. This means adding about 85 per cent more ohms. The plugging resistor should be automatically short-circuited when the motor is started from rest; this can be done by using a relay responsive to zero armature voltage and in other ways.

The field flux of the d-c series motor is proportional to the armature current and would increase when the motor is plugged unless the current was limited by additional resistance. An increase in field flux, if it is permitted, will increase the armature voltage that is added to the line

Fig. 9-11. General Electric reversing and plugging magnet controller for a d-c motor.

volts and thus increase the current up to the saturation point of the iron in the field circuit. It is, therefore, more important to control the plugging current in a series motor than in a shunt motor. A compound motor might have its series turns oppose the shunt-field turns and thus reduce the plugging current.

The energy required to stop the motor during plugging is usually the mechanical energy stored in the motor armature and the driven load.

The plugging resistor can be short-circuited in more than one step if it is desirable to have the motor stop more quickly. Usually the reverse connections exert sufficient torque for this purpose.

Plugging can be prevented with a magnet energized by the armature voltage and arranged to lock the reverse contactors open until the motor is nearly stopped. This is usually done when dynamic braking is used.

The a-c induction motor performs entirely differently when plugged. Reversing the rotation of the a-c field gives the secondary double the slip it had at rest and decreases the torque of a squirrel-cage motor to less than that obtained at starting, unless the secondary has unusually high resistance. The motor-power factor drops and increases the wattless current. The motor can be designed to have a plugging torque low enough to prevent damage to the machine gearing.

When plugging is used only for stopping, automatic means, such as the zero-speed switch, must be provided to open the primary connections when zero speed is reached. The wound-secondary motor can have its secondary resistance adjusted during plugging, to control both the torque and the current. The secondary voltage is almost double, and it should be insulated for this condition.

Applications. In applying a brake to a motor, advantage can be taken of the friction in the machinery. In starting a load, the motor must overcome both the load torque and the friction in the machinery. In stopping this load, the friction of the machinery assists the brake. To illustrate, let us assume a hoist having 80 per cent efficiency. If the torque required to accelerate the load is represented as 100 per cent, the torque required to stop the load in the same length of time would be represented as 64 per cent. In order to provide a reasonable factor of safety, the friction brakes should be selected having a torque equal to the full-load torque of the motor. This assumption is based on the fact that many motors used on hoists and similar applications exert more than their full-load torque during the accelerating period and therefore the brake should have full-load torque in order to provide a margin of safety.

If a friction brake is used to lower a load any considerable distance, the energy required to maintain a fixed speed must be absorbed by the brake. This means that a great deal of energy will be absorbed by the brake and must be radiated from it. The size of the brake for such an application would be fixed not by the torque but by its ability to radiate energy. Steam hoists that use a lowering brake have a much larger brake than is common to motor applications. A comparison of this kind illustrates the advantages of using dynamic braking for lowering the load and employing a friction brake only for making the final stop and for holding the load. Dynamic braking adds to the average heating load on the motor.

CHAPTER 10

REGENERATION

The term "regeneration" is usually applied to a system of motor drive where the load exerts a negative torque and drives the motor as a generator, returning power to the system. It is similar to dynamic braking where the motor delivers power to a resistor, which transforms the energy into heat. A system using regeneration must have sufficient positive load to absorb all the energy delivered, or else a resistor should be arranged to absorb the surplus energy.

When regeneration is used for lowering a load, such as the cage of a hoist or a railroad train going downgrade, the retarding torque will be lost if the circuit is open. It is necessary, therefore, to provide protective devices to hold the load by mechanical braking should the electric circuit become disconnected.

In order to obtain regeneration, the induced voltage of the motor or motors must be in excess of the voltage at which power is delivered, or to state it in another way, the motors driven as generators will deliver power to the line only if their voltage is in excess of the voltage at which the positive load is operating. Regeneration may be obtained from motors with shunt characteristics by operating them above their normal speed. For instance, an induction motor or a d-c shunt motor when lowering a load will return power to the line and hold the load at a constant speed slightly in excess of the normal full speed of these motors. Reduced speeds can be obtained by increasing the field strength of a d-c motor so that the required voltage will still be generated when the motor is operated below the maximum running speed. Several d-c motors may be connected in series or in parallel combinations, or in the case of an induction motor, the number of poles may be changed.

The regenerative system must provide for inherent current regulation so that the machines will quickly adapt themselves to any sudden drop in line voltage. This is usually taken care of by automatically changing the field strength of the motors. The line voltage may change too quickly to permit control apparatus to insert armature resistance to protect the motor.

Regeneration may be used to maintain the load at the maximum operating speed, or it may be used to reduce the speed so that part of

167

the energy stored in the moving load will be returned to the line.   The stored energy is proportional to the square of the speed, so that a reduction in speed to one-half of the maximum would mean absorbing three-fourths of the stored energy.   If the speed is reduced to 20 per cent of the maximum before the final stop is made with friction brakes, only 4 per cent of the stored energy will be wasted.

There are many examples of regeneration with shunt d-c motors or induction motors, such as hoists, elevators, etc.   A notable example is that of freight locomotives using induction motors and regenerating when taking a train downgrade.   The inherent characteristic of these motors is such that regeneration is obtained with little or no additional complication.

Where it is desirable to make a material reduction in the speed by means of regeneration, additional features are necessary in designing the equipment.   There are a number of different schemes for obtaining regeneration, but for purposes of simplicity they will be grouped under two main headings: (1) field control and (2) voltage control.

FIELD CONTROL

In its simplest form, this control consists of a d-c shunt motor controlled by varying the strength of the shunt field.   This is illustrated

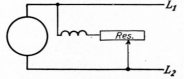

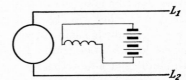

FIG.   10-1.   Field-control   regeneration—scheme 1.

FIG.   10-2.   Field-control   regeneration—scheme 2.

diagrammatically in Fig. 10-1.   Commercial motors of this type can be obtained with a speed range of 4 to 1.   Such a motor can have its speed on regeneration varied in approximately this ratio.   When it is operating at its maximum speed on a weak field, the field can be strengthened so that approximately 80 per cent of the stored energy of the load is returned to the line.

Modifications of this scheme are shown in Figs. 10-2 and 10-3.   In Fig. 10-2 the field is excited from a storage battery, and is therefore independent of the line voltage.   Figure 10-3 shows the field energized from an exciter.   The field of the exciter is connected to the line and is, therefore, affected by variations in line voltage.   If the exciter were self-excited, it would be independent of the line voltage, provided that it were maintained at a uniform speed.   This exciter may be operated by a motor connected to the line with shunt, series, or compound winding, or it may be driven by the main motor through suitable gearing. If it is located on a vehicle, it may be driven by one of the axles. When schemes of control are shown involving an exciter, it will be assumed that the exciter may be driven by any one of the above methods. Each arrangement has its advantages; the method used must be selected for the particular application. If all the various schemes for regenerative control were shown, together with the various methods of driving the exciter, the subject matter would be complicated and difficult to follow.

The scheme shown in Fig. 10-1 is limited to a shunt motor. In the scheme in Fig. 10-2 or 10-3, the motor may be either shunt or series.

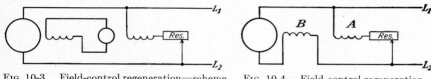

FIG. 10-3. Field-control regeneration—scheme 3.

FIG. 10-4. Field-control regeneration—scheme 4.

The three schemes just considered do not provide means for inherent regulation to protect the motor from overloads caused by a sudden drop in line voltage. Figure 10-4 is the same as Fig. 10-1, with the exception that the motor has a double winding, the series winding B opposing the shunt winding A and weakening the field strength on overloads. A drop

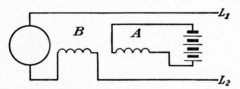

FIG. 10-5. Field-control regeneration—scheme 5.

in the line voltage will increase the motor current, and the strength of the compound winding, which opposes the shunt winding, will cause a reduction in the field strength, which in turn reduces the emf of the motor and maintains the current at a normal value. This regulating action, while inherently in the proper direction, will ordinarily be too slow, on account of the inductive effect of the shunt-field winding.

The field A may be energized from a storage battery (Fig. 10-5) or from a separate exciter (Fig. 10-6). If it is energized from a storage battery, the windings may be either shunt or series. If it is series-wound, the inductive effect is relatively small and the regulating characteristics will change the field strength fast enough to prevent abnormal rises in current. The use of the battery makes the field strength independent of the line voltage.   The arrangement of Fig. 10-6 is usually applied to a series motor and is dependent upon the line voltage, the fields of the exciter in this case being connected across the line.   If these fields were self-excited, a different set of characteristics would be obtained.   Where the field strength is affected by the line voltage, as in Figs. 10-4 and 10-6, a drop in line voltage tends to reduce the field strength in itself, in addition to the action of the differential compound winding B. The arrangement in Fig. 10-5 depends entirely upon the differential winding B for its inherent regulation.

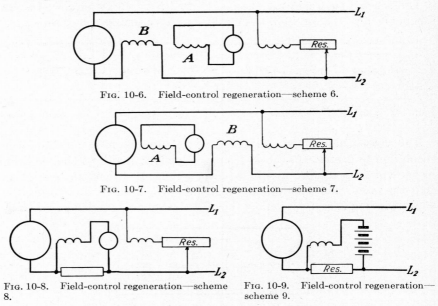

Fig. 10-6.   Field-control regeneration—scheme 6.

Fig. 10-7.   Field-control regeneration—scheme 7.

Fig. 10-8.   Field-control regeneration—scheme 8.

Fig. 10-9.   Field-control regeneration—scheme 9.

It is desirable to make the main motor as simple as possible and not to interfere with its use in motoring.   For this reason, it is better to put the compound winding on the fields of the exciter than on the main motor.   The arrangement shown in Fig. 10-7 is similar to that in Fig. 10-6, the difference being that the compound winding B, which decreases the motor-field strength on overloads, is on the exciter field and not on the motor field.

Other arrangements for limiting the current when a decrease in line voltage takes place are shown in Figs. 10-8 and 10-9.   The main motor field is connected in series with the exciter and in shunt with a small amount of resistance.   The voltage on the field is equal to the voltage of the exciter minus the voltage drop caused by the current flowing through the series resistor.   If the line current increases, the drop through this resistor also increases, and assuming that the exciter voltage remains constant, the voltage on the field will decrease in proportion to the increase in line current. Figure 10-8 shows an exciter with its field connected to the line. Figure 10-9 has a battery substituted for the exciter. The arrangement in Fig. 10-8 is affected by changes in line voltage, whereas the excitation in Fig. 10-9 is independent of the line voltage. The arrangement shown in Fig. 10-8 has been used very successfully on large locomotives; it responds quickly to the changes in current caused by fluctuation in the line voltage. The use of a resistance in series with the motor armature also acts as a buffer, although the value of this resistance is very low and the losses represent only about 1 per cent of the losses in the motor.

The schemes that provide for automatic regulation of the armature current with fluctuations in line voltage not only operate to hold the current down to a safe value when the line voltage decreases, but they tend to maintain the line current close to the required value of an increase in line voltage. The increase in line voltage through the action of the compound winding or series resistance operates to increase the field strength and thus restore the current to its former value.

The speed of the motor on regeneration is adjusted by changing the field strength. Where a battery is used, the number of cells in circuit can be changed. In other cases a rheostat is used in the field of the exciter. When the arrangement shown in Figs. 10-8 and 10-9 is used, adjustments can also be made by changing the ohms in the series resistor. Each particular application must be carefully worked out, and a selection must be made of the scheme of control that is best adapted for that particular application. After the method of control has been determined, the characteristics of the motor on regeneration can be adjusted by varying the amount of compounding where that form of control is used, or the series resistance in Fig. 10-8 or 10-9 may be changed. In addition to these two methods of adjustment, the exciter is capable of a wide degree of adaptation by changing its driving means.

VOLTAGE CONTROL

This method of control may be considered under three subheadings: (1) the motor-generator set, (2) the booster, and (3) the combination of motor-generator set and booster.

The Motor-generator Set. A d-c shunt-wound generator (see Fig. 10-10) has its commutator connected directly to the commutator of a d-c shunt-wound motor. Any standard type of motor may be used to drive the motor-generator set. The motor connected to the load has a constant field strength and a variable voltage impressed on its armature by varying the field strength of the generator.   To reverse the motor, the generator fields are reversed.

The control scheme is a well-known method of obtaining regeneration and is explained fully in Chap. 11.   The speed range obtained on regeneration is practically the whole speed range of the motor in either direction of operation.

The Booster.   A d-c machine may be used as a booster (see Fig. 10-11) or a bucker in series with the main motor, which usually is a d-c shunt-

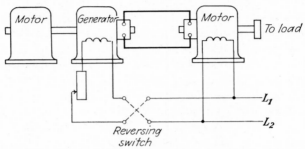

Fig 10-10.   Voltage-control regeneration using a motor-generator set.

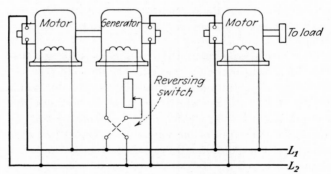

Fig. 10-11.   Voltage-control regeneration using a booster.

wound machine.   When it is at rest, the voltage of the booster is approximately that of the supply circuit.   As the field strength of the booster is decreased, its voltage goes down and the voltage on the motor increases until the motor is operating at line voltage.   The fields of the booster may be reversed and gradually increase the voltage on the motor to approximately double the line voltage.

Regeneration with this method may cover the entire speed range of the motor in both directions of operation.   The booster may be driven by any form of motor, usually a d-c shunt-wound machine.

The Motor-generator Set and Booster.   In this arrangement (see Fig. 10-12) two d-c shunt-wound machines are coupled together and connected in series across the supply lines. The working motor C is connected across the armature of machine B of this set; its field is shunt wound and has a constant value. The fields of the two d-c machines forming the motor-generator set are varied inversely to each other. When the working motor C is at rest, the field of machine A is fully excited and machine B has its minimum field strength, which impresses a low voltage on the motor C. The field of machine A is gradually reduced and that of machine B increased until motor C is accelerated to full speed and the voltage of machine A becomes zero. When regenerating, the voltage of machine A may be reversed so that it will assist

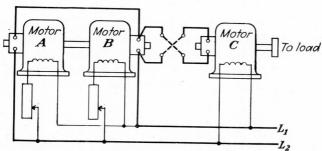

Fig. 10-12. Voltage-control regeneration using the combination of motor-generator set and booster.

machine C in delivering power to the line. The speed reduction during regeneration depends upon the voltage of machine A, and may extend over a wide range. Motor C may have its direction of operation reversed by reversing the connections to its armature.

The schemes shown in Figs. 10-10 and 10-11 require the generator or the booster to carry the full motor current all the time, and to deliver full voltage part of the time. These two limitations fix the size of this machine. The arrangement shown in Fig. 10-12 divides the motor current between machines A and B. When the motor C starts from rest, its total current is supplied by both machines A and B in the inverse ratio of their voltages, the machine B supplying most of the current at slow speeds. This distribution of current permits smaller machines to be used than in the schemes shown in Figs. 10-10 and 10-11.

The last two arrangements show the motor and the generator with shunt-field windings only. These machines can be compound wound to obtain better operating characteristics from the motor driving the load. If this motor is operating a hoist, its speed will change with a change in load, owing to the resistance in the armature circuit. This change in speed is known as "regulation." The load may change from the maximum value in the positive direction to a negative load of perhaps 50 per cent of the maximum, so that a considerable change in speed may result. If series windings are used, the motor can be given approximately a flat speed characteristic over the entire range of load.

When it is regenerating, a sudden drop in line voltage may cause an abnormal increase in the regenerating current. This condition can be taken care of in much the same way as was described under field control. The service conditions will often determine the amount and frequency of voltage disturbances. In railway work, a considerable drop in line voltage must be provided for, while in power work, particularly with the smaller hoists, elevators, etc., the voltage regulation is good. In many cases these motors are operated from the same lines that supply the lighting system. If an induction motor is used for the motor-generator set shown in Fig. 10-10, the ordinary changes in line voltage will be readily taken care of by the inherent characteristics of the motor. For large installations the induction motor is provided with a slip regulator, which automatically adjusts the current fast enough to protect the motor from damage from voltage fluctuations.

GENERAL

The various forms of field control, with the exception of that shown in Fig. 10-11, have their widest application in railway work. For the latter it is preferable to use series motors, as they are freer from flashing troubles than are shunt motors. These systems of control require the use of a rheostat for acceleration and speed regulation when motoring. The resistors are also required during regeneration, when the motors are first connected to the line, and also when the motor combinations are changed from parallel to series, etc.

The voltage methods of control have found their principal applications in the industrial field. The scheme illustrated in Fig. 10-10 is the one commonly used for elevators, large mining hoists, and reversing steel mills. Voltage control does not require a resistor in the armature circuit of the motor. The only rheostats used are in the field circuits, and they consume very little energy. During acceleration and regeneration, the ordinary rheostat losses are eliminated, so that these systems operate very efficiently while the motor is connected to the line. During the time when the working motor is idle, the operation of the motor-generator sets consumes power and represents a direct loss. The control system can be arranged to shut down the motor-generator set during idle periods, to avoid stand-by losses, if sufficient time can be allowed for starting the set before starting the working motor.

CHAPTER 11

VOLTAGE CONTROL FOR DIRECT-CURRENT MOTORS

If a d-c motor has its field excited at a constant voltage, its speed will be proportional to the voltage impressed on its armature. The methods of obtaining a reduced voltage by means of resistance in series with the armature have already been described. Another method that is little used at present is to provide a source of power, using four or more power wires, the voltage between the different wires being proportioned so that a considerable number of operating voltages can be obtained by connecting the motor armature to different pairs of wires. This method is known as the "multivoltage system." It is objectionable because it requires a number of power wires and special generator equipment, as well. There are also power circuits provided with two outside wires and a central or neutral wire, the voltage between the outside wire being double that between either wire and the neutral. These systems usually have voltages of 115 and 230, respectively, and are used for a limited number of industrial applications.

THE MOTOR-GENERATOR SYSTEM

The increasing size of d-c motors for planers, hoisting, and the application of motor drive to reversing steel mills, during the last 20 years, has brought into general use a system of voltage control in which a separate generator is provided for each motor. This generator may be driven from any source of power but is usually driven by a constant-speed a-c motor. The armature of the generator is connected directly to the d-c motor, as shown in Fig. 11-1, both machines having their fields supplied from a constant-voltage exciter. The slow speeds of the motor are obtained by reducing the strength of the generator field. If the generator field is reduced to zero and energized in the reverse direction, the rotation of the motor will be reversed. The controller in Fig. 11-1 shows one means of doing this. The rheostat consists of a closed circuit in the form of a circle. Points A and B are connected to the + and to the − side of the exciter, and C and D are connected to the generator field. When the rheostat is in the position shown, the generator field is zero, and consequently the motor speed is zero. If contact 1 is moved to coincide with point A, contact 2 with C, contact 3 with B, and contact 4 with D, current will flow from the exciter to A through 1 and 2 to C, thence through the generator field to D, and from contact 4 to 3 to B, and thence to the exciter. This will give the maximum field strength to

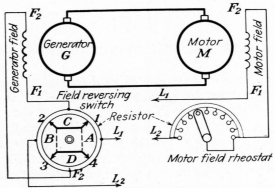

FIG. 11-1. Connections for reversing a steel-mill motor.

the generator and cause the motor to operate in a forward direction at full speed. Any position between the one shown in the diagram and the one just described will give intermediate values of field strength and cause the motor to operate at reduced speeds. If the controller is moved so that contact 1 coincides with point C, contact 4 with point A, etc., current will flow from the exciter to A through contacts 4 and 3 to D, through the generator field to C, through contacts 1 and 2 to B and then to the exciter. This will cause the motor to operate at full speed in the reverse direction. Intermediate positions of the control will give intermediate speeds.

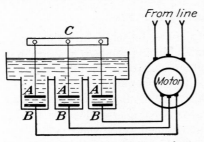

FIG. 11-2. Connections of slip regulator to induction motor.

The advantage of such a method of control is obvious. The speed and direction of rotation of the large motor M in Fig. 11-1 is controlled by switching the small field current of generator G. This current may be in the neighborhood of 100 amp, while the armature current flowing from G to M may be several thousand amperes. This method gives a large number of fixed running speeds, and the only losses that occur are the usual losses in the generator and the motor, in addition to the rheostatic losses in the field control.

The speed of motor M may be retarded by reducing the generator voltage to a lower value than the counter emf of the motor. This causes the motor to regenerate and produces dynamic braking.   If the generator *G* is driven by a suitable motor, this method of slowing down will return power to the line.   If it is driven by an engine, the generator cannot absorb the power, and the regenerated current must be wasted in a resistance.

The field of motor *M* can also be varied to increase the speed range of the combination.   It is found in practice that the motor *M* can be

Fig. 11-3.   Westinghouse liquid-slip regulator with torque motor for automatic control. Figure 11-4 shows the operating parts of this regulator.

arranged for speed control of 1 to 1.5 or 1 to 2 by varying its shunt field, without much additional expense.   If less than the full range of operating speed is obtained from the generator, a smaller generator can be used. Therefore, the combined field control of the generator and field control of the motor gives cheaper commercial apparatus than would obtaining the entire range of speed control from the generator.   This double method of control may seem complicated, but as it is usually combined in one master switch, very little additional apparatus is required.

Figure 11-6 shows a magnetic amplifier (Chap. 13) controlling a series of contactors to vary the resistance in an induction motor secondary. This arrangement can be used instead of the liquid-slip regulator (Fig.

11-3); it is a modification of Fig. 6-41 arranged to increase or decrease the resistance in the motor secondary.

The "step-type" slip regulator was used on the first rolling-mill equipment to limit the power input. The relays and interlocks available at that time required considerable attention and caused the development of the liquid-slip regulator. Now the magnetic amplifier has so simplified the "step-type" of slip regulator that it may again be used.

Flywheel Power Storage. When a large generator G is driven by a motor, this method of controlling the operating motor is usually combined with a system for reducing the maximum power demand from the generat-

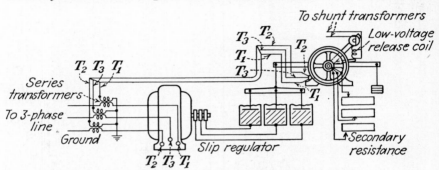

Fig. 11-4.   Diagrammatic view of regulator shown in Fig. 11-3.

ing station. The power supplied for large installations is usually alternating current, so the generator G in Fig. 11-1 is driven by an induction motor, shown in Fig. 11-5. On the motor-generator shaft is placed a large flywheel, which is used for storing energy during the low-demand period of the cycle and for supplying energy during the maximum-demand periods. This flywheel performs a similar function to a storage battery floating on the d-c system. The flywheel gives out energy or absorbs energy, depending upon the speed of the motor-generator set.

The driving motor for this set is provided with a wound secondary, and a slip regulator is introduced in its secondary circuit. If the resistance in this secondary circuit is varied automatically with the load, the motor will take an approximately constant amount of power from the line. This is desirable only above full load on the motor. If the demand for power is in excess of this load, the slip regulator introduces more resistance in the motor secondary and allows the motor-generator set to slow down, so that the flywheel can supply this excess of power. When the demand on the generator is less than normal, the resistance in the secondary of the induction motor is decreased and the excess power input is used in accelerating the flywheel, thus storing up mechanical energy to be given out later when an excess demand occurs.

A diagram combining the control of the motor-generator set with the control of the operating motor is shown in Fig. 11-5. This diagram is merely a scheme of connections intended to illustrate the principle, and does not show any of the control apparatus in detail. The slip regulator in the secondary of the induction motor consists of three fixed electrodes marked *B* in Fig. 11-2. Each of these electrodes is insulated and con-

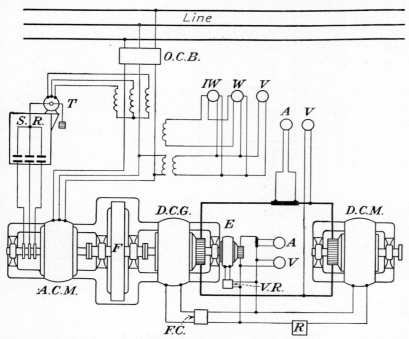

Fig. 11-5. Connections of equalizer flywheel hoisting set. *A.C.M.*, wound-secondary induction motor; *F*, flywheel *D.C.G.*, separately excited d-c generator; *E*, exciter; *D.C.M* separately excited d-c motor; *S.R.*, automatic liquid-slip regulator; *T*, torque motor for ship regulator; *O.C.B.*, oil circuit breaker; *F.C.*, reversing field controller for generator *R*, rheostat for motor field; *V.R.*, voltage regulator for exciter; *A*, ammeter; *V*, voltmeter; *W*, watt-hour meter; *IW*, integrating wattmeter.

nected to one of the slip rings of the induction motor. Above them in the liquid are suspended three electrodes marked *A*, attached to a common support *C*, and electrically connected through this support. The liquid in the tank, known as the "electrolyte," is a solution of washing soda and water. By referring to Fig. 11-5, it will be seen that the movable electrodes are raised or lowered by a small torque motor *T*, which is energized from three series transformers in the primary circuit of the induction motor. The weight of the moving element is partly counterbalanced, but it is still sufficient to move the plates together. The torque motor tends to separate the plates.   This motor operates in the same manner as an ammeter; the plates move up or down until the torque of the motor just balances the weight of the moving element, which occurs at substantially the same current values for all positions of the plates.   The friction in a commercial regulator does not require more than 5 per cent difference between the torque for raising and that for lowering the plates.

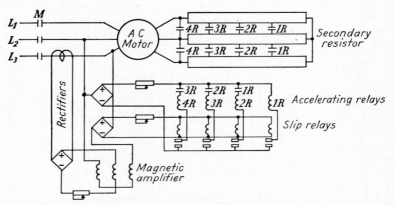

FIG. 11-6.   "Slip regulator" for a wound-rotor induction motor.
    The motor drives a generator has a flywheel on its shaft.   When the load exceeds a fixed value, resistance is inserted in the motor secondary in steps to reduce its speed and permit the flywheel to supply some of the power.   When the load decreases, the resistor is short-circuited in steps to accelerate the flywheel and store up energy for the next peak load.   The slip regulator is a power equalizer.
    The contactors $1R$, $2R$, $3R$, and $4R$ are controlled by the motor current as explained in Fig. 6-41 except that slip relays are used as shown instead of lock-out coils, so that the resistance can be changed in and out of the circuit.

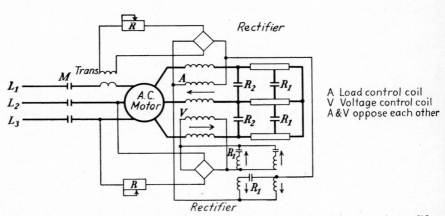

FIG. 11-7.   Slip regulator for wound-secondary induction motor with magnetic-amplifier control.   This diagram shows the magnetic amplifier in the motor secondary as part of the impedance of this circuit.

The upper curve in Fig. 11-10*a* shows the regulation obtained with one of these slip regulators in commercial work, as compared with the regulation obtained with a magnetic-contactor control for cutting resistance in and out of the secondary of the motor, as shown in the lower curve. These curves, which reveal the advantages of the liquid regulator, show that the maximum-power input is quite uniform. The minimum-power input depends largely upon the way in which the load comes on and off the operating motor, so that these low peaks decrease to a very small value if the demand for power is small over a considerable period of time.

Fig. 11-8. Equalizer flywheel hoisting set showing automatic liquid-slip regulator.

An exciter is shown mounted on the shaft of the motor-generator set in Fig. 11-5. As the speed of this exciter varies with the speed of the motor-generator set, it is necessary to provide a voltage regulator, in order that the voltage of this exciter will remain constant over the speed range that is obtained in practice. This is a simpler arrangement than the use of a separately driven exciter.

It is the practice of power companies to make a charge based upon the maximum demand required from the power system. This is a just method of charging for power, as the size of the generating station must be determined by the maximum demand of the customers. Where a large motor is applied to a hoist, considerable power is taken from the line to accelerate the hoist if the motor is connected directly to the supply system. The charge for power may be large on account of this maximum demand. If the motor is operated from a flywheel motor-generator set, as was previously described, the maximum demand can be kept quite low, as is shown in Fig. 11-10, particularly if a liquid regulator is used, so that a reduction is made in the power bills by using this system. Another saving results from the regeneration of power when the

F<small>IG</small>. 11-9. Equalizer flywheel hoisting set showing automatic liquid-slip regulator.

load is reversed. In the operation of a mine hoist with this voltage system of controlling, there is very little rheostatic loss, so that less power is taken and a large percentage of the energy given out by the descending hoist is returned to the line by regeneration.

It is not difficult to determine the size of a flywheel to absorb the peak loads when used in connection with a motor-generator set. A curve should be drawn showing the relation between the horsepower required at any particular instant and the time. It is usual to plot the horsepower as ordinates and the time as abscissas. From this curve the average input can be obtained and the maximum demand over any given period of time.

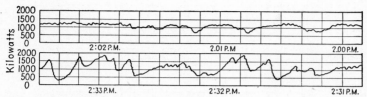

FIG. 11-10a. Power-demand curves of a typical hoisting set. The upper curve shows regulation using a slip regulator; the lower curve, regulation using magnetic-contractor control.

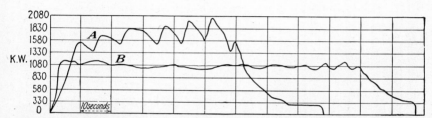

FIG. 11-10b. Curve *A* was taken when starting a 2,000-hp plate-mill motor with magnetic control. Curve *B* shows the same motor starting under load operated with a liquid regulator.

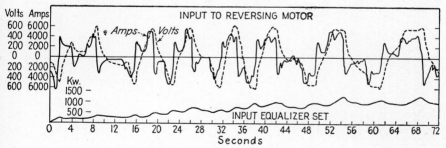

FIG. 11-11. Input to reversing motor.

To illustrate, in Fig. 11-12 is given a load-time curve of a hoisting set, to lift 5,000 lb at 1,200 ft per min. The accelerating and retarding periods will be equal to 1,760 hp-sec, and the constant speed periods will be 3,540 hp-sec, making a total of 5,300 hp-sec in excess of the average requirements. This represents the total energy that must be given out by the flywheel over the maximum-demand period. This

energy must be returned to the flywheel during the periods when the
power demand is less than the average.

The weight of the flywheel depends upon the type of construction and
the maximum peripheral speed.   Let V_1 equal the velocity in feet per

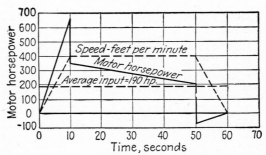

FIG. 11-12.   Load-time curve of a typical hoisting set.

FIG. 11-13.   Westinghouse control panel for a reversing steel-mill motor for main-roll
drive.

second at a radius of gyration for maximum speed, and V_2 for the minimum speed.   The simplest form of flywheel and one of the best is
made up of solid circular plates.   For this type of wheel, the radius of
gyration is equal to 0.707 of the wheel radius.   If 20,000 ft per min is

selected as the maximum peripheral speed, which corresponds to good practice, the maximum velocity at the radius of gyration will be

$$V_1 = \frac{20,000 \times 0.707}{60} = 236 \text{ ft per sec}$$

If a minimum speed is assumed equal to 85 per cent of the maximum speed, which is good practice, the minimum peripheral speed will be

$$V_2 = 236 \times 0.85 = 200 \text{ ft per sec}$$

The weight of the flywheel can now be calculated as follows:

$$W = \frac{\text{hp-sec to be supplied} \times 550 \times 2g}{V_1{}^2 - V_2{}^2} = \frac{5300 \times 35,400}{(236)^2 - (200)^2} = 12,050$$

The rotating element of the motor and the generator furnish some flywheel effect, so that the horsepower-seconds of the flywheel effect obtained from these two units can be subtracted from the total in calculating the size of the flywheel if it is desirable to figure very closely.[1]

MULTIPLE OPERATION OF MOTORS AND GENERATORS IN SERIES

The scheme of control illustrated in Fig. 11-5 is applicable to mine hoists and similar reversing sets for driving the main rolls in steel mills. Many steel-mill applications require much larger equipments. If the diameters of the rotating parts are increased, the stored energy will increase as the square of the diameter, which materially increases the work required for reversing the requipment. It is, therefore, better engineering practice to divide motor and generator into two units. Figure 11-14 shows a diagram of the double-unit set. The main circuits between the generators and the motors might be arranged so that each generator operated its own motor, or the generators and motors might be coupled in series. The series arrangement is preferable, as it ensures an even distribution of load among all four machines. The objection to this arrangement is the large armature current if the voltage per machine is 250 or a total of 500 volts to ground, but if the voltage per machine is 500 volts, additional insulation is required. The arrangement shown in Fig. 11-14 avoids both these difficulties by connecting the motors and generators alternately in series, the current passing from generator No. 1 to motor No. 1, thence to generator No. 2 and motor No. 2, back to generator

---

[1] With a slip regulator it is possible to keep the motor load almost constant at the average value. Without a slip regulator the motor load increases with the decreasing speed, and the calculation is more complicated. See S. A. Fletcher and C. R. Riker, Relation of Flywheel and Motor Capacity for Industrial Loads, *Elec. J.*, March, 1912, p. 270.

No. 1. This arrangement can be readily extended to additional machines if a larger output is required.

In rolling steel, it is very desirable that the motors shall have compound characteristics, but the armature currents are too large to reverse the series field each time the shunt field is reversed, so that another arrangement must be used. This consists of a small generator K (see

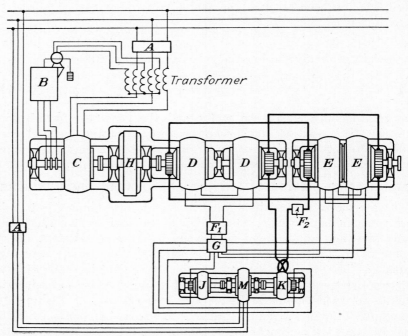

Fig. 11-14. Connections for double-unit reversing motor. A, oil circuit breaker with no-voltage trip; B, automatic liquid-slip regulator; C, a-c wound-rotor induction motor; D, d-c separately excited generators; E, d-c separately excited motors; F_1, circuit breaker in generator fields; F_2, circuit breaker in main circuit; G, field controller; H, flywheel; J, shunt exciter for generator and motor fields; K, series exciter; M, a-c squirrel-cage induction motor.

Fig. 11-14), forming part of the exciter set. The fields of this generator are in series with the armature current of the main motors. The voltage of the machine K is, therefore, proportional to the load on the main motors, and this machine can be used to excite windings on the motors. These windings carry only a small current and can be reversed when the fields of the shunt generators are reversed.

The detailed scheme of connections for this reversing set is shown in Fig. 11-15. The control consists of a series of magnetic contactors, some of which are used for reversing the fields, others for changing the resistance in series with these fields, others for purposes that will be described later.

In order to make the generator voltage respond quickly to a change in the controller, it is necessary to wind this field for a low voltage and use a resistance in series with it. If this resistance is short-circuited while the field is being strengthened, it will increase the speed at which the change of flux takes place and therefore hasten the increase in voltage on the generator. This method of manipulating the field is called "field forcing." In order to prevent the field from building up beyond the value

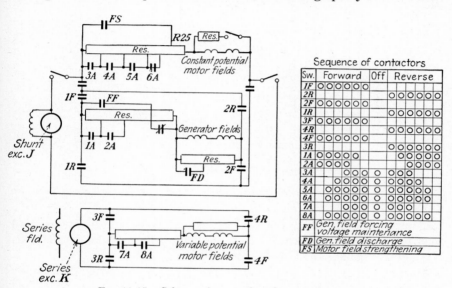

Sequence of contactors

Sw.	Forward						Off	Reverse					
1F	O	O	O	O	O	O							
2R								O	O	O	O	O	O
2F	O	O	O	O	O	O							
1R								O	O	O	O	O	O
3F	O	O	O	O	O	O							
4R								O	O	O	O	O	O
4F	O	O	O	O	O	O							
3R								O	O	O	O	O	O
1A	O	O	O	O	O				O	O	O	O	O
2A	O	O	O	O						O	O	O	O
3A			O	O	O		O		O	O	O		
4A		O	O	O	O		O		O	O	O		
5A		O	O	O	O		O		O	O	O	O	
6A	O	O	O	O	O		O		O	O	O	O	
7A			O	O	O		O		O	O	O		
8A	O	O	O	O	O		O		O	O	O	O	
FF	Gen. field forcing												
	voltage maintenance												
FD	Gen. field discharge												
FS	Motor field strengthening												

Fig. 11-15. Scheme of connections for reversing set.

for which the master switch is set, an automatic arrangement is used, which is shown in Fig. 11-16. The coils for the contactors, 9 and 10, controlling the field, are shown as 9 and 10. These coils are in series with the solenoid *S*, which operates the contact mechanism 30, and is opposed by solenoid *T*. The strength of *S* depends upon the coils 9 and 10 of contactors 9 and 10 being energized by the master switch. When a contactor is first closed, the coil *S* predominates over *T* and closes contact 30, which energizes coil 17 of contactor 17. This closes contactor 17 and short-circuits resistance in series with the generator fields. As these fields build up, the magnet *T* exerts an increasing pull until the desired voltage is reached, at which point magnet *T* overcomes *S* and opens contactor 17.

This contactor 17 is also used to maintain the generated voltage constant on long passes in the mill. As has been previously described, the motor-generator set is equipped with a flywheel, which by slowing down furnishes the excess power above normal load. But the slowing down of the motor-generator set has a tendency to lower the voltage on the generators if the field strength remains constant. In order to overcome this difficulty and obtain constant voltage, which means constant speed of the mill motor, a voltage regulator is used, which momentarily closes contactor 17 whenever the voltage drops below normal. The voltage then tends to increase above normal so that by the repeated closing and

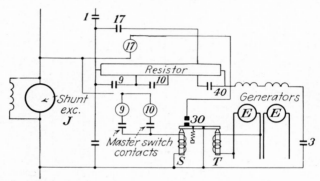

FIG. 11-16. A method of preventing the field from building up beyond the value for which the master switch is set.

opening of this contactor the field has a tendency first to increase and then to decrease, but because of the inductive effect of the field circuit, the voltage remains practically constant.

An overload relay is used to limit the armature current. This relay is shunt wound, with as little inductance as possible, and is connected across the interpole windings of one of the motors, which acts as an inductive shunt, giving the relay a slight anticipation of a change in the current. But the change in flux in the generator fields has a time lag owing to the inductance of the field windings; therefore, when an overload occurs, if we arrest the increase of current in the field windings, the field flux will continue to increase on account of this stored energy. An overload relay that inserts resistance in series with the field circuit will not respond quickly enough to correct momentary current peaks. It is, therefore, necessary to add a contactor which short-circuits a section of the resistor in shunt to the field windings; this immediately arrests an increase in flux. The contactor may open and close a number of times during a change in speed. It is found in practice that the various field windings can be timed so that dangerous overloads do not occur except during deceleration, when the motors are operating on weakened fields. This overload device is, therefore, arranged so that it operates only when the motors are delivering power to the generators.

The generator field has two sets of resistance in series with it. One set is controlled by contactors 9 and 10, operated by the master switch for the purpose of regulating the motor speed. The second set of resistance is normally short-circuited by contactor 40. When an overload occurs, it opens contactor 40, which inserts a resistance in the field, and this, in turn, reduces the current through the armature. Under normal operation, this contactor is closed.

The motors have two field windings, one connected to the constant potential source of power exciter J (see Fig. 11-14), the other connected to the compound exciter K. After the motors have reached normal speed on full field value, the speed may be further increased by weakening the motor fields. This requires the insertion of resistance in both field windings. If the fields are weakened too rapidly during acceleration, excessive current will flow through the armature. Contactor FS is therefore provided for short-circuiting the resistance in series with the constant potential motor fields. This contactor is controlled by an overload relay and opens and closes in rapid succession during acceleration, maintaining the armature current practically constant.

If the master switch is operated to decrease the speed of the motors, they will regenerate and in doing so reverse the polarity of the field windings supplied from the exciter K. This may cause an abnormal weakening of the motor field. To prevent this, a reverse-voltage relay opens contactor $5A$ or $6A$ and disconnects these field windings whenever the motor voltage reverses with reference to the generator voltage without the master switch's being reversed. As was explained previously, when the master switch is reversed, the polarity of these fields is automatically reversed; therefore, the current in these fields is in the correct direction.

The control of the reversing equipment for steel-mill service has been given at some length in order to illustrate the nature of the problems arising in such a control system. This control system is used for mine hoists and elevators with one working motor and no field control. Commercial controllers differ in many details, but the principles of this control are typical. Some of these problems are similar to problems met with in the control of small adjustable-speed motors. As an illustration, contactor FS, which prevents too rapid weakening of the motor field, has its counterpart in the ordinary fluttering relay used with adjustable-speed motors.

The control equipment for the rapid reversing required in steel-mill service differs in some details from the controller used with mine hoists, where the change in speed is much more gradual and the motor does not have compound characteristics.   The mine-hoist controller provides automatic slow-down and stop at either limit of travel.   This is accomplished by a current relay, which reduces the generator voltage to zero at the proper rate to keep the armature current at a constant value.

In order to prevent the generator fields from being disconnected from the line by throwing the master switch to the Off position when the motor is still running, a voltage relay is used, which automatically maintains the generator-field circuit and allows the decelerating current relay to slow the set down before disconnecting the fields.

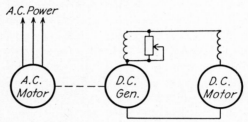

FIG. 11-17.   Variable-voltage control using a series-wound d-c generator and motor.   No exciter is required.

When the generator field is disconnected from the line, there is a residual magnetism, which causes the motor to rotate at a very slow, creeping speed.   This is a desirable feature in steel-mill work, as the slow turning of the main rolls prevents overheating and consequent injury to the rolls.   When it is applied to a mine hoist, this creeping action is very objectionable.   It is eliminated by automatically connecting the generator fields across the motor armature in the reverse direction.   This causes a small current to flow through the field coils in the proper direction to kill this magnetism.

Steel mills, mine hoists, elevators, and planers are some of the principal applications using this method of control.

Small variable-voltage motor-generator sets can be economically built with a series motor and generator.   No exciter is required with this arrangement (see Fig. 11-17).   The motor speed is adjusted by a rheostat in parallel with the generator field.   The generator is usually driven by an a-c induction motor.

CHAPTER 12

AMPLIFIERS USED FOR MOTOR CONTROL

METHODS OF REGULATION BY MEANS OF AN AMPLIFIER

The American Standards Association definition of an Amplifier is
" . . . a device for increasing the power associated with a phenomenon
without appreciably altering its quality through control by the amplifier
input of a larger amount of power supplied by a local source to the
amplifier output."

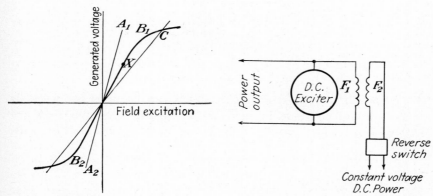

FIG. 12-1. Saturation curve of an exciter.   FIG. 12-2. A regulating exciter with two fields F_1 and F_2 and means for reversing F_2. The rheostat in the circuit of F_1 is not shown.

Three methods of amplification are now in use for motor control as
follows:

1. Electronic amplifiers (static electronic means). See Chap. 21, also
Fig. 21-10.

2. The separately excited dynamoelectric machine such as the Amplidyne, the Regulex, and the Rototrol (rotating magnetic means). See
the following text.

3. The magnetic amplifier (static magnetic means). See Chap. 13.

R. M. Saunders compares methods 1 and 2 in *Elec. Eng.*, April, p. 351,
as follows:

The d-c generator as a dynamoelectric amplifier is analogous to the electronic amplifier except that the power supplied is mechanical instead of electrical. . . . Control is effected by a current instead of a voltage, and the control circuits contain inductance rather than capacitance. (This applies also to magnetic amplifiers.)

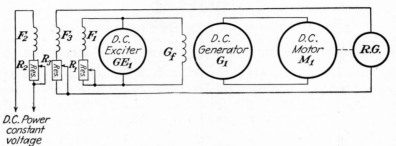

FIG. 12-3.   Method of regulating for constant speed. F_1, self-excited field; F_2, pattern field; F_3, regulating field; RG, generator with constant field drive by motor M_1.

The generator G_1 and the exciter GE_1 are driven at constant speed. R_1 adjusts F_1 so that the self-excited voltage is on the saturation-curve (see Fig. 12-1) line B_1-B_2. R_2 adjusts the speed of M_1 and RG. F_3 opposes F_2, and the two are made equal by R_3 when the speed of M_1 is correct.   An increase in the speed of M_1 reduces field GF and returns M_1 to the correct speed.   A reduction in the speed of M_1 increases field GF and corrects the speed of M_1.

The electronic tube is responsive to voltage, and the other two methods respond to minute changes in current.   For example, a tube responds directly to the change in voltage of a tachometer generator used to meas-

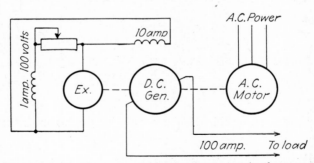

FIG. 12-4.   How 1 amp in the exciter field controls 10 amp in the generator field and 100 amp in the generator armature—an amplification of 100 to 1.   This is one method of amplification where a slow response is satisfactory.

ure a motor speed.   Methods 2 and 3 respond to a change in current in the motor circuit.   Voltage can be converted to current by a shunt across the motor terminals, and current can be measured by the voltage drop in a series-field winding or a resistor, so that any of these three methods can be used.   All three methods, in general, are used to change the field strength of a generator or motor to regulate its speed or output quickly so as to maintain or achieve a definite result with a high degree of accuracy. Electronic tubes can be used in combination with the other methods.

DYNAMOELECTRIC METHODS OF REGULATION BY ROTOTROL AND REGULEX

The motor-generator method of speed control of motors has developed wide possibilities. The generator can have a series field winding, to

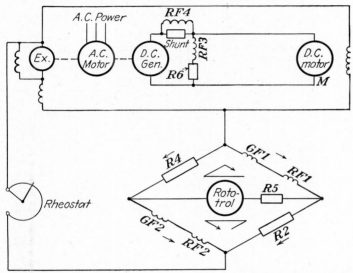

Fig. 12-5.   Rototrol with bridge connections.   The generator has two shunt fields $GF1$ and $GF2$; the ampere turns add together.   The Rototrol has four shunt fields: $RF1$, $RF2$, and $RF4$ ampere turns add together, and $RF3$ ampere turns oppose the others.

At no load, $R5$ and $R6$ are adjusted so that $RF1 + RF2 - RF3 = 0$ and the Rototrol generates no voltage.   The speed of the motor M is controlled by a rheostat.   The no-load losses cause a current to flow in the shunt, which builds up $RF4$ and opposes $RF3$, causing the Rototrol to generate voltage and send current through $GF1$-$RF1$ and $GF2$-$RF2$, increasing the generator voltage to overcome the load-current voltage drop. $RF1$ and $RF2$ also increase to bring the Rototrol voltage back to zero when M returns to its present speed. The working load on M causes a further increase in the generator volts to compensate for the added voltage drop in the armature circuits.

If the load on M is negative, as when lowering a load, the ampere turns in $RF4$ are reversed, causing a reduction in generator volts to hold M at its present speed.

increase its voltage as the load increases, nearly to compensate for the voltage drop in the armature circuit and maintain approximately constant speed. This speed regulation is close enough for some applications, but where closer regulation is required, there are several designs of regulators available of the exciter type. Electronic tubes also can be used. It is desirable to keep the regulating power small and to amplify its effect on the generator voltage. These regulators can maintain exact preset speed or constant torque. They can regulate for any function that can be expressed electrically. The elements of the exciter type of regulators are as follows:

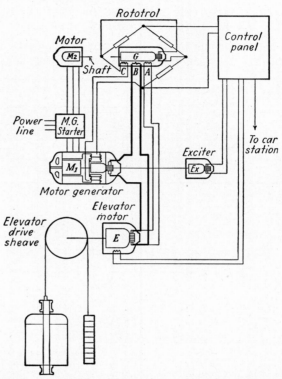

FIG. 12-6. Schematic outline for rototrol system. How Rototrol works: The system depends on a small d-c generator G to furnish the "brains" which automatically regulate the elevator motor speed.

The "eyes" are fields A and B which enable the system to "see" the speed at which the car is operating.

The "hand" that automatically corrects for any deviaiton from a predetermined speed pattern (field C) is the voltage generated by the small d-c generator G which operates in the bridge circuit.

The d-c exciter, in Fig. 12-2, driven at constant speed, can have its self-excited field F_1 adjusted with a rheostat so that its magnetizing force coincides with the saturation curve in Fig. 12-1, line B_1-B_2. In standard practice the resistance is less and the line intersects the saturation curve at C. When the resistance is high, the magnetizing force moves toward line A_1-A_2, and the field flux becomes zero, as it will not self-excite. The field can be built up along B_1-B_2 to the point X by means of the momentary use of field F_2, which can move X up or down on B_1-B_2 by adding or opposing F_1. A small change in F_2 shifts the line of magnetizing force sidewise and a small field can make a large change in the exciter voltage. Field F_2 gives a regulating means requiring very little energy to affect the exciter voltage and is, therefore, very sensitive.

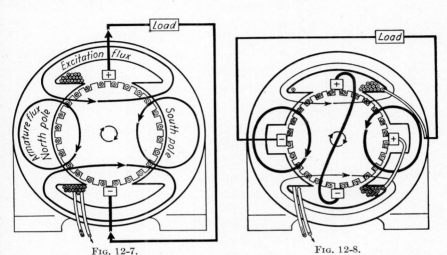

FIG. 12-7.   FIG. 12-8.

FIG. 12-7.   A conventional d-c generator (10 kw) driven at constant speed may be shown schematically in the form above, with the armature serving also as the commutator, for sake of simplicity.   About 100 watts of excitation power supplied to the field coil creates the excitation flux.   This flux is producing full-load voltage of 100 volts, which circulates 100 amp (full-load current) through a 1-ohm resistance.   The load current, in flowing through the armature conductors, creates an armature flux of about the same magnitude as the excitation flux.   To put this flux to work see Fig. 12-8.

FIG. 12-8.   Two brushes are added, one in the center of each armature flux loop.   The armature flux now produces 100 volts between these new brushes, which are connected to the load through a compensating field: this circulates 100 amp through the load.   This new 100-amp load adds or subtracts from the short-circuit current (Fig. 12-13).

The compensating winding prevents the load current from causing an armature flux opposing the control flux.

If the excitation current is doubled, it doubles the short-circuit current, producing double voltage and double load current.   An increase of 3 watts in the control circuit therefore increases the output from 10 to 40 kw.

The exciter in Fig. 12-3 has been given a third field F_3, which opposes F_1 and F_2.   The rheostat R_2 selects the speed of the motor M_1.   When this speed is reached, the voltage of RG causes F_3 to neutralize F_2 so that X in Fig. 12-1 remains on line B_1-B_2 at the point that gives the generator voltage necessary to run motor M_1 at its selected speed.   When a change in load affects this speed, the voltage RG changes and the point X is moved to return RG to the set speed corresponding to the setting of R_2.   In this way RG changes the position of X in Fig. 12-1 to excite G_1

to the proper voltage to cause F_3 to neutralize F_2 at the setting given R_2 and keeps the motor M_1 at its selected speed.

Changing the position of R_2 will select a new speed, at which the motor will be held constant. The Westinghouse Rototrol and the Allis-Chalmers Regulex both use this method of control, *i.e.*, a self-excited generator with the field magnetizing force coinciding with the straight part of the saturation curve and two additional field windings, the pattern field winding, which is adjustable, and an opposing or differential

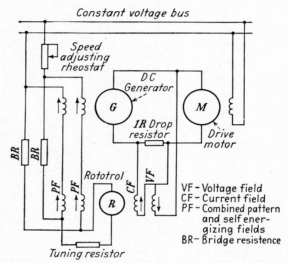

Fig. 12-9. Elementary diagram of blast-furnace skip hoist drive with Rototrol speed control.

field winding, which is responsive to the function that is to be regulated. These last two fields, operating on the differential principle, require very little power. They neutralize each other when the regulation is correct. These machines are, therefore, amplifiers as well as exciters. If it is desirable, the self-excitation may be obtained by the use of a series field instead of a shunt field, as shown in Fig. 12-4.

The Westinghouse Company also uses the Rototrol in a Wheatstone-bridge connection, explained briefly in Fig. 12-5.[1] This bridge connection is very useful for certain applications.

The shunt winding assists in adjusting the voltage of the generator to meet the different load conditions. When the load is positive, a higher landing speed is necessary than with negative load. With a positive load

[1] For a more detailed explanation, see G. A. Caldwell and W. H. Fornhals, Electrical Drives for Wide Speed Ranges, A.I.E.E. Paper, January, 1942.

the car tends to stop itself.   Under negative load the car tends to continue its motion.   This same system of control is used for "skip hoists."

ROTOTROL AND REGULEX APPLICATION

Variable-voltage Elevator Control (Fig. 12-6).   The elevator motor E
receives its power from the motor-generator set which is operated by a

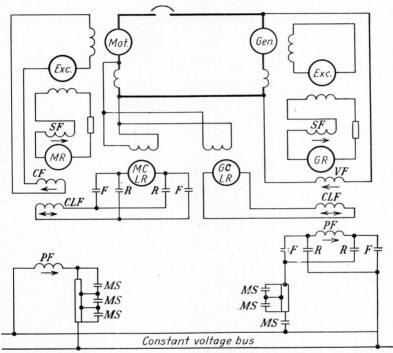

Fig. 12-10. Simplified blooming-mill control diagram illustrating Rototrol generator
voltage and motor-field current regulation with current-limit Rototrol.
    The exciter serving the generator has its field energized by Rototrol GR which has four
fields; SF keeps the excitation on the steep part of its excitation curve (Fig. 12-1); VF
opposes SF and stabilizes the motor speed by measuring the generator voltage; CLF
measures the motor load through another Rototrol $GCLR$ and prevents overload; PF is the
"pattern field" which is controlled by the master switch and selects the direction of the
generator field and its strength.
    The exciter for the motor field is controlled by Rototrol MR with four fields; SF keeps
the excitation on the steep part of its excitation curve (Fig. 12-1); CF is in series with the
motor field; CLF changes with the motor load; PF is the pattern field controlled from the
master switch to give additional speed by motor-field weakening after the generator reaches
its maximum voltage.

constant-speed a-c motor.   The speed of the elevator is controlled by
changing the voltage of the generator.   To reverse the elevator motor,
the generator voltage is reversed.

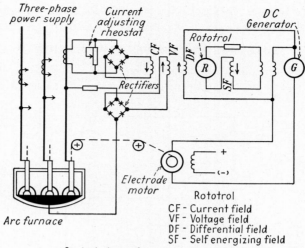

CF - Current field
VF - Voltage field
DF - Differential field
SF - Self energizing field

Control shown for one phase only

FIG. 12-11.   Elementary circuits for Rototrol arc furnace regulator.   The current is balanced against the arc voltage in the two generator fields   When out of balance the motor moves the electrodes to establish a balance.

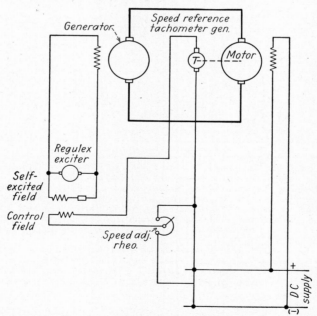

FIG. 12-12.   Schematic diagram showing Regulex speed control frequently used on calender drives.   Generator voltage is varied to hold motor speed constant by balancing tachometer voltage against d-c reference through adjusting rheostat.

The load on the elevator motor may be positive or negative. Hoisting a car and load heavier than the counterweight gives a positive load to the generator. Hoisting a car and load less than the counterweight gives a negative load to the generator. The problem is to stop the elevator automatically at a floor level with this variation in load. The solution is

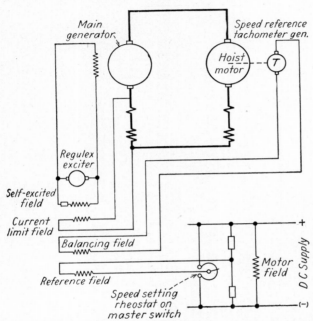

Fig. 12-13. Schematic diagram of variable-voltage hoist control using Regulex exciter for speed and acceleration control.

obtained by using a second exciter called a Rototrol that controls a separate winding on the generator field. The Rototrol is connected in a "bridge circuit," as shown, to adjust it for different generator voltages required for normal car operation. It has three field windings:

1. Measures the elevator motor voltage.

2. Measures the elevator motor current either positive or negative.

3. Measures the amount and direction of Rototrol excitation of the elevator motor.

At landing speed: with a maximum positive load on the elevator the generator has its maximum landing voltage; with a decreasing load the winding A decreases, reducing the generator voltage. With a negative load the series winding A reverses and causes a reverse current to flow from the elevator motor through the generator for the purpose of holding the elevator at the fixed speed required for landing. This operates the same as a series winding on the generator.

Hoists (Fig. 12-13). Regulex exciter control on variable-voltage mine hoists gives accurate speed control corresponding to master switch posi-

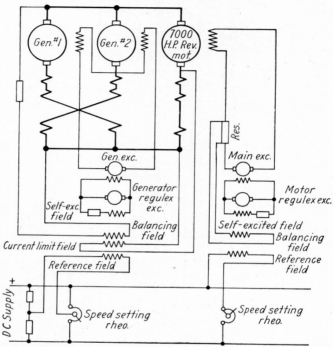

Fig. 12-14. Schematic diagram of reversing blooming mill using Regulex exciters to control speed and reversing of mill motor.

tion. This selected operating speed is maintained constant and does not vary with varying load on the hoist. Current-limit control by Regulex exciter pre vents overloading of rotating machines and hoist equipment, yet allows operation with maximum, safe loading.

This accurate current-limit control permits utilizing peak outputs of machines for rapid acceleration and deceleration, thereby decreasing the hoisting time cycle and increasing the output.

Skip Hoist. The essential circuits of the drive are shown in Fig. 12-9. The Rototrol is used as a speed regulator and furnishes regulating power only to the generator field. The motor emf, which is proportional to its speed, is measured by the combined effect of Rototrol voltage field *VF* and current field *CF*. This eliminates a pilot generator, which results in simplification of the drive equipment and circuits and saves space about the machine. This system provides a drive with a very wide speed range, good regulation at all speeds, and high running and break-away torques at minimum speed settings. The slow speeds are uniformly maintained regardless of the transition from motoring to regenerative loads in the dumping horns or variation in generator residual voltage.

Blooming Mill (Fig. 12-10). Ingot production was increased from 162 to 200 tons per hr on an old blooming mill after the drive control was

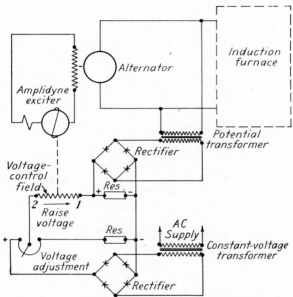

Fig 12-15. Amplidyne control field (1-2) is excited by the difference between a reference voltage and a voltage proportional to the a-c voltage being controlled. The amplidyne output controls the alternator field. The same scheme (without certain transformers and rectifiers) applies to d-c generators.

modernized by the addition of the Rototrol. This performance was obtained by the forcing action of the Rototrol, which resulted in faster, more uniform reversals and improved maintenance of generator voltage and motor speed on long passes, regardless of the speed of the flywheel motor-generator set. In addition, maintenance has been reduced by elimination of the vibrating relays and contactors and by better control of current peaks.

Arc Furnace (Fig. 12-11). Rototrol regulators are used to control the power input to arc furnaces. A standard line of these regulators is available for any size of electrode positioning motor. Advantages of the Rototrol regulator are reduced electrode breakage, low maintenance because of the smoothness of operation and elimination of contactors and relays, and quick and accurate electrode positioning to accommodate changes in furnace conditions.

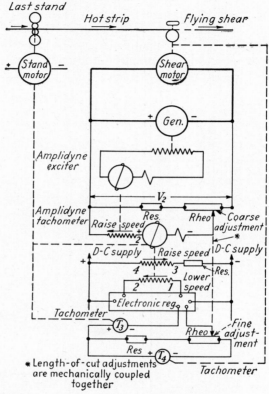

FIG. 12-16. Amplidyne used for the speed matching of two d-c motors for flying-shear control to give extreme accuracy of cut at strip speeds of 2,000 ft per min. Amplidynes can be used wherever speeds must be controlled or matched—on paper machines, textile machines, machine tools, and Diesel-engine governors.

The voltage difference between the amplidyne tachometer generator and voltage V_2 operates on voltage field $(1-2)$ of the amplidyne exciter, tending to hold speed 10 per cent above that of the stand motor. The small voltage difference between tachometers T_3 and T_4 is amplified in the electronic regulator and then is used to control the excitation of the amplidyne tachometer generator. This reduces the "coarse" speed differential until close synchronism is obtained.

THE AMPLIDYNE

The General Electric Company uses a machine of the Rosenburg-generator or Pestarini-Metadyne type in which the armature cross field, set up by a pair of short-circuited brushes, supplies the power for the generator field. This machine, which is called an "amplidyne," is shown in Figs. 12-13 and 12-14 in simplified form. More complete information will be found in various technical papers.[1] The small amount of power used in the initiating field is greatly amplified by this machine.

Voltage Control (Fig. 12-15). Control of voltage is one of the amplidyne's fundamental functions. It is used as a voltage controller on a

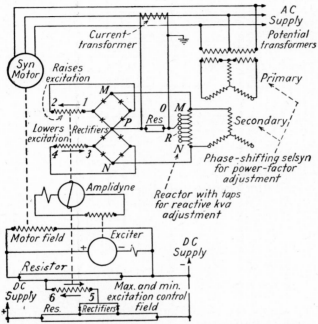

Fig. 12-17. Diagram of power-factor control using an amplidyne.

large, high-frequency generator, where it is applied for the following reasons (Fig. 12–15):

1. By its forcing action it speeds up the response of machines that have very long time constants.

2. It smoothly and swiftly corrects for either wide load swings or small deviations.

3. The amplidyne system is simple and easy to operate.

In this arrangement the amplidyne fields are used to compare the generator output voltage with a reference voltage. The difference excites the

[1] See Alexanderson, E. F. W., M. A. Edwards, and K. K. Bowman, The Amplidyne Generator—a Dynamoelectric Amplifier for Power Control, *Gen. Elec. Rev.*, March, 1940; also Fisher, Alec, Design Characteristics of Amplidyne Generators, *Gen. Elec. Rev.*, March, 1940.

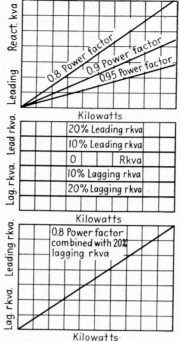

FIG. 12-18. Power-factor and reactive kilovolt-ampere control obtainable with the amplidyne.

amplidyne to supply the stepped-up excitation power required for the generator. Thus, the generator can be made to maintain closely a fixed voltage or to follow a changing voltage adjustment rapidly.

Speed Control (Fig. 12-16). The amplidyne can be the "electric coupling" that matches the speeds of two or more d-c motors, or it can provide a simple means of holding speeds to desired values. Speeds are translated into voltages by tachometer generators, and these voltages are used in the amplidyne.

Power-factor Control (Fig. 12-17). Automatic control of power factor (shown here as it would be applied to a synchronous motor) illustrates the use of four amplidyne control fields. With this arrangement:

1. Power factor can be held constant to increase system capacity.

2. Reactive kilovolt-amperes can be held constant to improve voltage regulation.

3. Combinations of these two can be used to give lagging reactive kilovolt-amperes at no load (thus maintaining normal voltage) or to give leading reactive kilovolt-amperes at heavy loads.

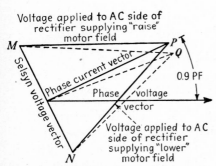

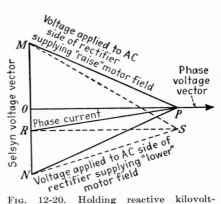

FIG. 12-19. Holding the power factor constant. The power factor is set by manually adjusting and locking the selsyn rotor to bring the selsyn voltage vector *MN* into the desired position. The phase-current vector is automatically held at right angles to *MN*, because in this position *MP* and *NP* are equal and the "raise" and "lower" amplidyne fields which they supply are balanced.

Any tendency for the power factor to shift from *P* to *Q* will create excess of *MQ* over *NQ*, raising the excitation to restore the preset power factor.

FIG. 12-20. Holding reactive kilovolt-amperes constant. Constant reactive kilovolt-amperes, regardless of load, is maintained by setting the handle on the tap changer away from mid-tap. If the handle is set on tap *R*, the current vector will be held in position *RP*, where *MP* and *NP* are equal and amplidyne fields are balanced. (*Note that reactive component of current is always "OR," regardless of load; thus constant reactive kilovolt-ampere is held.*)

4. Synchronous-motor field current can be increased to increase pull-out torque.

5. Operating efficiency can be improved by reduction of light-load losses.

CHAPTER 13

MAGNETIC AMPLIFIERS

Industry has a new means for motor control; it is a saturable-core transformer called a "magnetic amplifier." It is similar to a commercial transformer and has no moving parts like the Amplidyne, Rototrol, or Regulex, and it does not use electronic tubes. It is often combined with a static rectifier to convert from a-c to d-c power for the low-power-control circuits.

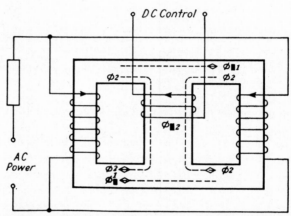

Fig. 13-1. Elementary construction of a magnetic amplifier. The alternating current passing through the load also goes through the two coils on the reactor. The impedance of these coils is controlled by the saturation of the iron core. This saturation is altered by direct current in the control coil on the center leg of the iron core.

An increase in the direct current increases the saturation of the iron, reduces the impedance of the a-c coils, and increases the load current. A decrease in the direct current decreases the impedance and the load current.

When the iron is worked close to its saturation point, a small change of direct current can cause a large change in the load current.

Figure 13-1 shows a simple type of magnetic amplifier having a center leg double the size of the outside legs. This center leg contains the d-c control coil which varies the impedance in the outside legs by means of the d-c flux $\phi 2$. During one-half cycle the a-c and d-c flux in one outside core are in the same direction and cause no change in the a-c impedance, as this core is oversaturated and there is only a minor change in the total flux. During this part of the cycle the a-c flux opposes the d-c flux

206

in the other outside leg and causes a large change in the a-c impedance, depending upon the amount of d-c flux. The combined effect results in an adjustable impedance in the a-c circuit. This impedance is controlled by the direct current, a small change in which will cause a large change in the a-c impedance because the iron is worked near the knee of the saturation curve.

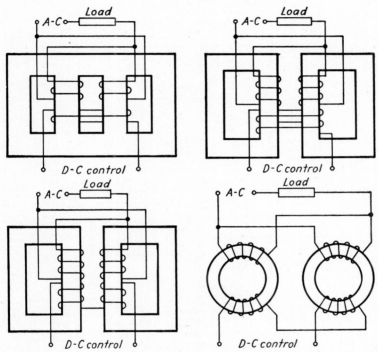

FIG. 13-2. Types of core construction of a magnetic amplifier that can be used.

This amplifier is fast in operation, as the normal time element of a commercial amplifier is less than $\frac{1}{12}$ sec, or about 5 cycles of a 60-cycle power circuit, and this speed of response can be increased when necessary. The speed of operation can be made faster than the time element of the device controlled, so that no "hunting" occurs. It can have a "feedback" circuit (Figs. 13-8 to 13-11) that will increase the "forcing action," resulting in quicker response. Its response is similar to tube amplifiers (Chap. 21) and rotating exciters (Chap. 12). This magnetic amplifier will be welcomed by the trade because it requires little or no maintenance and is not sensitive to vibration and shock. When the response time of a regulating device is considered, its sensitiveness is an important factor. A device like the electronic tube, the dynamoelectric regulator, or the magnetic amplifier is very sensitive to a deviation from the "pattern" and corrects for very small deviations; it is not often required to work over a wide range.   The response time needed for many applications can easily be estimated as shorter than necessary.   Moving parts have inertia that introduces a time element, and the load itself may exert a correcting force such as a change in the tension of a strip of

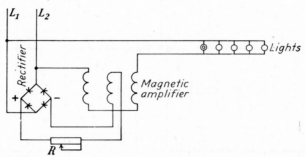

FIG. 13-3.   Theater dimmer.   The magnetic amplifier replaces the resistor previously used to dim theater lights.   The power loss is very much less with this type of dimmer, as a small d-c control current can cause a large change in lamp voltage.

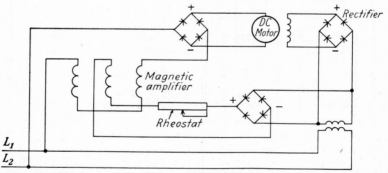

FIG. 13-4.   Variable-voltage control of a d-c motor from a-c power.   This is a voltage controller.   The voltage is adjusted by the rheostat to give different motor speeds.

material being rolled.   A fan or pump changes its torque as the square of the speed and usually does not require so close speed regulation as a paper machine.

Quick response is necessary to prevent "hunting," but the tendency to hunt differs with the various applications.   The electronic tube is much quicker than the other two regulators and can transmit speech, but these other two types are fast enough to regulate mechanical devices.

Many magnetic amplifiers were used during the war for military and naval equipment.   So far they have had very limited application to manufacturing operations in replacing the existing means of control for steel mills, paper machines, elevators, skip hoists, electric furnaces, etc., as it takes time to introduce such a departure from existing practice. The design engineers who understand the magnetic amplifier predict its wide use for industrial applications in place of electronic tubes and

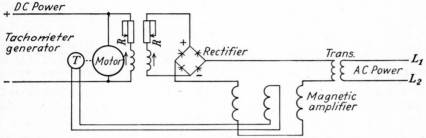

Fig. 13-5. Speed controller with rheostatic adjustment. The tachometer generator is connected to the amplifier control winding; as the motor speed increases, the magnetic amplifier increases the current in its controlled field, which strengthens the motor field and slows the motor speed. A decrease in motor speed weakens its field and accelerates it to normal speed.

If this motor is part of a variable-voltage system of control, its generator field can be adjusted by the magnetic amplifier to maintain the motor speed constant. In the generator system of control the regulating field would oppose the regulator generator field, thus reducing the voltage on overspeed and increasing it when the speed dropped below normal.

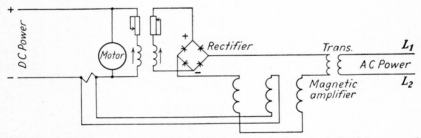

Fig. 13-6. Load control with rheostatic adjustment. An increase in load increases the voltage drop across the interpole windings, increasing the saturation in the magnetic amplifier; this increases the current in the motor field and reduces its speed. A decrease in load weakens the motor field, increasing its speed and the work it is doing. In an adjustable-voltage system of control the generator voltage can be controlled to adjust the speed as in Fig. 13-5.

dynamoelectric exciters. It has the same rugged qualities as existing motor control and requires no more attention than any other transformer. It is particularly desirable where automatic performance is necessary.

The magnetic amplifier uses the principle of a saturated iron core to change the current flowing through an a-c winding. The greater the saturation, the more alternating current flows through its winding and

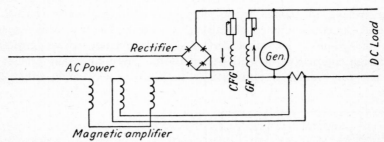

FIG. 13-7.   Load control applied to a generator field.   An increase in current, measured by the voltage rise across the interpole windings, increases the control current of the amplifier, and this increases the strength of the control field *CFG* and reduces the generator voltage and power delivered.

A decrease in current reduces the control field *CFG*, strengthens the generator voltage, and increases the load.

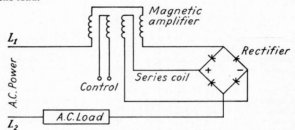

FIG. 13-8.   Series-feedback coil with a-c load.

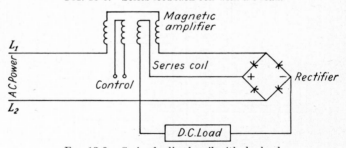

FIG. 13-9.   Series-feedback coil with d-c load.

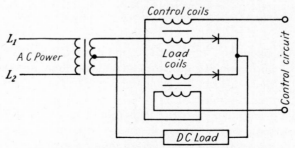

FIG. 13-10.   Self-saturating amplifier for d-c load.

the less the voltage drop across this winding. The degree of saturation is usually controlled by a direct current obtained from a rectifier (page 219), and the iron core is operated near the saturation point, so that a small change in the direct current will cause a large change in the alternating current. This method of control has been used to dim theater

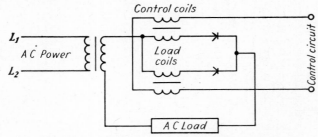

FIG. 13-11. Self-saturating amplifier for a-c load.

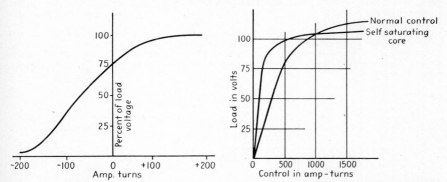

FIG. 13-12. Per cent control in ampere turns.

FIG. 13-13. Comparison of normal control and self-saturating control.

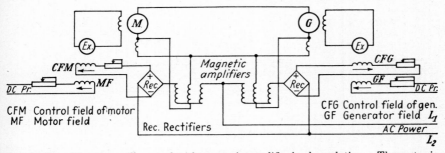

CFM Control field of motor
MF Motor field
Rec. Rectifiers

CFG Control field of gen.
GF Generator field L_1
AC Power
L_2

FIG. 13-14. Blooming-mill control with magnetic-amplifier load regulation. The motor is started, stopped, reversed and its speed adjusted by controlling the generator field. After the motor reaches full speed with its maximum field strength, its speed can be increased by reducing its field strength. The load is kept constant by the magnetic amplifier, changing fields *CFG* and *CFM* in proportion to the load as shown in Fig. 13-7. Reversing means is not shown.

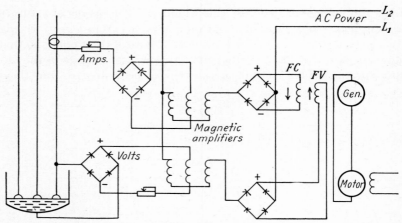

FIG. 13-15.   Electric-arc-furnace control.   In an arc furnace it is necessary to adjust the electrodes to the proper depth in the furnace in order to maintain the desired power input.

The electrode motor is served by its own generator.   When the two generator fields are equal and opposed, there is no voltage to rotate the motor.

If the current is too great, the field *FC* is built up and the motor moves the electrodes up so as to increase arc resistance.   If the voltage is too great, the field *FV* is built up and the motor moves the electrodes down so as to reduce the voltage drop.   The magnetic amplifier greatly increases the effect of a change in current or voltage to obtain quick action and accurate regulation.

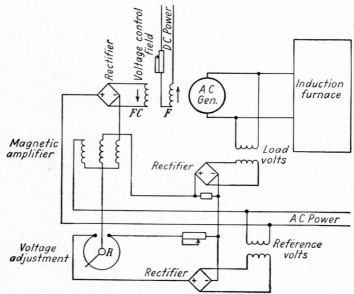

FIG. 13-16.   Induction furnace heating.   The magnetic amplifier maintains a balance between the reference voltage and the load voltage to keep the power input to the furnace constant.   This input is regulated by rheostat *R*.

lights (Fig. 13-3) for over 20 years and is more efficient than using a
rheostat in the lamp circuit.

Small-size d-c motors are controlled in the same way. The alternating current that flows through the amplifier is rectified and supplies
an adjustable voltage to the d-c motor to control its speed. An automatic device can be used to maintain the motor at any fixed speed or

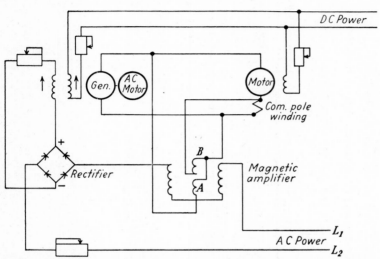

Fig. 13-17. Skip hoist controller. The magnetic amplifier gives accurate speed adjustment for dumping the skip and making the lower landing. This same controller can be used
for other types of hoists and elevators.

With maximum "positive load," coils A and B add to give maximum field strength in
order to overcome the IR drop in the armature circuit.

With less load and IR drop the field of the generator is reduced.

With "negative load" due to overbalance of the counterweight, the coils A and B oppose
each other and substantially reduce the generator field. The load current is reversed, as
the motor now becomes a generator driving the other generator and returning power to the
power-supply system.

The series resistor shown can be replaced by any series winding on the motor. A series
transformer can be used to accelerate the change of flux in the magnetic amplifier.

to change the speed in order to keep the load constant (see the diagrams
of Fig. 13-4).

The next steps are easy to follow. Assume that a d-c motor receives
power from a constant-voltage power source (Fig. 13-5) and has its field
connected to a rectified alternating current that passes through the magnetic amplifier. Changing the control circuit of this amplifier will change
the motor-field current and can be used to maintain the speed or load
constant by automatic means as follows: A tachometer speed generator
can be connected to the control circuit of the amplifier (Fig. 13-5) to
adjust the motor field current so as to keep the speed constant. The

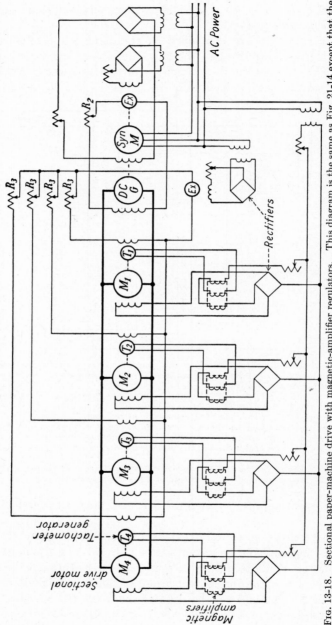

FIG. 13-18.   Sectional paper-machine drive with magnetic-amplifier regulators.   This diagram is the same as Fig. 21-14 except that the tube control has been replaced by magnetic amplifiers.   Each paper-mill section receives d-c power from a common motor-generator set. The speed of each motor is regulated by a tachometer generator T driven by the motor.   This tachometer generator is connected to the control coil of its magnetic amplifier, which serves the motor field.   A change of motor speed is corrected by changing the saturation in the magnetic-amplifier iron core (see page 354 for other details of Fig. 13-18).

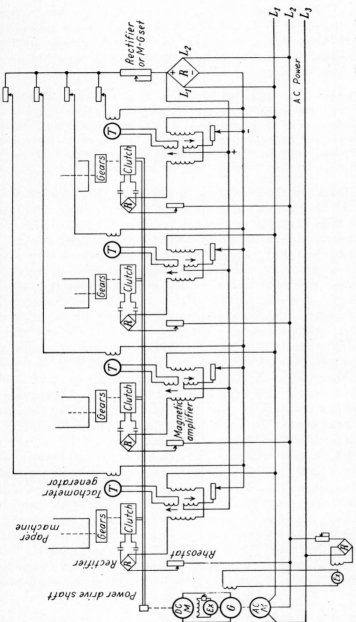

FIG. 13-19. Sectional paper-machine drive using magnetic clutches to couple each section to a common drive shaft. These clutches maintain each section at its correct relative speed by adjusting the slip of the clutch. The speed is regulated by a tachometer generator through a magnetic amplifier that adjusts the clutch slip. The drive-shaft speed is adjusted by changing the voltage of the generator that furnishes power to the motor driving this shaft.

control circuit of the amplifier can be connected across the interpole windings of the motor so as to maintain the load constant (Fig. 13-6). A very small change in the d-c control circuit will be greatly amplified in the rectified current passing through the main windings of the amplifier.   F. N. McClure states:[1]

. . . small amplifier units can be built with time delays of only a few cycles and amplifications of 1,000 to 10,000 per stage.   Where longer time delays do not prevent successful operation, as in the case of equipments such as lighting controls, larger reactors can be built. . . . Time delays can be reduced in various ways. . . . Amplification can be increased by feedback; *i.e.*, by feeding back part of the output through auxiliary windings or by self-saturation.

A series feedback coil can be added (Figs. 13-8 and 13-9) to increase the amplification.[2]   Self-saturating circuits are shown in Figs. 13-10 and 13-11.   The effect of negative saturation is shown in Fig. 13-12.   A comparison of normal and self-saturating control is shown in Fig. 13-13.

Let us assume that the "working" motor is large and receives its power from a motor-generator set with a direct-connected exciter.   This exciter receives its field current from the rectified current flowing through the a-c windings of a magnetic amplifier (Fig. 13-14).   A small change in the d-c control current in the amplifier causes a much greater change in the exciter voltage, which is again amplified through the generator field in order to alter the generator voltage.   In this way a large generator can be made to respond to a minute change in voltage applied to the control winding of the magnetic amplifier and force a large change in generator voltage so as to correct a fault in operating conditions.   Engineers and maintenance men are very familiar with the action of a series winding on a generator or motor.   It causes a quick change in the field strength of the generator to correct sudden changes in load.   An overload strengthens the field and increases the voltage, which overcomes the additional voltage drop in the circuit.   This winding on a motor slows down the speed in order to reduce an increase in the load and increases the field strength to give more torque.   The magnetic amplifier as stated is also similarly able (Figs. 13-8 and 13-9) to meet changes in load or speed quickly. Additional accelerated action shown in Figs. 13-10 and 13-11 can be obtained by a "feedback" circuit which adds its magnetomotive force to the control coil in order to increase the rate of change of magnetism in the amplifier.   These changes in the motor drive and the response are

[1] *Westinghouse Eng.*, May, 1949.

[2] These illustrations are taken from "Magnetic Amplifiers," published by Vickers Inc., who have spent many years in research work on magnetic amplifiers in conjunction with the Ward Leonard Company.

so quick that the correction takes place in the motor drive before it has had time to overcorrect the condition.

The diagrams of magnetic amplifiers show the most elementary design in order to simplify the illustration and indicate how this amplifier can be applied to well-known motor drives. The design of the amplifier itself is a separate problem as is the design of the motor.

TRANSDUCTORS

The transductor is a modified magnetic amplifier in which the d-c ampere turns are produced by the direct current passing through the

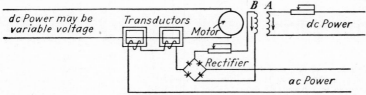

Fɪɢ. 13-20.   Transductor load regulator for an adjustable-speed d-c motor.   The motor speed is adjusted by changing the field *A*.
The motor load is kept constant by the transductor that controls field *B* and maintains constant armature current.

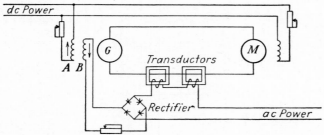

Fɪɢ. 13-21.   Transductor load regulator for a variable-voltage-controller motor.   Field *A* of the generator is changed to change the motor speed.
The current is maintained constant by means of the transductor, which adjusts field *B*. An increase in armature current increases field *B* and reduces the generator voltage.   A decrease in armature current decreases field *B* and raises the generator voltage.

opening in the iron core. This core is saturated by a very small direct current. The a-c coils are connected so that for each half cycle the a-c ampere turns on one core aid the d-c ampere turns while the other core opposes them. The coil in which the ampere turns are aiding the d-c turns will have no voltage induced in it because there is no change in flux due to saturation of the core. The current in the coil opposing the d-c turns will increase until the a-c ampere turns equal the d-c ampere turns. This induces a back voltage in the a-c coil, as the flux changes proportionally to the d-c current. The rectified alternating current adjusts the motor field (Fig. 13-20) so as to maintain a constant motor current. Figure 13-21 shows a motor-generator set with the generator field adjusted to maintain constant current. These two diagrams are combined in Fig. 13-22 for a blooming-mill control similar to Fig. 13-14.

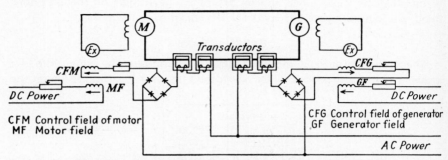

FIG. 13-22. Blooming-mill control with a transductor load regulator. The motor is started and accelerated to 100 rpm by increasing the generator field. The motor speed is then increased to 150 rpm by reducing the motor field. This diagram shows a combination of Figs. 13-20 and 13-21.

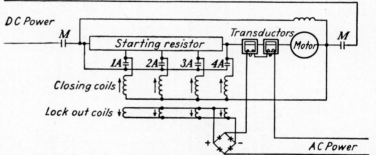

FIG. 13-23. This diagram is similar to Fig. 6-41 for accelerating a d-c motor, except that a transductor is substituted for the magnetic amplifier.

When the current drops sufficiently to permit 1A to close, the voltage on closing coil 2A increases but its lock-out coil holds it open until the current again decreases to permit 2A to close. 3A and 4A close in the same manner.

An automatic d-c motor starter is shown in Fig. 13-23. This is similar to Fig. 6-40, where a magnetic amplifier is used.

RECTIFIERS

Rectifiers are an important part of the magnetic-amplifier circuit. They consist of a stack of thin plates coated with a material that permits current to flow in only one direction. They are indicated on diagrams as follows:

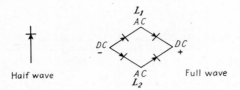

Half wave   Full wave

They are used to convert alternating to direct current and are shown on a number of diagrams in this chapter. Two types are available:

1. Copper oxide rectifiers, consisting of copper disks coated on one side with copper oxide (Fig. 13-24).

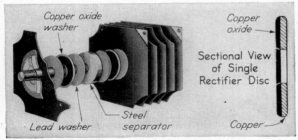

Fig. 13-24. Copper oxide rectifier.

2. Rectifiers with a selenium coating covered by an alloy coating (Figs. 13-25 and 13-26).

Electronic tubes are also used to convert from a-c power to d-c power (see Chap. 21).

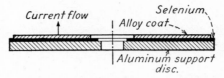

Fig. 13-25.   Selenium rectifier.

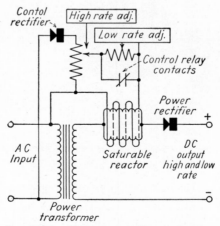

Fig. 13-26.   Half-wave rectifier application.

CHAPTER 14

SERIES-PARALLEL CONTROL AND THE ELECTROPNEUMATIC CONTACTOR

SERIES-PARALLEL CONTROL

The series-parallel system of control is applied to two motors, or groups of motors, so arranged that they are connected in series across the line for acceleration to half speed and operation at this speed. The motors may then be connected in parallel and accelerated to full speed. The motors must be mechanically connected together. Otherwise, one motor may accelerate faster than the other. This results in unequal distribution of load. This control is usually applied to cars moving along a relatively horizontal track, such as street railway, interurban, and mainline cars and locomotives. It is also used for cars in steel mills, coke plants, etc., for the purpose of conveying material from one point to another. These latter cars may be controlled automatically by a push button or by a standard streetcar controller. This system of control is sometimes used for slope hoists, where the angle of the slope is small, and for the bridge travel of large ore bridges.

Some controllers are arranged for operation in either series or parallel, the motors being connected permanently in series or in parallel by means of a change-over switch. This switch is interlocked so that the controller must be turned to the Off position before the connections are changed. An arrangement of this kind is known as "series-and-parallel" control. It has a very limited application. If the resistor is designed for accelerating with one combination of motors, it gives poor acceleration on the other combination, unless the connections to the resistor are changed, which further complicates the control. The only occasion for using such a control would be where there are considerable periods of time during which the apparatus is required to operate at half speed, which can be obtained by series connection.

The series-parallel control is usually associated with street railway and steam railway electrifications; the system, however, is applicable to many industrial railways, to mining locomotives, automobile trucks, and similar applications.

Advantages. The advantages of the series-parallel control are obtained when the period of acceleration extends over a considerable period of time

221

and represents an appreciable part of the complete duty cycle. This is obtained in horizontal traction and in many of the applications already enumerated. A saving is accomplished when the motors are connected in series, since the current drawn from the line is one-half the value that would be taken if the motors were connected in parallel. This is particularly desirable for starting a car or a train of cars where the static friction requires a considerable torque in excess of the running torque. Where the period of acceleration is short, the saving is often counterbalanced by the loss during the transition period.

The series-parallel control gives operation at one-half normal speed. This is desirable where trolley cars are operated through a congested portion of the city. If the industrial car is operated automatically, the series combination would give a low speed, from which the stop could be made more gradually than from the parallel combination. The reduction in starting current may sometimes permit the use of smaller feeders for a trolley system or other power distribution. The acceleration of the motors in series to half speed, and then in parallel to full speed, results in a saving in the weight of the resistors, which is considerably more than the additional weight to the control equipment, so that a net saving in the total equipment is obtained.

Limitations. The disadvantage of the series-parallel control is the added complication in additional parts to the controller. Where rapid acceleration is required, the transition period from series to parallel introduces a time element, which is objectionable. For instance, many industrial motors are accelerated in approximately 3 sec. If 1 sec were taken for the transition period, this would add 33 per cent to the total time of acceleration. If the complete cycle were completed in 6 sec or 10 times a minute, the introduction of this extra second would eliminate 1 cycle per minute, which might be very undesirable. Even where the bridging system is used and no loss is experienced in the progressive acceleration, the additional time required for the operation of the extra switches would still add a considerable time element to the cycle. Where the motor operates a vertical hoist or has a similar load, the reduction in torque, which usually occurs at the transition period, would cause a slowing down of the motors. This would be very undesirable and would more than compensate for any saving that might be effected during the period of acceleration of the motors in series.

Where the series-parallel system is considered for a new application, careful analysis should be made of the accelerating conditions, to determine whether this system of control is the most desirable.

Methods of Transition. There are three common methods of changing motors from series to parallel. They are known as

1. Open-circuit transition.
2. Shunt transition.
3. Bridging transition.

Open-circuit Transition.   This was the first method to be introduced. It is illustrated in Fig. 14-1, while Fig. 14-2 shows the relation between speed and torque during acceleration.   In passing from the full series to the first parallel notch, the circuits of both motors are opened.

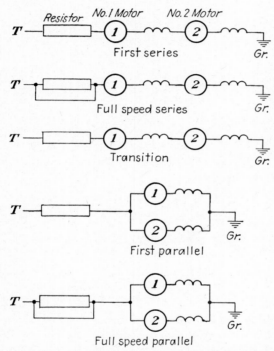

Fig. 14-1.   Steps in the open-circuit transition method of series-parallel control.

This method is in use for small motors in ordinary service.   It is objectionable because the motor circuits are opened, causing arcing at the contacts of the controller and a loss of torque in the motors.   The method of control is simple and easily understood.   The motors are permanently connected in series and started by inserting resistance in series with them.   This resistance is gradually short-circuited, as in rheostatic control.   This gives half speed with both motors the line in series.   The motor circuits are then opened, and the motors are connected in parallel and accelerated from half speed to full speed by introducing resistance in series with each motor and gradually short-circuiting it.

Shunt Transition. The method of shunt transition is an improvement over that of open-circuit transition. It is based on the principle that a short circuit can be placed around the armature and fields of a series motor without injuring the motor. The short circuiting of the armature through the field reverses the field current, which, in turn, reduces the fields and counter emf to zero. The method of control is shown in Figs. 14-3 and 14-4. This system allows one motor to remain active while the other is being short-circuited, and in this way an active

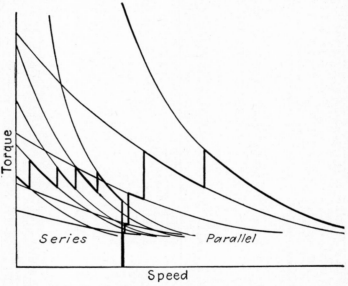

Fig. 14-2.   Speed-torque curves with open-circuit transition.

torque is maintained on the apparatus during the transition period. This gives half speed with both motors in series. In passing from full-speed series to the first notch in parallel, the proper amount of series resistance is first inserted and then motor No. 2 is short-circuited. This resistance limits the current to compensate for the absence of the counter emf of motor No. 2. This motor is then connected in parallel with motor No. 1, and the series resistance gradually is short-circuited until the motors are connected across the line, giving full speed. This method of control is employed in the type *K* drum controllers, which are still in extensive use on trolley cars.

One of the type *HL* electropneumatic controllers uses this principle of control. Figure 14-5 shows the connections in detail. An improvement has been made in this controller by using some of the sections of resistors several times. This is permissible, as the use of resistors in series requires the short-circuiting of these resistors in sections.   Ordinarily, the first section of the resistor has the maximum resistance and is in circuit the shortest length of time.   In order that cast-iron grids may be used for these resistors, this first section usually has more capacity, and requires less capacity in proportion, than the balance of resistors, as it is impractical to obtain high ohmic value with a small number of grids.   If

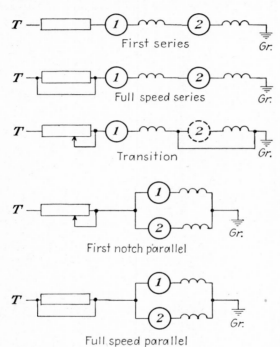

Fig. 14-3.   Steps in the shunt-transition method of series-parallel control.

this section of resistor is now used in another part of the acceleration by being connected in parallel with other resistors, the weight of metal is used to better advantage and the total weight of the resistor is reduced.

The advantages of this method of transition are that

1. An active torque is maintained upon one motor during the transition period.

2. It is the simplest method in general use.

The disadvantages of this method of transition are that

1. A reduction in torque is obtained during transition, as only one motor is active.

2. This active motor is subject momentarily to a very heavy overload.

3. The change in torque on the short-circuited motor during transition usually results in the motor's being momentarily driven by the other motor, which takes up the lost motion in the driving gears in the reverse direction. When the motor becomes active again, this lost motion is again taken up in the positive direction. This double action results in two shocks in the driving machinery and has a tendency to cause excessive wear and loosening of parts.

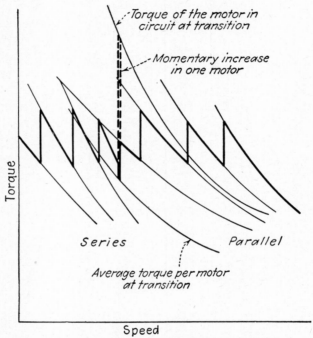

FIG. 14-4.   Speed-torque curves with shunt transition.

Bridging Transition. The transition from series to parallel by this system consists in placing a shunt, or bridge, between the motors so that all the motors are active during the transition period. This is illustrated in Figs. 14-6 and 14-7. Its operation is similar to that of a Wheatstone bridge. The two sides of the bridge consist of the motor plus a resistor. If the drop in voltage through the resistor is equal to the drop through the motor, the two parts of the circuit connected by the bridge will be at the same potential and no current will flow. It is difficult to obtain this exact balance with manual operation; it can be closely approximated, however, where automatic acceleration is used. The arrangement of circuits for this method consists in a portion of the series resistance being inserted between the two motors. Passing from the full-speed series position to the first parallel notch, the two sections of resistance are inserted

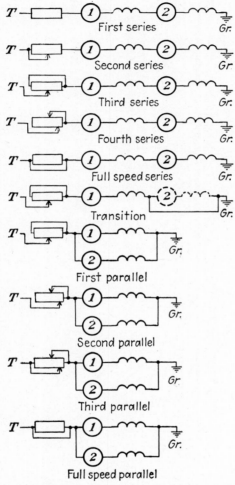

First series

Second series

Third series

Fourth series

Full speed series

Transition

First parallel

Second parallel

Third parallel

Full speed parallel

FIG. 14-5. Steps in shunt transition using an electropneumatic controller.

in parallel with the motors, so that each motor has a circuit from trolley to ground through the motor and a section of resistance, the final series connection forming the bridge of the circuit. This bridge circuit is then opened and the resistance is gradually short-circuited until the motor is brought up to full speed. In practice, extra resistance is inserted ahead

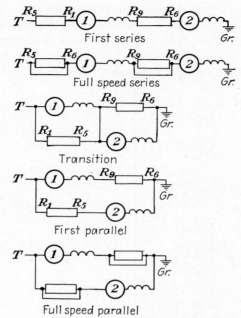

FIG. 14-6.   Steps in the bridging-transition method of series-parallel control.

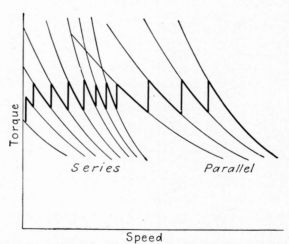

FIG. 14-7.   Speed-torque curves with bridging transition.

of the first motor, to obtain adequate starting resistance and to protect the first motor on resetting the circuit breaker.

If the resistors are so adjusted that more current passes through the two resistors than through the two motors during the bridging period, the opening of the bridging switch will interrupt this excess current and give an increased torque on the motors, equivalent to an additional notch of the controller. This notch can be so adjusted as to be equal to the other accelerating notches, so that the acceleration through the transition period compares favorably with that during other periods.

The advantages of this method of control are that

1. An active torque is maintained on the two motors during the transition period.
2. By proper adjustment of the resistors at the time of transition, an active accelerating notch is obtained at this time, which gives a smooth acceleration. Since both motors are active, no jerks are produced. These advantages make this method of transition the best for heavy-traction applications.

The disadvantages of this method of control are

1. Added complication.
2. Additional switches.
3. Increased arcing. This latter is objectionable only where drum controllers are used. Contactor switches are well adapted for this service and the arc can be properly distributed so as not to cause excessive wear.

ELECTROPNEUMATIC CONTROL

The use of series-parallel control in railway work has identified it with the electropneumatic controller. This controller is in general use for railway work but is also used for some industrial applications where compressed air is available or where the installation is of sufficient size to warrant the use of compressed air. Often compressed air proves a valuable means for operating mechanical brakes, clutches, and similar apparatus, so that on some large ore bridges and similar industrial applications, the electropneumatic controller has been used instead of the magnetic-contactor controller.

Electropneumatic Switches. When the railway industry developed from small individual cars to multiunit operation, it became necessary to design control apparatus that could be operated from a master switch placed on the platform of the leading car. Several methods of operating the control were tried. The two principal methods used at that time, both of which are now in successful operation, were the magnet-operated contactors and the electropneumatic switch. Other methods, such as the pilot motor-operated and air-cylinder-operated controllers, have been used and still have a limited application, but the railway industry today has been built up on the foundation of individual contactors or switches operated either by a magnet directly or by air pressure controlled by an electromagnet.

The switch is illustrated in Fig. 14-8, which gives a cross-section drawing of the switch.   The contacts are of the rolling type, having the same

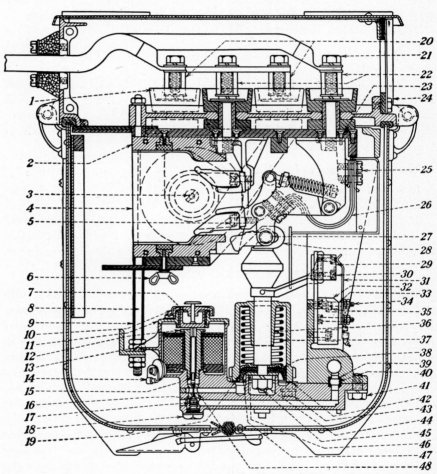

FIG. 14-8.   Cross section of an electropneumatic switch: 1, insulating washers; 2, arc chute 3, screw holding pole piece on blowout coil; 4, arc-chute side; 5, bolts holding switch contacts; 6, wing nut holding arc chute in place; 7, armature of magnet valve; 8, bolt holding angle iron that supports front end of valve-magnet casting; 9, insulating tube; 10, magnet-valve cap; 11, iron cover of valve magnet; 12, magnet-valve core; 13, foot supporting front end of magnet bracket; 14, magnet-coil terminal.

design as those of the magnetic contactor. They are opened by a spring in the air cylinder and closed by air pressure underneath the piston. Air is admitted to the cylinder by a small valve operated by a magnet. The work done by this magnet is so small that a very low wattage in the coil is sufficient for the purpose. This makes it possible to design a small magnet that will operate over a wide range of voltage and one that can be used on a low potential circuit. The design of the switch is such that a failure of air pressure results in opening the switch. The magnetic blowout is smaller in design than those used for magnetic contactors, with possibly one exception. The opening in the arc box confines the arc to a movement in the horizontal direction. This is necessary in order to permit the mounting of the switch underneath a car or in rows in a locomotive cab. As was explained in a previous chapter, the arc is ruptured by stretching it and cooling it. On account of the arc's being moved only in the horizontal direction, the arc box on the railway contactor is usually larger than that for the corresponding industrial contactor, which permits the arc to be moved both horizontally and vertically. In other words, the industrial contactor has a box that is opened at the top as well as the side.

The width of the switches for railway service is kept down to a minimum, in order to reduce the over-all length of the controller, which is made up by mounting switches side by side. Weight also is an important factor influencing the construction of the switch. This is evident from the minimum amount of iron used in the framework. The latest designs of these switches are of the self-contained unit type, the switch parts being clamped to insulated steel bars, which form the framework of the switch and give the maximum strength with a minimum weight. This unit construction permits the air-operated switch to be assembled in a variety of ways, the more readily to adapt it to different classes of service. The former method of building these switches in groups of eight to ten in a cast-iron frame resulted in a heavier controller—one that lacked flexibility.

The arrangement of air-operated switches shown in Fig. 14-9 is typical for an ordinary surface car. The switches are mounted in a sheet-metal enclosure, which protects them from dirt and water. The sides of the box are hinged, to make the operating parts of the switch accessible for inspection and renewals.

The controller is divided into two groups, one of which carries the reverse switch and the other the sequence switch. The sequence switch is a small drum controller actuated by air cylinders and controlled by magnet valves. The contact fingers energize the air switches in the proper sequence for accelerating the motors. The speed at which the sequence-switch drum rotates is adjusted to give the desired rate of accel-eration.   When the master switch is moved to the Off position, the sequence switch returns to its initial starting position.   This ensures that the motors are started in the proper manner each time the master switch is moved from the Off position to one of the running notches.   The sequence switch will stop at intermediate notches corresponding to posi-tions on the master switch.   The reverse switch is interlocked with the line switches, so that it is operated only when the controller is discon-nected from the line.

The valve magnets are operated on a low-potential circuit, which is supplied either by a storage battery or from a resistance that is connected

Fig. 14-9.   Arrangement of air-operated switches in the ordinary surface car.

across the line, the valve magnets being in shunt with the portion of this resistance at the grounded end.   The voltage used on the valve magnets is normally 20 volts.   On account of the low voltage at which the valve magnets operate, there is very little arcing on the interlock fingers, which permits their being arranged in a very compact manner.

The use of air as an auxiliary for operating the controller has been applied to a number of different types of control.   Air pressure is avail-able at the present time on practically all except very small surface cars. The amount of air used in operating a controller is small in comparison with the amount taken by the air brake, so there is little objection to using air as an auxiliary for operating the controller.   The only extra precaution required is to see that the piping is installed so as to drain the moisture from the air system.   Air cools very rapidly when it is expanded and has a tendency to cause frost or ice particles to form in the ports to the valve and the cylinder, particularly when the outside temperature is very low.   This difficulty is sometimes experienced when the piping is installed by persons not familiar with this system of control. If it is properly installed, the air is cooled after being compressed, which precipitates the moisture in the form of water that can be readily drained off. The only other source of trouble is dirt, which can be easily removed by a fine-mesh strainer.

An important detail of these switches is the piston leather. There is perhaps no detail of the entire switch that has received more thought and on which more research work has been done than on the piston leather and the method of mounting this leather in the cylinder. Leather is porous, and if it is used in its natural condition, it will have excessive air leakage through these pores. It is therefore necessary to treat this leather, partly for the purpose of filling up the pores and partly for the purpose of giving it the proper mechanical structure. The practice at this time is to use a piston leather made up of three layers, or thicknesses, of leather. This gives the desired flexibility as well as reducing the leakage to a minimum. The piston leather has a phosphor-bronze expander, mounted inside the cup. This causes the leather to exert an initial pressure against the inside of the cylinder. When air is applied, this pressure is increased and makes a tight joint between the leather and the walls of the cylinder. The compound with which the leather is impregnated must withstand a considerable variation in temperature. In cold weather the cars may be idle for a long time and the temperature within the cylinder may go to zero or even lower. When the car is in service, the current that passes through the controller heats up all the parts in the switch group, and if the outside temperature is warm, especially in the southern states, the temperature inside the cylinder becomes very high in comparison. The ordinary compound with which leathers are impregnated has a tendency to be very stiff at low temperatures and very soft at high temperatures. It is therefore necessary to use a process for impregnating that will give satisfactory operation over wide range of temperature.

Advantages. The electropneumatic control has a number of fundamental advantages, which may be briefly summarized as follows:

1. High pressures can be used between the contacts carrying the main current.

2. A strong spring can be used in opening the contacts.

3. The valves require very little force to operate them, and the magnets require only a small wattage for their successful operation.

4. On account of the above, successful operation can be obtained with a wide range of voltage on the control circuits.

5. The power available for operating the switch permits a rugged construction of the interlock contacts.

6. The low voltage at which the valve magnets operate permits of a very compact arrangement of interlock details.

7. The design of the switch is such that its operation is independent of its position and is also independent of vibration.

8. The speeds at which the switch opens and closes can be independently adjusted by changing the size of the air inlet and exhaust.

9. The switch closes at a positive uniform speed and eliminates the hammer blow present in magnet-operated contactors. This reduces the bouncing of the contacts during closing to a minimum and in many cases entirely eliminates it.

10. The pressure on the contacts carrying the main current is independent of the line voltage. With control of this type, being independent of voltage, the car can be operated at any voltage that will cause the motors to turn over. On the other hand, the movements of the switch will be uniform and satisfactory at voltages greatly in excess of normal.

11. On account of the small size of the valve magnet, it has very little induction and therefore responds quickly both in opening and in closing the valve; the small inductive effect does not interfere with the coils connected in multiple.

Limitations. The limitations of this form of control may be summarized as follows:

1. It requires a reliable source of air pressure for operation. The normal air pressure is usually 70 lb. This air pressure should not drop below 50 lb and should not exceed 100 lb. In practice, a governor maintains the air at normal pressure, so that the switches may operate under the most favorable conditions.

2. The air must be clean and dry.

3. The use of air as an auxiliary requires piping connections to be made to the controller, in addition to the wiring connections. This is offset to a considerable extent by the use of low-voltage control circuits, which simplifies the wiring details.

4. Piston leathers need renewing from time to time. This, too, is offset somewhat by the absence of trouble with the valve magnets and interlocks on account of the small power used in this circuit.

CHAPTER 15

ADJUSTABLE-SPEED ALTERNATING-CURRENT MOTORS OF THE WOUND-ROTOR TYPE

ANALOGY WITH D-C ADJUSTABLE-SPEED SETS

The wound-rotor induction motor can have its speed adjusted by connecting the secondary circuit to an external source of power having suitable characteristics. The principle of operation may be illustrated by referring to a similar scheme using d-c machines. If we assume a d-c motor A (see Fig. 15-1), having a d-c machine B in series with its armature, and assume that this d-c machine is operated at a constant speed by another d-c machine C, it can be readily seen that by changing the voltage of this regulating machine B, the speed of the main motor A can

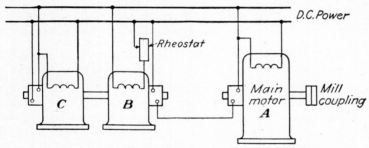

Fig. 15-1. Direct-current adjustable-speed set, constant torque.

be adjusted. Assuming that B runs at constant speed, that its field is capable of adjustment over a wide range, and that it is provided with interpoles, so that it will operate successfully at zero field strength, we can then obtain a voltage from B that either opposes the flow of current through the motor A or assists that current. In other words, the machine B interposes an active voltage in the armature circuit of machine A. This voltage may oppose the line voltage, reducing the speed of A below normal, or it may add to the line voltage, increasing the speed of A above normal voltage. If we wish to reduce the speed of motor A 50 per cent, the machine B would have half the capacity of A. When the motor A is operating below normal speed, the difference in power represented by this difference in speed is absorbed by the machine B, which acts as a motor driving the machine C as a generator and returning this power to the line.

If the motor A is operated above normal speed, power is taken from machine B, which then becomes the generator, and machine C a motor receiving current from the line. The torque of machine A remains constant throughout the speed range, as this torque is fixed by the field strength, which is assumed to be constant, and the current-carrying capacity of the armature. Therefore, this equipment operates at a constant torque throughout its range, the horsepower varying with the speed. (These statements and those which follow are all based on the assumption that the equipment is operating at its rated full-load current.)

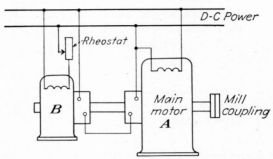

FIG. 15-2.   Direct-current adjustable-speed set, constant horsepower.

If we couple the machine B to the main motor A, as shown in Fig. 15-2, the speed of A can be adjusted in a manner similar to that shown in Fig. 15-1, by varying the field strength of machine B. In this case, the difference between the operating speed and the normal speed of the main motor A is absorbed by the machine B and converted into mechanical work. The torque of A remains constant, but the torque of B will change with the change of speed, the resultant torque of the equipment being inversely proportional to the speed and the horsepower remaining constant.

In the schemes shown in Figs. 15-1 and 15-2, it will be noted that the main current passes through machines A and B in series. Assuming that this current is always equal to full-load current and that the supply voltage is constant, it will be seen that the power supplied to this circuit has a constant value. In Fig. 15-2 there are no other connections to the line, and therefore, if the losses are kept small, this scheme should deliver a constant horsepower corresponding to the constant-power input. The arrangement in Fig. 15-1, however, provides an additional circuit through machine C. There is a constant-power input to machines A and B, either to which the power input of machine C should be added or from which it should be subtracted, depending on whether machine A is running above or below normal speed. The total power received from the line is, therefore, a function of the speed. The torque, however, is obtained from one machine only, *viz.*, the main motor *A*. Therefore, this equipment delivers a constant torque, as compared with the constant horsepower delivered by the equipment in Fig. 15-2.

If these two schemes are kept in mind in considering the a-c motor, it will be found that the methods used for controlling this motor are either constant torque or constant horsepower and that they function in a manner similar to that of the d-c motor.

The line voltage connected to the primary of an induction motor must be balanced by a countervoltage set up in the windings caused by the alteration of the flux through these windings. This countervoltage is a little less than the line voltage, the difference being consumed by the ohmic and leakage reactance drops caused by the load current. Assum-

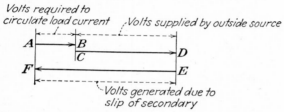

Fig. 15-3. Secondary-voltage distribution, motor operating below synchronism.

ing that the line voltage, the frequency, and the load on the motor remain constant, the primary flux remains constant. Most of this flux also passes through the secondary. If the secondary revolves at synchronous speed, its conductors do not cut this flux and there is no secondary voltage or current; therefore, no work is done by the motor. In practice, the secondary revolves at a little less than synchronous speed. This difference in speed generates a secondary voltage, which causes the secondary load current to circulate. This, in turn, requires a corresponding increase in the primary current in the ratio of transformation. The difference between synchronous speed and actual speed is commonly called the "slip" of the motor. Let us assume that this slip amounts to 3 per cent of the synchronous speed of the motor. The motor, therefore, operates at 97 per cent of synchronous speed at full load. If we now connect the secondary circuit to a source of power of the same frequency, we can impress an external voltage upon the secondary windings. If this impressed voltage has the proper phase relation, the secondary will revolve at a less speed, as more slip will be required to generate the additional voltage made necessary by that supplied from the external source. This can be more easily understood by referring to Fig. 15-3. We shall let the line *AB* represent the amount and direction of voltage required in the secondary to circulate the load currents and the line *CD* the voltage supplied from the external source.   We must then generate in the secondary circuit a voltage *EF*, which is opposite to the two previous voltages and equal to their sum.   In order to generate this voltage, the secondary must run at a lesser speed.   The motor can be operated above synchronism by changing the direction of the voltage supplied from the external source.   Figure 15-4 shows a similar analysis.   The line *AB* represents the value and direction of voltage required to circulate the load current. This is the same as in Fig. 15-3.   The line *CD* now represents the value and direction of the voltage supplied from the external source.   The sec-

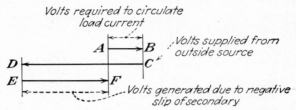

FIG. 15-4.   Secondary-voltage distribution, motor operating above synchronism.

ondary of the motor must, therefore, develop a voltage having a value and direction corresponding to *EF*.   As this voltage is in the opposite direction to that in Fig. 15-3, it is necessary for the motor to operate above synchronism.

Figures 15-3 and 15-4 show that, when the motor is operating below synchronism, the voltage required to circulate the load current is obtained by a decrease in speed and, therefore, by less work being delivered by the motor.   When it is operated above synchronism, this voltage is supplied as part of the power obtained from the external source.   In both cases the voltage required to circulate the load current represents a loss; in one case the loss appears as less mechanical work, while in the other case the loss is made up from a source of power external to the motor itself.

ALTERNATING-CURRENT ADJUSTABLE-SPEED SETS

The performance of the a-c machine is similar to that of the d-c machines previously described, with the additional limitation that in the a-c machine we must take into consideration the power factor and frequency of the circuits in the secondary of the motor, in addition to the voltage.   In the d-c machine we are concerned only with voltages.   In both a-c and d-c machines the speed of the motor can be adjusted either above or below normal speed by changing the voltage impressed upon part of the motor windings from an external source.

Several different methods have been used for introducing the variable voltage in the secondary circuit of a wound-rotor motor. Some of these methods also include means for changing the power factor so that the normal power factor of the motor may be improved or even changed to a leading power factor. In all these methods the main motor is started from rest by connecting the secondary through a resistor with means for

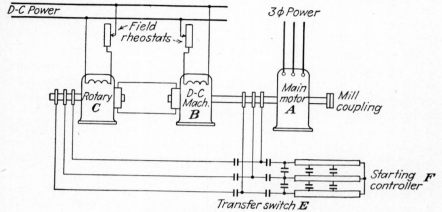

Fig. 15-5.   Method I, constant horsepower.

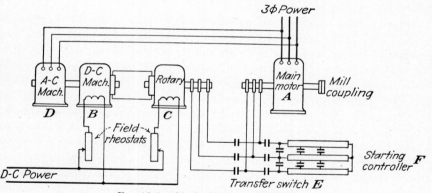

Fig. 15-6.   Method II, constant torque.

short-circuiting this resistor, as is done with standard equipments. The diagrams in Figs. 15-5 and 15-6 show this resistance, together with a change-over switch for connecting the motor to the adjustable control after it has come up to speed. This method of starting has been omitted from all except Figs. 15-5 and 15-6 for the purpose of simplicity, as the means of starting has nothing to do with the principle of speed adjustment.

In describing the following methods no attempt will be made to develop the theory or to furnish vector diagrams illustrating the phase relation between the different voltages and currents. A very complete analysis of these problems is given in the A.I.E.E. proceedings.[1]

Method I. This method consists of a main driving motor coupled to a d-c machine. The secondary of the main motor is connected to the slip rings of a rotary converter. The d-c side of the rotary converter is connected to the armature of the d-c machine. The fields of the rotary and the d-c machine are excited from a constant-voltage source of direct current. Diagrammatically, this scheme is illustrated in Fig. 15-5.

In starting from rest, the secondary of the main motor A is connected to a resistor, which is gradually short-circuited by means of magnetic contactors in the usual manner. After the main motor has been brought up to speed, its secondary is transferred to the rotary converter.

The voltage on the d-c side of the rotary is changed by varying the field of the d-c machine B. This changes the voltage impressed on the secondary motor A, which changes the speed of this motor. At the same time, the change in voltage on the rotary changes the speed of the rotary. These two actions take place simultaneously. The a-c side of the rotary is connected to the secondary of the main motor A. Therefore, the frequency in the two machines remains the same and the change in speed takes place simultaneously.

To reduce the speed of the main motor, the field of the d-c machine B is increased. This causes an increased voltage to be applied to the secondary of the main motor through the rotary converter, which in turn reduces the load current or may momentarily reverse this current. The main motor will then slow down until the sum of the generated voltage and the supplied voltage in its secondary is enough less than the ratio of transformation to cause full-load current to flow through the secondary. The reduction in speed, in turn, reduces the voltage of the d-c machine so that a balance running speed is soon reached. The speed is increased by reducing the strength of the d-c motor field. The power represented by the difference between full speed and actual speed is converted into work through the rotary converter and the d-c machine, causing this machine to give a torque, which adds to or subtracts from the torque of the main motor A. If the set is running at 75 per cent of normal speed, the main motor will be delivering 75 per cent of its rated output and 25 per cent will be delivered by the d-c machine. The torque of the main motor remains constant, as this is fixed by the excitation of the primary and the design characteristics of the machine, both of which remain constant. The d-c motor, however, increases its torque as the speed of the main motor decreases. When the main motor A is operated above synchronous

[1] *Trans. A.I.E.E.*, Vol. 39, Pt. II, pp. 1135ff.

speed, the torque of the d-c machine B is subtracted from the torque of A. The torque delivered by the d-c machine is directly proportional to the change in speed of the main motor, so that the horsepower output of the combined unit remains practically constant.

The power factor of the main motor can be altered by changing the excitation of the rotary fields. In this way the power factor of the motor may be increased so that it is above 90 per cent, but ordinarily a leading power factor is not obtained.

This method can be used to operate the main motor above synchronism as well as below synchronism. If operation at normal speed is desired, the regulating set can be disconnected and the secondary of the main motor can be short-circuited.

Method II. This method is similar to Method I, except that for the d-c machine coupled to the main motor a motor-generator set, not coupled, is substituted. The scheme of connections is shown in Fig. 15-6. The operation is very similar. The rotary converter C supplies power to the d-c machine B, which drives the a-c machine D and returns power to the line. The speed of the main motor is adjusted by changing the field strength of the d-c machine B. The difference between these two schemes is that, in the first method, power is converted into mechanical work and returned to the main-motor shaft. This gives a constant horsepower throughout the range of the equipment. In Method II, power is returned to the line. The main motor operates at constant torque, but the horsepower decreases with the speed. The power returned to the line is the difference between the horsepower that the motor would deliver at full speed and the horsepower that it actually delivers at the reduced speed. In both methods, the losses are very small and most of this difference in power is saved. By reversing the polarity of the power supplied to the secondary of the a-c motor, it may be made to operate above synchronism. This may be accomplished in several ways; the additional power in this case will be taken from the line by the motor-generator set.

Method III. This equipment (see Fig. 15-7) consists of a main driving motor A, having mounted on its shaft a small frequency changer D. Separate from this main motor is a set consisting of an a-c induction or synchronous machine C coupled to an a-c commutator machine B. The a-c commutator machine B is operated at nearly constant speed by the a-c machine C, to which it is coupled. The field strength of this commutator machine is varied in order to supply different voltages to the secondary of the main motor. The method of varying this field consists in connecting one end of each field coil to an autotransformer, in the secondary of the main motor. The other end of each field coil is connected through a resistance to the low-frequency, or commutator, end of the fre-

quency changer D, mounted on the main-motor shaft. The frequency
changer is so connected that, when the main motor is operated at synchronous speed, the commutator end of the frequency changer supplies
direct current. At any other speed of the main motor, an alternating

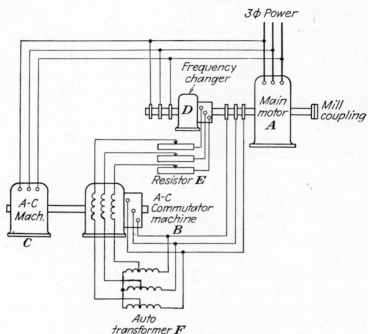

FIG. 15-7.   Method III, constant torque.

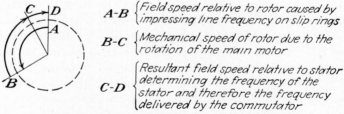

FIG. 15-8.   Analysis of frequencies in frequency changer.

current is supplied to the field, which has the same frequency as the secondary of the main motor. This can be better understood by referring
to Fig. 15-8. When the main motor is operating below synchronism,
we can let the line AB represent the frequency due to the rotation of the
a-c field and the line BC the frequency due to the rotation of the fre-

quency-changer armature, which is coupled to the main machine A and rotates at the same speed as that machine. The line CD will then represent the difference in these frequencies and will be the frequency that is delivered at the commutator end of the frequency changer. Since this frequency is equal to the difference between synchronous speed and the actual speed of the main motor, it will be the same as the frequency in the secondary of the main motor for all speeds of the main motor.

Since the field of the commutating machine B is excited by two sources of power out of phase with each other and independently adjustable (phase relation of the frequency changer by shifting the brushes, current from the frequency changer by varying the resistor, and voltage from the auxiliary commutator circuit by adjusting the autotransformer), both the phase relation and the strength of the excitation can be controlled. This adjusts the phase and the amount of voltage impressed on the slip rings of the main motor A and provides a ready means for adjusting its speed and power factor. Motor A may be operated at a leading power factor when this is desired.

The speed of the main motor can be adjusted from below synchronism to above synchronism while it is operating under load. In order to pass through synchronism, the voltage impressed upon the secondary of the main motor must equal zero when the main motor is operating at about 3 per cent below synchronous speed, in order that there will be sufficient voltage to circulate the load current. When the main motor reaches synchronous speed, the frequency of the secondary circuit is zero and the voltage from the autotransformer F is zero; therefore, the commutating machine B is excited entirely from the frequency changer D on the main-motor shaft; the voltage supplied from machine B must now be sufficient to circulate the load current. This voltage is in the opposite direction to that impressed on the secondary below synchronism. The transition can be illustrated by Figs. 15-3 and 15-4. As the motor approaches synchronous speed (see Fig. 15-3), the line BC is reduced in length until it reaches zero. The line EF then equals AB, and the voltage of machine B is zero. In order to obtain a further increase in speed, the voltage supplied by machine B is reversed, and the line EF reduces to zero and then reverses, as is shown in Fig. 15-4.

The torque of the main motor remains constant throughout the range, and the horsepower varies directly with the speed. The difference in horsepower represented by a speed slower than synchronism is returned to the line through the commutator machine and the induction machine that it drives. When it is operating above synchronism, the extra power is obtained from the line through the synchronous, or induction, machine to the commutator machine and then to the main motor. The power input to the primary and the torque of the main motor remains the same for all speeds, the horsepower varying with the speed.

Method IV. This method is the same as the Method III, except that the commutator machine *B* is coupled to the main-motor shaft instead of being driven by a separate a-c machine. The scheme is illustrated diagrammatically in Fig. 15-9. The energy represented by the difference in

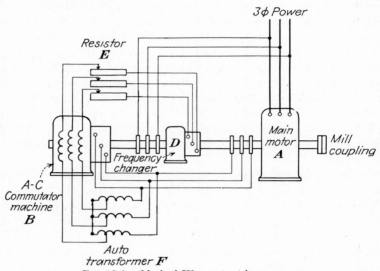

Fig. 15-9. Method IV, constant horsepower.

speed is converted into work by the a-c commutator machine *B*, which either adds to or subtracts from the torque of the main motor *A*, depending on whether the set is operating below or above synchronism. The equipment, therefore, operates on a constant-horsepower basis, no energy being returned to the line.

Method V. The main driving motor *A* has a synchronous machine *B* coupled to the same shaft. Mounted separately is a frequency changer *C*, driven by a small synchronous motor. The diagram of connections is shown in Fig. 15-10. The secondary of the main motor is connected to the commutator end of the frequency changer. The slip-ring side of the frequency changer is connected to the synchronous machine on the main-motor shaft. The d-c field of this synchronous machine *B* can be varied by means of the field rheostat.

The frequency changer runs at a constant speed corresponding to the synchronous speed of the line. The synchronous machine coupled to the main motor operates at a speed greater or less than synchronism, corresponding to the slip of the main motor. If we represent the slip of the main motor by S, then the frequency of the synchronous machine is equal to 1 plus or minus S.   This frequency is imposed upon the slip-ring side of the frequency changer, which in turn delivers a frequency equal to the slip in the secondary of the main motor, on account of the frequency changer operating at synchronous speed.   This arrangement ensures that the frequency of power supplied to the main motor is of the correct value.

The voltage delivered by the synchronous machine coupled to the main motor is adjusted by changing the strength of the d-c field.   This

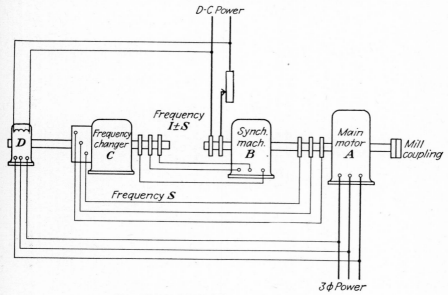

Fig. 15-10.   Method V, constant horsepower.

voltage is transmitted through the frequency changer to the secondary of the main motor, which rotates at the proper speed to develop a voltage sufficiently above or below that supplied by the frequency changer to circulate the load current (see Figs. 15-3 and 15-4).   By adjustment of the value and the direction of the voltage of the synchronous machine, the main motor may be operated either above or below synchronism at any speed within the range of the equipment.

The power factor of the main motor may be adjusted either by shifting the brushes on the commutator end of the frequency changer or by shifting the poles in the synchronous motor D, driving this machine. This motor is very small compared with the frequency changer, as it has only to overcome the friction and windage losses; therefore, the poles can be shifted economically by winding the field coils in sections and connecting them to a small rheostat.

The power taken from the supply lines remains constant.   The difference in power delivered by the main motor, owing to a reduction in speed, is converted into mechanical energy by the synchronous machine, coupled to the motor shaft.   In this way a constant horsepower is delivered to the mill coupling at all speeds.

Method VI.   This method (see Fig. 15-11) uses a frequency changer having a wound stator and a rotor with a commutator on one end and slip rings on the other end.   The commutator end is connected to the slip

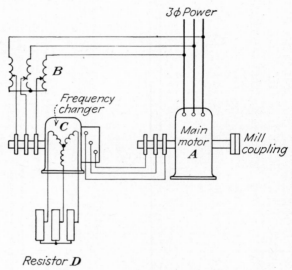

FIG. 15-11.   Method VI, constant torque.

rings of the main motor and the slip-ring end to the line, through an autotransformer.   The speed of rotation of the frequency changer is controlled by changing the resistance in the stator winding.   Its performance is similar to a wound-rotor induction motor, the slip rings supplying energy to the rotor, which in this case is the primary member, the stator being the secondary.   The amount of slip, or speed, is fixed by the resistance in the secondary circuit.

Another method would be to excite the stator from the commutator end of the frequency changer and change the speed by a resistance in this circuit.

The voltage supplied to the secondary of the main motor depends upon the voltage imposed on the slip rings of the frequency changer by the autotransformer B; at the same time the speed at which the frequency changer operates must be adjusted to maintain its secondary frequency the same as that of the main-motor secondary. When it is operating above synchronism, energy is taken from the line.

A modification of this method consists in coupling the frequency changer C to the shaft of the motor A and omitting the stator windings. The frequency changer in this case operates exactly the same way as the machine D in Fig. 15-7, Method III, with the exception that in Method III this machine furnishes power to the fields of the a-c commutator machine B, while in Fig. 15-7 the frequency changer C would supply the power directly to the secondary of the main motor A. In the latter case, the frequency changer must be large enough to supply the power represented by the difference in speed required either above or below normal speed of the main motor A. The speed is fixed by that of the main motor A, which is usually quite slow, so that the frequency changer might be quite large and expensive. The arrangement, however, is very simple and can be easily operated through synchronism, stable operation being obtained at all speeds.

These methods of control of wound-rotor induction motors were first developed for large motors, used for driving the main rolls in steel mills. There are two general methods of rolling steel. One consists in passing the metal back and forth through one set of rolls, and the other method uses a number of sets of rolls, the metal passing continuously from one set to the next. This latter is known as a "continuous mill." Where a single stand of rolls is used, two rolls only may be employed, the motion of the metal back and forth being obtained by reversing these rolls. When this method of rolling steel is used, the driving motor must be reversed quickly and frequently; therefore, d-c motors are used with the voltage method of control described in Chap. 11.

If three rolls are used and the metal passes one way between the bottom pair and then back between the upper pair, the rotation is continuous in this direction and the a-c motor can be used. The speed of this motor may be adjusted by any one of the methods described above. In most cases, the speed is adjusted for a particular class of work and is not changed between passes. The speed is adjusted when rolling begins and remains fixed until the class of work is changed. In most cases, it is not necessary to adjust the speed under load, which simplifies the controller.

When the continuous process of rolling steel is used, the roughing rolls, or those through which the steel is passed first, are often driven at a constant speed by an a-c motor and only the finishing rolls are provided with adjustable-speed a-c motors.

The speed regulation of a-c motors between no load and full load can be made very close, the difference being due to the voltage required to circulate the load current. In some cases, the load varies over a consider-

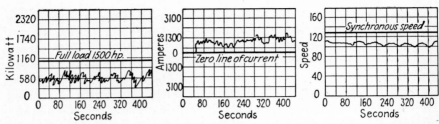

FIG. 15.12.   Characteristic curves of a 1,500-hp constant-horsepower adjustable-speed set.

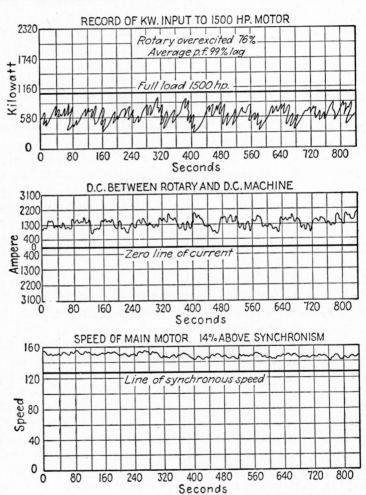

FIG. 15-13.   Characteristic curves of 1,500-hp constant-horsepower adjustable-speed set operating at 14 per cent above synchronism.

able range and it is desirable to provide a flywheel to absorb the peak load. In order to have this flywheel effective, it is necessary for the motor to drop in speed when the load comes on. This result can be obtained either by increasing the resistance in the path of the load current or else by designing the regulating machine to have the proper characteristics to give this result. The curves in Figs. 15-12 and 15-13 show the speed variations of one of these adjustable sets operating below and above synchronism.

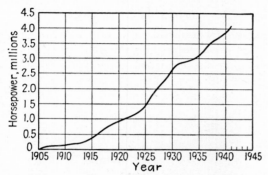

Fig. 15-14. The cumulative curve of main-drive motors over 300 hp shows a 1942 total of 4,045,665 hp. This curve is typical of the increased use of electric drive in industry. (*From Iron Steel Engr. Year Book*, 1942, *p.* 35.)

Electric motors have almost entirely replaced steam engines for rolling steel where new equipments are installed. The curves in Fig. 15-14 show this increase in total horsepower over a period of years. The efficiency and the flexibility of the electric drive has made an entire change in engineering practice. The slow-speed reciprocating engine has been supplanted by the high-speed turbine. Steam as a prime mover is used now almost exclusively for the development of electric energy, which in turn is applied to the work by means of the motor. The application to steel mills is only one illustration of this change.

CHAPTER 16

RESISTORS[1]

TYPES OF RESISTORS

The most common form of resistor is the cast-iron grid, shown in Figs. 16-1 to 16-4. Cast iron is admirably adapted for this purpose on account of its cheapness, high electrical resistance, freedom from corrosion, and small temperature coefficient. The resistance of cast iron increases about 15 per cent with a change of temperature of about 250°. Its principal

Fig. 16-1. Cast-iron grid resistor unit.

limitation is that it is not suitable for small apparatus where a large ohmic value is required with a small capacity, requiring high-resistance units of small size.

Where a large ohmic value is required in a small space, the embedded type of resistor is used. It is made in various forms, the resistance material usually consisting of a wire or ribbon embedded in enamel or in some similar compound, as in Fig. 16-5. It is also common to make

---

[1] A resistor is "an aggregation of one or more units possessing the property of resistance, used in an electric circuit for the purpose of operation, protection, or control of that circuit." This term was coined to express properly the part of a controller often referred to as the "resistance." The word "resistance" expresses the property of a substance and should not be used to denote the material itself.

up units in the form of plates. Embedding the resistance material gives increased thermal capacity and mechanical protection. It also prevents conducting material, such as metal dust, from collecting on the unit and reducing the resistance. Most of these embedded units can be heated to destruction without any external flash or drippings.

Cast Grid Resistors. These grids (see Figs. 16-1 to 16-4) are cast from iron or from an iron alloy; they may be in several sizes for different ratings; they usually have two widths of boss, which controls the spacing between grids. Alloy grids will stand more mechanical shock and can be given greater ohmic value, but they cost more. The ohmic value is

FIG. 16-2.   Electric Controller and Manufacturing Company tab weld resistor.

changed by using different cross sections of the grid loops, as well as by using alloys.

The grids are threaded on insulated tie rods attached to end frames. The contact between grid bosses is by pressure from the tie rods; mica washers are used to insulate between grids to give the current a zigzag path. Metal terminals, usually with slotted ends, are inserted between grids and make pressure contact with the grid boss. The slots permit a terminal to be relocated or additional ones to be added by slacking off the tie-rod pressure. Grids are usually given a coating of aluminum paint.

Edge-wound Ribbon Resistors. Ribbon resistors (see Fig. 16-3) occupy a position midway between cast grids and wire-wound tubes. They can be furnished with higher ohmic resistance than can grid resistors and have greater ampere capacity than do wire-wound tubes. They will stand greater mechanical shock than alloy grids and are suitable for some applications where grids would be broken. They have greater continuous rating and less short-time rating than have grid resistors of comparable size.

The ribbon is wound edgewise, in a spiral, and is screwed on porcelain insulators or is wound edgewise in loops between porcelain blocks. It

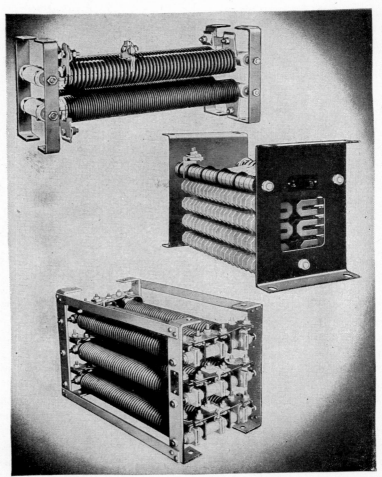

Fig. 16-3.   Grid and edge-wound resistors.   (*Courtesy of Westinghouse Electric and Manufacturing Company.*)

may also take other special forms.   The ribbon material can be stainless steel, Nichrome, or a copper-nickel steel alloy; any suitable metal may be used to give a wide range of ohmic values.   The units are assembled in end frames, similar to grid resistors.

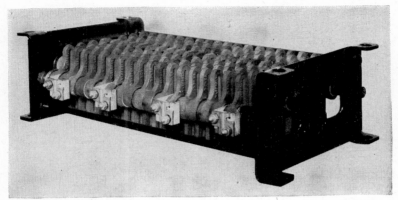

FIG. 16-4.   Grid-type resistor.   (*Courtesy of General Electric Company.*)

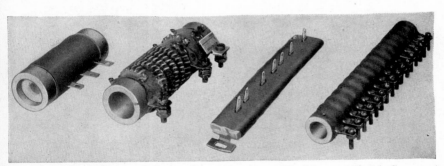

FIG. 16-5.   Vitrohm wire-wound resistors.   (*Courtesy of Ward Leonard Electric Company.*)

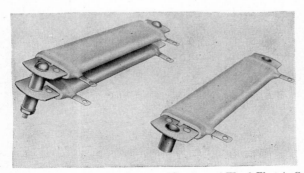

FIG. 16-6.   Vitrohm strip-type resistors.   (*Courtesy of Ward Electric Company.*)

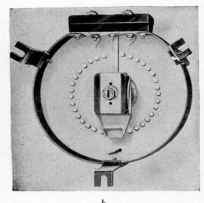

a

b

c

d

e

Fig. 16-7.   Front-of-board Vitrohm field rheostat: *a*, Front view. *b*, Rear view. *c*,
Stages of manufacture: (1) Pressed-steel plate
forms a rigid base.   After the entire surface is
(2) sandblasted to remove foreign particles,
the (3) ground coat of enamel is applied which
protects the surface of the plate and forms an
electrical-insulating heat-conducting surface
upon which to mount the (4) resistance element of alloy wire.   To these wires the heavy
contacts are fastened; this gives a mechanically and electrically perfect joint.   (5)
Vitrohm insulation is applied over the resistance wire.   It holds the wire and contacts securely and protects them against corrosion
and mechanical inquiry. *d*, Vitrohm field
rheostat with small rectangular contacts.   *e*,
Motor-operated Vitrohm field rheostat that is
used with a reversing planer control. (*Courtesy of Ward Leonard Electric Company.*)

FIG. 16-8. *a*, Ribohm field rheostat, single faceplate, front view. *b*, Motor-operated Ribohm rheostat combining a generator-field rheostat and a motor-field rheostat.

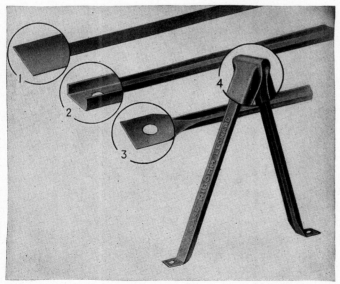

FIG. 16-9. (1) A metal ribbon of suitable size and alloy (2) is punched and formed into a channel and (3) after being flattened at the ends and center, (4) is bent into a V shape. This construction possesses the advantages of light weight, rigidity, and strength. Resistor used in Fig. 16-8. (*Courtesy of Ward Leonard Electric Company.*)

Wire-wound Resistors. The wire is wound on a clay or porcelain base and is embedded in a surface coat of baked enamel. It is usually in the form of a tube or a plate. The embedding is desirable to protect the fine wire from corrosion and mechanical damage; the covering greatly increases the thermal capacity of the resistor and prevents the wire from creeping out of place when it is hot. Skill and long experience are required for making good embedded resistors.

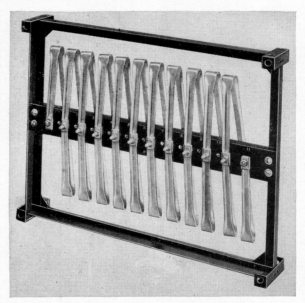

FIG. 16-10. Ward Leonard Electric Company loopohm resistor.

Heavy wire is sometimes wound on an asbestos-insulated tube or some other shape and is covered with a special cement. Many different types of wire-wound resistors have been made, some of which are not very satisfactory. This type of resistor gives a high ohmic value in a small space and can have many taps. Wire made from different alloys suitable for this purpose is available. The capacity depends upon the outside surface area. The mounting can be made to suit the application.

Resistors of the Compression Type. Some rheostats and controllers have resistors composed of graphite disks. The change in ohms is obtained by changing the pressure on the column of the disks. These disks are illustrated in Fig. 16-19 and a rheostat of this type in Fig. 16-21. The change in ohms with pressure is shown in the curve of Fig. 16-11. If a rheostat were designed so that the pressure on the column was changed in a uniform manner, the resistance would not be altered so as

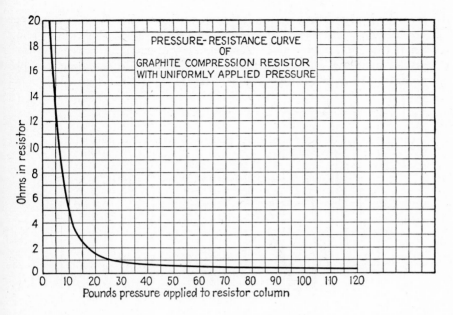

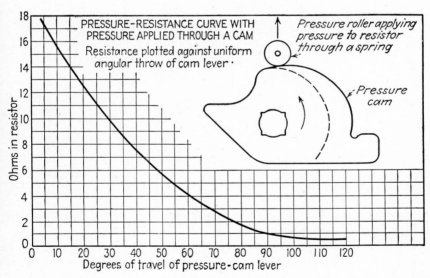

Fig. 16-11. Pressure-resistance curve of graphite-compression resistor. This curve shows the relation between the resistance of the carbon pile and a uniformly increased pressure applied to the column. When used in apparatus requiring a uniform decrease in resistance with a uniform travel of the controlling level, the increments of pressure should not be uniform but should be carried through suitable cams and springs as shown in the lower curve.

to give the best starting or regulating conditions. In order to improve this condition, a cam is used for compressing the resistance column. This cam acts through a spring and is so designed that equal movements of the controller handle give approximately equal changes in resistance. The curve in Fig. 16-11 shows the change in resistance with the movements of

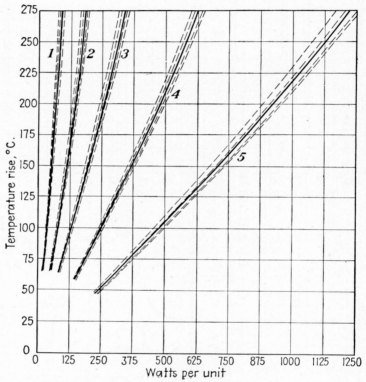

Fig. 16-12. Relation of the temperature use and the energy loss per resistor unit for five different classes of service.

the controller handle. Controllers using this form of resistor are shown in Figs. 16-21, 19-16, and 19-17.

A rheostat is defined as a resistor provided with means for varying its resistance. This usually takes the form of a series of contacts mounted on the surface of an insulating material having an arm arranged for making connection between a central post, which forms the pivot of the arm, and the various contacts, which are arranged in a circle. Mounted back of this face plate is a series of resistor units, as shown in Fig. 16-22. For small sizes, the contacts and resistance material are both embedded in a compound, forming a complete unit, known as a "plate-type rheostat" (see Fig. 16-7).

In applying resistors, two points should be considered: (1) the ability to radiate and conduct the heat from the unit to the surrounding atmosphere, (2) the ability to absorb heat. Usually the mass of the resistor is small compared with that of a motor or controller for dissipating the same amount of heat energy, so the energy absorbed by the resistor will raise its temperature more rapidly. When the resistor is used for starting purposes only, the absorption forms a very important item in the design. For intermittent duty, radiation is the controlling feature. The relation between temperature rise in degrees centigrade and the watts per unit for five different conditions of operation is shown in Fig. 16-12. The heavy line is the average value and the dotted lines on either side represent the variations due to the different cross sections of the grids used. These curves, of course, apply only to one particular size of grid and are shown for the purpose of illustrating the effect that different classes of service have upon the capacity of a resistor of a given size. Curve 1 is for continuous service; curve 2, for a cycle of duty, in which the resistor is in circuit for 2 min out of every 4 min, with 2 min of rest between. Curve 3 represents a duty cycle of an ordinary shop crane of 1-min service and 3 min of rest. Curve 4 represents a duty of 30 sec with 3 to 5 min of rest. Curve 5 is a duty of 15 sec in each 4 min. Curve 5 corresponds to ordinary starting duty. In making these tests, it was found that the spacing between the grids was an important factor and preliminary tests were made to determine the most economical spacing. Similar data should be obtained for any form of resistor used, so that an intelligent application can be made.

The effect that the spacing of the grids has upon their radiating capacity is shown in Fig. 16-15. Standard grids were used, and the spacing between the grids was changed by introducing washers. Curve *a* shows the minimum spacing. Curve *b* shows the effect of increasing this spacing by ¼ in. Curve *c* shows the effect of increasing it by ⅜ in. Further tests were made by increasing the spacing ½ in., but the results were practically the same as with the ⅜-in. increased spacing, showing that the economical limit had been reached for that particular design. The curves show very clearly the increase in capacity with a rise in temperature. Where the grids are spaced close together, the increase in capacity per degree rise of temperature is less than for the wider spacing. The tests show that if the resistor is used for continuous or intermittent duty, considerable material can be saved by a proper spacing of the grids.

The economical arrangement of the grids is more clearly shown in Fig. 16-13. The duty cycle is for light intermittent duty. The solid-line curve was obtained from a frame of 30 grids with narrow bosses, and the dotted-line curve from a frame of 18 grids with wide bosses. The frame was of the same length in both cases. The curves indicate that the frame of wide-boss grids radiated more energy than the one with narrow-boss grids. It is therefore a better frame, costs less, and is lighter in weight. The same relation could be shown if similar curves were plotted for heavy starting duty and heavy intermittent duty.

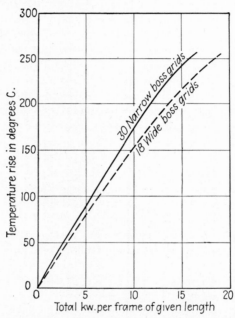

FIG. 16-13. Comparative radiating capacity of the same size resistor frames using different spacings of grids.

For light starting duty the time cycle is so short that most of the energy is absorbed by the resistor material itself and radiation has less effect. Therefore, the grids for this duty are spaced much closer together and the capacity is determined largely by the weight of the material and less by the radiation. From a heat-absorption standpoint, for light starting duty, the narrow-boss grids are better, as is shown in Fig. 16-14.

In the designing of resistors, certain arbitrary assumptions must be made, as it is manifestly impossible to predetermine the exact cycle of operation for many applications. The National Board of Fire Underwriters has adopted tests for starting rheostats that have proved very satisfactory for general-purpose starters. They are based on the average operating conditions that must be met when the motor is started and provide a sufficient factor of safety to give protection against fire hazard. Where the rheostat is used for speed regulation, its design is a simple matter if the load is known. Ordinarily, the requirements may be grouped as to duty into two classes—one known as "constant torque," where it is assumed that the current remains practically constant throughout the entire speed range and is equivalent to the full-load motor current, and another known as "fan" duty, where it is assumed that the current is approximately proportional to the speed of the motor.

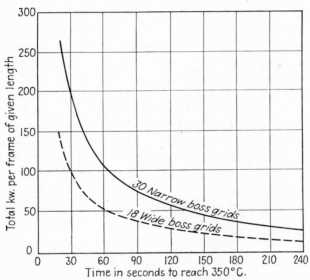

Fig. 16-14. Comparative heat absorption of two resistor frames of the same length having different number of grids.

The more difficult applications are for intermittent duty, such as crane service. The general-purpose crane used in an ordinary machine shop or foundry operates over a wide range of load and for varying intervals of time. An early analysis of this problem caused manufacturers to rate their resistors on the basis of different loads for different time intervals, assuming that, if a heavy load were being lifted, it would occur seldom and the time interval, therefore, could be made relatively short. The same resistor could be used for an average load operating for a longer period, etc. This method of rating became quite complicated and did not prove practical. An accumulation of data indicates that resistors for crane duty may be divided into two classes: those for general-purpose duty and those for heavy duty, such as those needed in certain operations in steel mills.

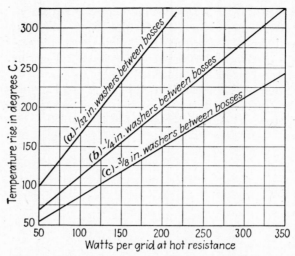

FIG. 16-15.   Relation between the spacing of cast-iron grids and temperature rise.

TABLE 16-1.   RESISTOR CLASSIFICATION TABLE ADOPTED BY THE NATIONAL
ELECTRICAL MANUFACTURERS ASSOCIATION

Approx. per cent full-load current on first point	Starting torque of full-load torque, per cent					Resistor classification numbers applying to duty cycles						
	D-c motors			A-c motors wound motor		5 sec on, 75 sec off	10 sec on, 70 sec off	15 sec on, 75 sec off	15 sec on, 45 sec off	15 sec on, 30 sec off	15 sec on, 15 sec off	Continuous duty
	Series	Compound	Shunt	One-phase starting*	Three-phase starting*							
25	8	12	25	15	25	111	131	141	151	161	171	91
50	30	40	50	30	50	112	132	142	152	162	172	92
70	50	60	70	40	70	113	133	143	153	163	173	93
100	100	100	100	55	100	114	134	144	154	164	174	94
150	170	160	150	85	150	115	135	145	155	165	175	95
200 or over	250	230	200	..	200	116	136	146	156	166	176	96

*This refers to the connections of the rotor circuit.

Other applications may be similarly analyzed.   In order to make it easy to express resistors in a definite way, The National Electrical Manufacturers Association adopted the resistor classification shown in Table 16-1.   The horizontal lines classify the resistors according to the percentage of full-load motor current that is obtained when all the resistor is in the circuit, and the vertical lines represent the service conditions.

The starting- and intermittent-duty resistors in the classification table are designed primarily for use with motors requiring an initial torque corresponding to the current value for the class of resistor specified and requiring a rms accelerating current not more than 125 per cent of the full-load motor current.

If the resistor is tested without its being connected to a motor, it should be connected to a line voltage that will give the initial current specified, and the steps should be cut out at equal intervals in the "time-on" period of the cycle specified; the current at no time during the cutting-out period should exceed 125 per cent of the rated value. This test should be repeated, at the intervals specified, for 1 hr. If resistors are desired for a longer time period than that shown in Table 16-1, the next higher class number to the right should be selected; if a higher starting torque is required, the next larger class number in the vertical column should be selected.

The amount of speed reduction obtained with a resistor in series with the armature or in the secondary of a slip-ring motor depends upon the load on the motor and may be obtained from the following formula:

$$\begin{matrix} \text{Speed reduction obtainable} \\ \text{in per cent of full-} \\ \text{load speed} \end{matrix} = \frac{\begin{matrix}\text{Actual load torque}\\\text{required in per cent}\\\text{of full load}\end{matrix}}{\begin{matrix}\text{Torque given in column}\\\text{under particular}\\\text{motor used}\end{matrix}} \times 100$$

For example, consider a wound-rotor motor with Class 95 resistor connected to a load requiring 70 per cent torque at slowest speed; this will give a speed reduction of

$$70/_{150} \times 100, \text{ or } 47 \text{ per cent}$$

The current taken from the line during the starting period is less than would be obtained by dividing the effective voltage by the ohms resistance. This reduction in current is caused by the inductive effect and the resistance in the lead wires and motor circuit. For the average application, the peak current during acceleration can be assumed as approximately two-thirds of the calculated value.

It is found in practice that the results obtained by different engineers agree very closely, so that the product of different manufacturing companies is on the same basis. The ordinary method of procedure is to divide the resistor into steps that follow a geometric progression. This can be worked out and tabulated for quick reference, as shown in Table 16-2.

TABLE 16-2.   METHOD OF PROPORTIONING STARTING RESISTORS, N.E.M.A. CLASS 135, FOR D-C SHUNT AND A-C WOUND-ROTOR MOTORS

	No. of steps	Step								
		1	2	3	4	5	6	7	8	9
Per cent ohms..........		100								
Per cent full-load amp.....	1	125								
Per cent ohms...........		72	28							
Per cent full-load amp.....	2	106	125							
Per cent ohms...........		55	30	15						
Per cent full-load amp.....	3	93	115	125						
Per cent ohms...........		45	28	17	10					
Per cent full-load amp.....	4	84	106	118	125					
Per cent ohms...........		37	26	17	12	8				
Per cent full-load amp.....	5	76	100	112	120	125				
Per cent ohms...........		32	24	17	12	9	6			
Per cent full-load amp.....	6	71	93	107	116	121	125			
Per cent ohms...........		28	21	16	13	9.5	7	5.5		
Per cent full-load amp.....	7	66	88	101	111	117	122	125		
Per cent ohms...........		25	20	15	12	9.5	7.5	6.5	4.5	
Per cent full-load amp.....	8	63	84	97	106	114	118	122	125	
Per cent ohms...........		23	18	15	12	9	8	6	5	4
Per cent full-load amp.....	9	60	80	93	103	110	115	119	123	125

The method of calculating the ohms per step in a given resistance takes the form of a geometric series, $R + RX_1 + RX_2 + RX_3$, etc., where R is the internal resistance of the motor and controller and X is the ratio of maximum and minimum accelerating current. The derivation of this formula can be obtained from textbooks on the subject or from electrical handbooks. The values obtained from such a formula are based entirely upon Ohm's law and do not take into account the effect of inductance in the circuit. The formula is sufficiently accurate, however, for most calculations.

The total number of ohms in a resistor is fixed by the classification number and the full-load current of the motor, and the number of sections of a resistor is determined by the steps on the controller, so that a designer can refer to the table, using the line corresponding to the steps in the resistor that he wishes to design, and then divide the resistor by taking the proper percentage for each step as indicated by the table. This results in a uniform product's being obtained with respect to the total ohms in the resistor, and its subdivision into steps.

It is more difficult to determine the capacity for each resistor step. Data for this part of the design must be obtained from actual tests. A resistor radiates heat in proportion to the fourth power of its absolute temperature (Fig. 16-16). This means that an increase in the hot-spot temperature from 250 to 350° C will materially increase the heat-dissipating ability of the resistor and, therefore, increase the factor of safety. Cast-iron grids show a dull-red heat at 600° C, which ordinarily will not damage the grids.

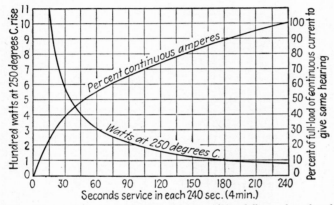

FIG. 16-16. Energy that can be dissipated in a grid for different lengths of service.

Unfortunately, this direct relation between temperature and radiating capacity is materially affected by the method of mounting and the circulation of the cooling air. If one cast-iron grid were located where there is a free circulation of air, this law would be followed very closely, but as they are ordinarily manufactured, cast-iron grids are assembled in frames of from 20 to 30 grids. These frames, in turn, are mounted in boxes with several other frames, so that the ultimate radiating capacity of the entire resistor depends upon the complete design.

The effect of increasing the time a grid resistor is in circuit is shown in Fig. 16-17. This curve was obtained by applying a definite load to the resistor for the time interval corresponding to each classification given in the table. The values plotted were the average hot-spot temperatures obtained. The actual temperature on test would first increase while the load was applied and then decrease during the off period. At first this difference in temperature was quite marked, but after the test was continued for 1 hr, only a small variation was observed between the maximum and minimum temperatures, the average of which, therefore, was considered as representing the actual temperature of the resistor for that class of service. A number of tests had to be made to determine the amount of energy that would correspond to a 250° C rise for each duty cycle. The curve shows that a resistor which has a continuous capacity

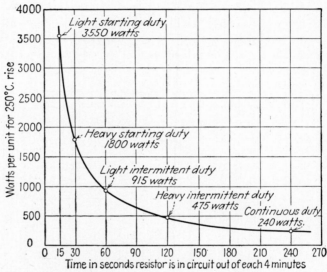

Fig. 16-17.   Relation between the time and the load required on a grid resistor to reach 250°C use.

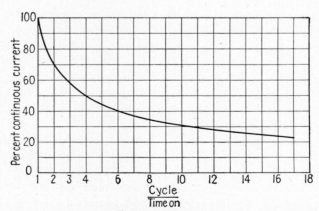

Fig. 16-18.   Relation between continuous and intermittent duty for various time cycles. Values are plotted for one particular size of resistor and are based on a temperature rise of 250°C.

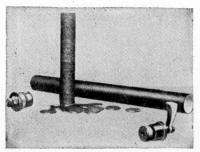

FIG. 16-19. Parts of a Bradleyunit compression disk resistor. Graphite disks, insulated steel tube, end plug, and pressure plug. (*Courtesy of Allen-Bradley Company.*)

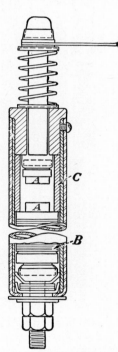

FIG. 16-20. Rear view of wall-mounted starter, showing Bradleyunits, starting lever, and pressure-equalizer assembly. Smooth motor acceleration is obtained. (*Courtesy of Allen-Bradley Company.*)

FIG. 16-21. Resistor element for Fig. 16-20 starter. The first motion of the operating handle closes the contacts *AA*; a further motion compresses the disk *B* of the resistor element. The insulating tube *C* is made of arc-resistant quartz, and the vaporized quartz has an arc-quenching effect when the contacts are opened.

of 240 watts will have 475 watts capacity on heavy intermittent duty and still higher values for the other classifications.

With test data of this kind available, a curve can be plotted, as in Fig. 16-18, showing the relation between the length of time in seconds during which the resistor is in circuit out of each 4-min period, and the percentage of continuous current to give equivalent heating.   This last curve

FIG. 16-22.   Westinghouse motor-operated rheostat.

forms the basis of an actual resistor design.   In Table 16-2, for each number of resistor steps two values are given.   One value is the percentage of total ohms in each step; the other is the percentage of full-load current that each step will carry continuously.   In designing resistors, it is assumed that the first step of starting- and intermittent-duty resistors will be in circuit a smaller number of seconds than the last step.   This gives a tapered capacity, so that the percentage of full load that the grid is capable of carrying should be smallest on the first step and increase with each step up to the last.   It will be noted from Table 16-2 that on the first step of a three-step resistor the current is 26 per cent of the full-load current and on the other steps, 35 to 44 per cent, the intermediate steps being tapered.

All the foregoing data were taken from one particular design and are not applicable to any other design. They are given because they show

FIG. 16-23. Electric Controller and Manufacturing Company controller with time-current acceleration and a motor-driven rheostat. Note the resistor mounted at the top in a ventilated enclosure to form an integral part of the controller.

clearly the relation that exists between the temperature of the grid and the current passing through the grid for different conditions, and they serve to illustrate how the design problem is worked out in practice. A different table is required for each size and type of resistor unit, and a different table for each resistor classification. For each ohmic value of grid of the same design it will be found that there is a slight variation in the watts per unit between the high and the low ohmic values, but this difference is not very great, and it is sufficiently accurate to use an average value.

As has been previously explained, the arrangement of the units in the resistor box or frame is determined by test. This also applies to the grouping of resistor frames; i.e., for light starting duty the resistors can be grouped close together, but for intermittent and continuous duty a greater space is required. The total energy dissipated in starting small motors is not great, and the arrangement of the frames is simple. Where large motors are used, it is desirable not to stack the resistor frames more than three high, and considerable space should be left between tiers of frames. Care should be taken to ensure a free circulation of air around all the resistor frames. Their capacity will be materially limited if they are located in the corner of a room or protected by partitions in such a way that the circulation of air is restricted. In arranging the grids in tiers, the frames should be located in such a way that the heat will be distributed equally among the tiers.

Each application for controllers must be studied and the classification of resistor should be selected after the operating data are obtained. The same classification of resistor may not be equally well adapted for the same type of service in different mills and industrial establishments. It is, therefore, difficult to give a definite classification for every application.

Any engineer having occasion to select control equipment for a particular application realizes the importance of such data. The manufacturer of the control equipment may not have actual test data available for the particular application and, therefore, must use the average data in his possession. The more generally these data are used, the more nearly will the table represent average conditions. With these average conditions and their probable limits of error known, the application of resistors from the classification table will be made relatively simple and both manufacturer and user will be benefited. Any engineer having difficulty with resistors on a particular application and finding that he has selected the correct classification may then examine this particular application with a view to determining in what way it differs from the normal. P. B. Harwood in his book, "Control of Electric Motors," gives additional information for resistor design.

CHAPTER 17

MANUAL CONTROLLERS

This chapter will deal particularly with manual controllers of the reversing type, which may be used for regulating the speed of the motor as well as starting, stopping, and reversing. A manual controller is one that has all its basic functions performed by hand. It is the opposite of a power-operated controller. The manual controller may be complete in itself or may form only part of the control equipment, as a master switch. The term "controller" is a broad designation. A controller used for accelerating a motor to normal speed in one direction is usually called a "starter." Types of faceplate starters are shown in Chap. 2.

TYPES OF MANUAL CONTROLLERS

The Drum Controller. The drum controller is the best known and, at present, the most commonly used form of manual controller. When it is used only for reversing a motor, it is known as a drum reverse switch, but generally it has additional points for acceleration and speed control. Types of drum controllers are shown in Fig. 17-1. The controller consists of a series of stationary fingers that engage segments on the surface of a cylinder or drum. The cylinder is revolved by a handle and is enclosed in an iron case with a sheet-iron cover. The fingers may be mounted in a single row on one side of the drum or in a double row, on opposite sides of the drum.

The drum cylinder usually consists of one or more castings clamped to an insulated square or hexagonal steel shaft; copper straps are attached to the outer surface for engaging the contact fingers and are sometimes provided with removable arcing tips. In some controllers the drum castings are made of brass or copper and engage the fingers directly without the use of removable contacts, but in most cases the drum is provided with removable contact segments.

The drum shaft has a notched wheel attached either above or below the drum. This is called a "star wheel," the notches corresponding to each of the operating positions of the controller handle. Whenever a set of contacts is in its proper position on the drum, a roller is forced into one of the notches on the star wheel by means of a spring. This indicates the exact operating position of the handle for each notch.

Fig. 17-1. General Electric drum controllers.

The most important item in the design of a drum controller is the contact finger, of which many different types have been made. Each manufacturer has a particular design which he features and which has its advantages and limitations. Figure 17-2 shows one type of finger that contains all the elements usually found in the various designs. There is a contact-carrying part that engages with the surface of the drum and is flexibly mounted on a finger base. The pressure between the drum and the finger is maintained by a spring, and the current passes from the

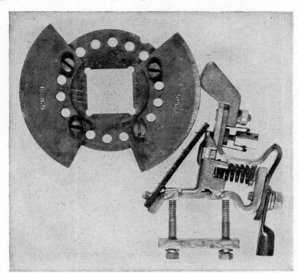

Fig. 17-2. Westinghouse drum-controller segment and contact finger.

finger to the terminal through a flexible shunt. The finger base is securely clamped to an insulated iron base and is sometimes provided with an arc shield between it and the drum.

When the controller is in the Off position, the fingers are not in contact with the surface of the drum, being opposite the cutaway portion of the drum. When the drum is rotated toward the finger base, the copper straps on the surface of the drum engage the contact fingers, lifting them and causing them to ride over the copper surfaces. The ends of the fingers are bent outward so as to strike the straps on the drum obliquely and are thus lifted without being stubbed. When the finger and the drum are in contact and the drum is rotated away from the finger base, the finger, being in tension, is under little strain; but when it is first engaged by the drum, it is in compression and must be of sufficiently rigid construction to withstand the strain then exerted upon it. When they are in contact, the fingers are lifted through a distance of $\frac{1}{16}$ in., a stop on the finger permitting it to be adjusted to obtain this condition. Sliding on the drum wears the finger away, so that it must be adjusted from time to time to maintain the proper contact pressure.

When returning the drum to the Off position, the contact segment in moving away from the finger forms an arc. This arc is established on one side of the contact surface of the finger and at the edge of the drum

Fig. 17-3.   Westinghouse cam controller.

segment, so that the burning does not take place on the parts ordinarily carrying current. A magnetic blowout is usually supplied with d-c controllers to extinguish this arc. The blowout may consist of a single coil and a common magnetic circuit for all the different fingers, or an individual blowout may be attached to each finger. The latter arrangement gives better results, but its extra expense may not be justified except for heavy duty.

The current that a contact finger will carry depends upon the width of the finger and the pressure between it and the surface of the drum. Tests indicate that if this pressure is in excess of 10 lb per in. of width some form of lubricant should be used or the cutting becomes excessive. The best form of lubricant is a good grade of vaseline spread thinly over the drum segments. Most controllers are designed for contact pressures less than that given above, so that the lubricant is not necessary, although if the drum is kept clean and lubricated, the contact fingers will last longer.

The armature resistor is almost always mounted separate from the drum controller. Where the controller provides for both armature and field control, the resistor for the field rheostat may be mounted as part of the controller. The ordinary reversing controller can be assumed to have a separate armature resistor.

The Cam Controller. Cam controllers have the same general appearance as the drum controllers and are mounted and operated in the same manner, but the contact element is different. In place of the rotating cylinder is a shaft carrying a set of cams, which engage and close a series of contactors that replace the drum fingers (see Fig. 17-3).

The contact mechanism is illustrated in detail in Figs. 17-4 to 17-6. It consists of a stationary element, which may or may not be provided with a blowout, and a movable element held open by a spring and closed by a cam. The action of this contact is exactly the same as that of the magnetic contactor, and the same contacts are used.

The illustration shows the three positions of the contact: (1) when open, (2) when just touching at the tip, and (3) when it is entirely closed, making contact at the heel. In opening it the process is reversed. This rolling action from the tip to the heel and back again in opening causes the arc to be broken at the tip and the current to be carried at the heel. By the use of rolling action instead of a sliding action in closing, the mechanical wear is eliminated and much heavier pressures can be used. A more complete discussion of this contact is given in Chap. 4.

The current is carried from the movable contact to the terminal by means of a flexible shunt; one end of the spring is insulated so that no current can pass through this member. On account of the spring's being located a considerable distance away from the contact, it is not directly affected by the temperature of the contact or the arcing and is, therefore, in no danger of having its temper drawn, owing to excessive loads.

The movable contact is attached to a block, which in turn is fastened to the hinge member. The surface between this block and the hinge member is corrugated and one of the holes is slotted so that this block can be adjusted to give the proper contact action. After this adjustment is made, it should not be necessary to change this block when renewing contacts, as all the contact wear takes place at the tip and does not affect the location of the current-carrying parts.

Various combinations of switches can be obtained by changing the number of contactors and the shape of the cams. The length of the frame can be adapted to the desired combination by changing the length of the insulating bars and the sheet-iron cover.

Fig. 17-4.

Fig. 17-5.   Fig. 17-6.

Figs. 17-4 to 17-6. Details of contactors used in cam controllers. The contactors may also be clamped to insulated plates instead of bars. These contacts are of the rolling type— note the action during closing. The contact is established at the tips and rapidly transferred to the heel or lower portion of the contacts during the closing process. This process takes place by a rolling action. When opening the process is reversed, throwing all of the arcing to the tip of the contact.

Both the drum type and the cam type of controllers can be provided with either a rotating handle or a lever handle. They may also be mounted vertically on the rear of the panel and operated by a handwheel on the front of the panel through suitable gearing. If the controller is mounted back of the panel with the shaft horizontal, the shaft can be extended directly through the panel without the use of gearing.

Both types of controllers have been built motor operated. In that case, the construction is the same as for manual operation, the handle being replaced by a reduction gear and a pilot motor.

The drum controller is more compact for certain switching combinations, such as reversing. The cam type is easily designed for complicated switching, and new combinations can be more easily made, as these combinations are accomplished by cutting cams of different shapes. The cam units can be removed individually without dismantling the controller. The same is true of the contact fingers of the drum controllers; however, the drum shaft must be taken out to replace drum segments, after which it is advisable to true the segments in a lathe before reassembling them in

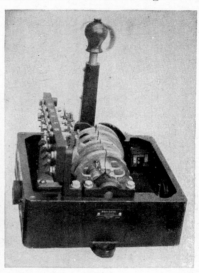

a   b

Fig. 17-7. Cutler-Hammer drum-type master switch; *a*, with cover in place; *b*, with cover removed.

the controller. The cam controller has a blowout that compares favorably with that of the magnetic contactor and that is always in the proper direction. Both types when enclosed have a restricted arcing space and are, therefore, more limited as to severity of service than are magnetic contactor controllers.

The Faceplate Controller. One of the most popular forms of manual controllers in steel-mill service is known as the Dinkey controller (Fig. 17-8). It somewhat resembles the ordinary faceplate rheostat, although it is much more rugged in construction. A series of stationary contacts are mounted on an insulated base, and a pair of brushes making contact with these rotate around a central shaft. The brushes make contact between an outer and an inner row of contacts. The handle usually projects from the top of the controller and actuates the brush arms by means of a pinion and gear segment, so that a relatively small motion of the handle is multiplied into a large motion of the brushes. The stationary contacts are made removable from the face of the controller without disturbing the electrical connection. The brushes can also be renewed when necessary. The resistor is mounted in the controller frame back of the faceplate, the whole forming a self-contained unit.

FIG. 17-8.   Electric Controller and Manufacturing Company faceplate controller—known to the trade as the "Dinkey controller."

A modification of this type of controller, known as the "grindstone" type, is now obsolete. The contacts of this controller are mounted around the periphery of an insulated base, in the semblance of a grindstone, to which fact it owes its name.

The Compression Type of Controller.   Controllers of the compression type (Fig. 16-20) differ from all other types of controllers. Instead of a number of contact segments connected to taps on the resistor, several columns of graphite disks are used, the change in resistance being obtained by varying the pressure between the disks. This form of resistor is shown in greater detail in Figs. 16-19 to 16-21.

The illustration shows the manual type of controller, but other forms of this controller are made, using contactors.

COMPARISON OF TYPES

The two controllers described last, above, have the resistor self-contained with the switching mechanism, whereas the first two usually have separately mounted resistors. The drum and cam types may have either a rotating or a lever handle, but the other two types are always provided with lever handles. The four are representative of many that are now being successfully used. Other forms of controllers are built and doubtless from time to time improvements will arise, but in the present state of the art the types described show the principles used in all manual controllers.

Manual Controllers versus Magnetic-contactor Controllers. The advantages and limitations of manual controllers depend to a large degree upon their sizes and application requirements. The following list of advantages and limitations should be interpreted broadly, as there are many applications for manual controllers that would not justify the use of contactor control.

Advantages. The advantages of a manual controller, as compared with a magnetic-contactor controller, are these:

1. The first cost is less.

2. The space occupied by the controller is usually less, and the weight is less. In some applications the weight and space requirements are often a determining factor.

3. They are more simple. Manual controllers usually have no electric interlocks, so that the wiring connections can be easily followed.

4. These controllers are readily enclosed to protect them against dust, dirt, and moisture. The drum and cam controllers are often made watertight for use on shipboard.

Limitations. The limitations are as follows:

1. The larger sizes of manual controllers require more effort to operate and may, therefore, tire the operator if frequent use is necessary.

2. The contacts will wear more rapidly, as their operation is not so positive. The quicker the contacts are opened and closed, the less is the maintenance cost.

3. The arcing takes place near the operator. This is not objectionable in small controllers, but it is safer to have the main arc-rupturing parts

located remote from the operator, where a considerable amount of power is being handled.

4. The larger sizes of manual controllers occupy more space than the master switch of the magnetic type, and on cranes and some other applications, therefore, a large manual controller may interfere with the operator's seeing his work.

5. A separate protective panel is required for manual controllers, to obtain over-load and low-voltage protection required in many applications. In some watertight controllers it has been found necessary to mount the protective panel in the same case as the master controller.

VENTILATING REQUIREMENTS

In rupturing the arc, ionized gases are produced, which must be removed by ventilation. Where the manual controller is enclosed, the air space surrounding the arc-rupturing parts is limited and the ventilation is poor. Where the circuit is opened and closed frequently, trouble may result from the accumulation of these gases. This difficulty does not arise with small controllers and may be avoided in the larger type by ventilating the enclosing cover. (These limitations may occur also in the magnetic type of controller where the enclosure is restricted.) This condition is sometimes overlooked so that a properly designed controller has been discredited, whereas improper application was the cause.

Whatever type or design of controller is used, provision must be made for disposing of these ionized gases. The more quickly the arc is ruptured, the less gas will be produced. When an enclosed controller is used, the arcing heats up the air space within the enclosure and limits the current-carrying capacity of the contacts and other parts. The more frequent the arcing, the greater the heating. This is a limitation sometimes overlooked.

Manual controllers are usually rated either for intermittent duty or for continuous duty. Continuous service presupposes only a small amount of arc rupturing. Intermittent service must assume a certain amount of heat to be generated by the arc. The more frequently the circuit is opened, the less time the current-carrying parts will be in circuit, and the increase in air temperature inside the enclosure due to arcing, therefore, will be counterbalanced by a smaller amount of energy lost in heating the current-carrying parts. Conditions may arise, however, under which the current is left on longer than was intended or the current is ruptured more frequently than was estimated when the controller was rated. Engineering skill, therefore, is required in selecting a controller, to determine whether any unusual conditions of this kind exist in a particular application.

CHAPTER 18

DIRECT-CURRENT MAGNETIC-CONTACTOR CONTROLLERS

TYPES OF MAGNETIC-CONTRACTOR CONTROLLERS

Magnetic-contactor controllers may be divided broadly into non-reversing and reversing controllers. Where several contactors are used for short-circuiting sections of the resistor in the armature circuit, the connections to the operating coils of these contactors can be made in suc-

FIG. 18-1. Cutler-Hammer magnetic-contactor controller for reversing and plugging service.

281

cession by means of a drum-type master switch.   In this case, the motor can be operated with more or less armature resistance, depending upon the number of contactors whose circuits are closed through the master switch.   The number of resistance steps can be altered to suit the application.   The authors believe that one step of resistance is sufficient for

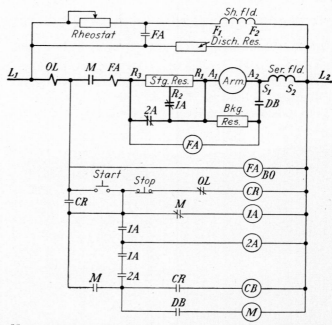

Fig. 18-2   Nonreversing magnetic starter with definite time acceleration. The definite time-accelerating contactors 1A, 2A and the dynamic braking contactor DB are spring-closed devices.   They must be opened (energized) before line contactor M is closed to start the motor.   Operation of the start button energizes control relay CR, contactors 1A, 2A, DB, and M in order to open 1A, 2A, and DB and close CR and M contacts.   The motor then starts with starting resistor R1-R2-R3 in series with the armature.   Interlock M in series with coil 1A opens to deenergize coil 1A and start its timing period, after which contacts 1A close to short-circuit resistor R1 to R2.   The timing period of 2A is started when control contacts 1A open.   Contacts 2A close after a definite time to short-circuit resistor R2 to R3.   The time-delay feature of contactors 1A and 2A is provided by magnetic flux decay principle illustrated in Figs. 18-3 to 18-4.   Operation of the stop button opens contactor M and allows DB to close to apply dynamic braking to provide a quick stop.

starting d-c motors up to 15 hp 230 volts, where the starting duty is light, and that two steps may be used for heavy starting.   If it is desirable to regulate the speed of the motor, additional steps should be provided. The acceleration of the motor quite frequently is automatic, even when several running points are provided.

Nonreversing Controllers.   Nonreversing controllers are usually connected on one side of the motor circuit only and consist of a line con-

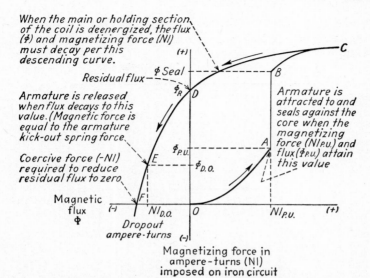

When the main or holding section of the coil is deenergized, the flux (ϕ) and magnetizing force (NI) must decay per this descending curve.

Residual flux—

ϕ Seal

Armature is released when flux decays to this value. (Magnetic force is equal to the armature kick-out spring force.

Coercive force (-NI) required to reduce residual flux to zero.

Armature is attracted to and seals against the core when the magnetizing force (NI$_{P.U.}$) and flux ($\phi_{P.U.}$) attain this value

Magnetic flux ϕ

Dropout ampere-turns

Fig. 18-3. Hysteresis curve for a type *AQ* timetactor magnetic circuit.

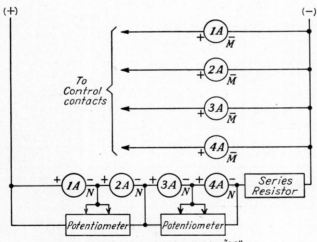

Main coil windings are indicated by "*M*"
Neutralizing coil windings are indicated by "*N*"

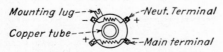

Coil terminal location (Front View)
Fig. 18-4. Connection diagram for timetactor coils.

Elementary controller diagram
to 230 v. d.c. supply

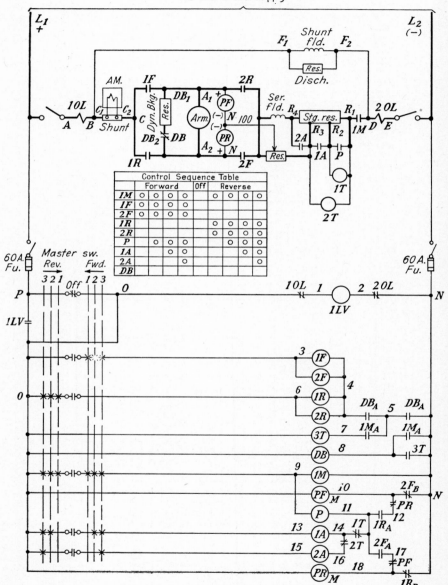

FIG. 18-5. Reversing magnetic controller with definite time acceleration, dynamic braking, plugging, and speed control.

A master switch with three points in each direction controls the operations. Under normal conditions speed control by means of the resistor $R1$-$R2$-$R3$-$R4$ in series with the tactor, a resistor, and one or more contactors for short-circuiting the resistor. A two-pole knife switch or circuit breaker, mounted separate from the control panel, is usually required with this type of controller, the knife switch being connected so that it will disconnect both sides of the motor and the controller from the line. The line contactor may be provided with a bottom contact for short-circuiting the armature of the motor through a fixed resistance, to give dynamic braking when the line switch is opened. A diagram of a controller arranged for dynamic braking is shown in Fig. 18-2.

In some cases it is desirable to open both sides of the motor circuit when the controller is in the Off position. This can be done by providing two line contactors. This arrangement, however, is not usually employed, as it adds to the expense and opening the knife switch by hand accomplishes the same result. The knife switch is needed so that the contactors can be disconnected from the line to renew the contacts or to make adjustments.

Reversing Controllers. In order to reverse the armature of a d-c motor it is necessary to disconnect both sides of the armature from the line. This necessitates the use of four single-pole contactors or two double-pole contactors, two contacts being closed for either direction of operation. It is the usual practice to arrange either a mechanical or an electrical interlock between these contactors, so that the forward and the reverse contactors cannot both be closed at the same time, as this would result in a short circuit and might injure the apparatus. The resistor in series with the armature is short-circuited in steps by magnetic contactors

---

armature is obtained because contactor P is closed on all positions of the master switch, contactor $1A$ on position three. Definite time acceleration is automatically provided by the flux decay timing relays $1T$ and $2T$ (Fig. 19-2) when the master switch is moved rapidly from a low speed to higher ones.

The plugging resistor $R1$-$R2$ is necessary to protect the motor from excessive currents when the master switch is moved quickly from a running position to the other direction of operation to apply power in the reverse direction to effect a quick reversal. Therefore when a normal start from rest is made the plugging resistor $R1$-$R2$ is not necessary, and plugging contactor P closes immediately to short-circuit it. When the plugging operation occurs, however, contactor P opens and remains open until the motor speed is near zero. Contactor P then closes, and definite time acceleration in the other direction occurs.

The operation of contactor P is controlled by plugging relays PF and PR, each of which has a main coil M and a neutralizing coil N. The neutralizing coils are connected in parallel with the armature. If plugging is from the forward direction, coil PRM will be deenergized by opening of interlock $1Rb$. Because of the holding action of coil PRN, relay PR will not close until the motor speed is near zero. Relay PF was opened when interlock $2Fb$ closed. Since neither relay PF nor PR is closed while the motor speed is decreasing to near zero, plugging contactor coil P is not energized and contactor P is open. Hence the entire resistor $R1$-$R2$-$R3$-$R4$ is effective, and the motor is protected against high currents while the motor is decelerating to near zero speed. During this time the counter emf of the motor and the line voltage are additive and approximately double the normal line voltage. Under such conditions the armature currents are held within safe values by the operation of plugging contactor P. A potentiometer provides means to adjust the low speed point at which the plugging contactor P will close.

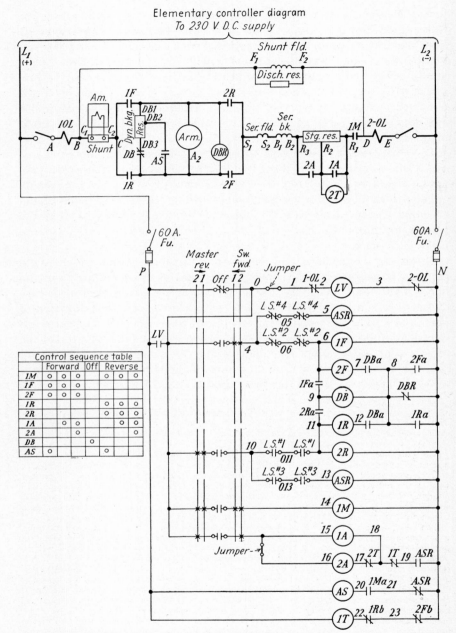

FIG. 18-6.   Reversing magnetic controller with definite time acceleration, dynamic braking, and armature shunt circuit for slow operation.

A master switch with two points in each direction controls the operations.   The first

in the same manner as for nonreversing controllers. Frequently the resistor is connected directly to one side of the motor, so that the line contactors in their Off position disconnect the armature entirely from the line, as is shown in Fig. 18-5. Since both sides of the motor circuit are opened by contactors, the shunt field cannot be connected so that it will discharge through the armature of the motor. It is, therefore, good practice to provide the shunt field with a parallel resistance to take up the inductive discharge when the field circuit is opened. If this resistance is omitted, a high voltage is generated in the field windings, which may ultimately result in puncturing the insulation.

The reversing controller can be arranged for dynamic braking by providing a bottom contact on one of the forward and one of the reverse direction switches, so connected that, when both of these switches are open, the armature will be short-circuited through a resistor, as shown in Fig. 18-6.

FIELD RHEOSTATS

Where a controller is used with an adjustable-speed motor, a field rheostat is used for changing the resistance of the field circuit to adjust the speed of the motor. This field rheostat may be mounted on the controller panel or separate from it. It is considered better practice to mount this rheostat separate from the control panel, so that the operator will not be required to place his hand close to the magnetic contactors when they are in operation. The separately mounted field rheostat can be covered, to prevent the operator from coming in contact with any live parts. Usually the contactor panel is quite large and must be mounted in a more or less inaccessible place. The field rheostat, however, is small and can be located close to the master switch. Sometimes the master switch and the field rheostat are combined in one unit.

CONTROLLER SUMMARY

To sum up: A controller is made up of a magnetic-contactor panel, either reversing or nonreversing, with or without dynamic brake. Some form of master switch is provided to operate the controller, and a field

---

position of the master switch opens the dynamic braking contactor *DB* and closes either the forward (1*F* and 2*F*) contactors or the reverse contactors (1*R* and 2*R*) depending upon which direction the master switch is moved. Definite time acceleration by the magnetic flux decay relays 1*T* and 2*T* is initiated when the master switch is moved to the first position and either interlock 1*Rb* or 2*Fb* is opened. For forward operation limit switch No. 4 and in the reverse direction limit switch No. 3 will operate relay *ASR*, contactors 1*A*, 2*A*, and *AS* to operate the motor at a slow speed prior to a final stop even though the master switch is left in a running position. Under these conditions starting resistor *R*1-*R*2-*R*3 will be in series with the motor and resistor *DB*1-*DB*2 will be in parallel with it. The motor will stop when the master switch is moved to the Off position or when either limit switch No. 1 or No. 2 opens. Dynamic braking is applied to stop the motor quickly by closure of contactor *DB*.

rheostat may be added.   This gives the essential elements for the control
of an electric motor.

MASTER SWITCHES

The master switch is an auxiliary switch that serves to govern the
operation of contactors and auxiliary devices of electric controllers.   It
usually takes the form of push button, float switch, pressure switch,

FIG. 18-7.   Square D type VG-2 starter for an adjustable-speed motor.   This starter has
resistor-shorting contactors closed in sequence at predetermined intervals after the line
contactor closes.   The timing period for each contactor is controlled by a pneumatic time-
delay unit (see Fig. 6-12).

thermostat, or drum switch.   Other forms, of course, are in use, and any
device that opens and closes the circuit may be used as a master switch.

The push-button switch is the most common and is perhaps used more
than all the other types combined.   An ordinary start-and-stop push
button is shown in Figs. 18-12 and 18-13.   More elaborate combinations
of push buttons are used for printing presses, electric elevators, and other
applications where a complicated sequence of operation is required.

A float switch is shown in Figs. 8-18 and 8-19 and a pressure switch in Fig. 8-17. These switches are used in connection with pumps and similar installations. The float switch, as its name implies, consists of a hollow

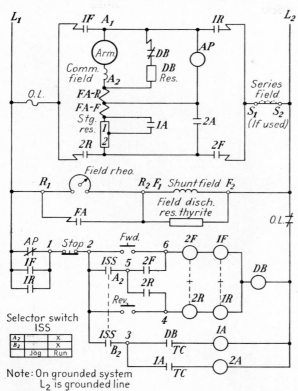

Fig. 18-8. Direct-current reversing controller with "time delay" acceleration and speed control by field adjustment.

SQUARE D COMPANY

This controller provides the following:

1. "Time-delay" (forced) acceleration, three steps.
2. Speed adjustment by field rheostat.
3. Dynamic braking.
4. Antiplugging relay.
5. Remote control for starting, stopping, reversing, and jogging.

The time delay is obtained from the relay of Fig. 6-12.

metal box used as a float, which opens and closes the master switch for different levels of the liquid in which it is placed. The pressure switch has a diaphragm, which opens the contacts at the maximum pressure and closes them at the minimum pressure for which it is adjusted. Various forms of thermostats are used in connection with refrigerating machinery for starting and stopping the motor-driven machinery at different temperatures.

A master switch of the drum type is shown in Fig. 18-10. This is usually in the form of a small drum controller and may be operated by

Fig. 18-9. Westinghouse cam-type master switch with lever handle and cover removed.

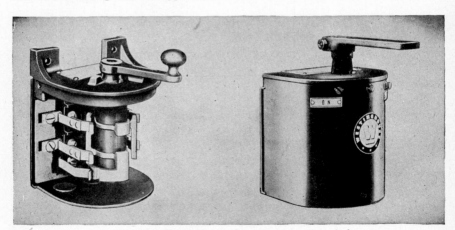

Fig. 18-10. Westinghouse drum-type master switch.

the rotation of a handle or with a forward-and-back motion of a lever (Fig. 17-7). Under this class should be included also switches in which the contacts are arranged on a faceplate instead of a drum and where the contacts are operated by cams. The drum type of master switch is usually applied where the sequence of operation is more or less complicated, also where frequent operation is required.

Methods of Operation. Most master switches may be connected to either reversing or nonreversing controllers. Two general methods are employed, one of which is known as "low-voltage release" and the other as "low-voltage protection." They are defined as follows:

Low-voltage Release. The effect of a device operative on the reduction or failure of voltage to cause the interruption of power to the main

FIG. 18-11. General Electric master switch for switchboard mounting.

FIG. 18-12. Westinghouse push-button station.

circuit, but not preventing the reestablishment of the main circuit on return of voltage.

Low-voltage Protection. The effect of a device operative on the reduction or failure of voltage to cause and maintain the interruption of power to the main circuit.

The reason for making the above distinction is largely a matter of safety. If the motor drives a woodworking machine, for instance, the machine may be at rest, owing to the absence of line voltage. Under these circumstances, the operator might be engaged in adjusting the machinery or for some other reason might have his hands close to the cutting tools. If the line voltage is restored at such a time, the operator may easily be injured. This applies to a variety of machinery. Gears are a source of danger from this cause. These gears are usually protected under operating conditions, but this protection might be removed when the machine is at rest. In order to guard against accident from this cause, the master switch is so connected to the controller as to afford low-voltage protection.   This requires the operator to perform a manual operation on the master switch in order to start the motor after it has once come to rest because of a failure of voltage.

Where the motor operates a fan or a pump, it is very desirable to have the apparatus start automatically after a failure of voltage.   In such

Fig. 18-13.   General Electric push-button stations.

Fig. 18-14.   General Electric heavy-duty push-button station.

cases there is little or no danger resulting from the automatic starting of the motor, and a great deal of inconvenience and possible danger might result from the failure of the motor to start when the voltage is restored to the line.   The master switch under such conditions is connected to give low-voltage release.   This arrangement automatically starts the motor again, when the line voltage is restored.

OVERLOAD PROTECTION

It is usually necessary to provide some form of overload protection in connection with the controller. The least expensive form of protection is the fuse, usually of the cartridge type. These fuses have a certain amount of time element and therefore can be used for control apparatus. When a motor is started or during its operation, heavy currents may be taken by the motor for a few seconds. These do not injure the motor or

FIG. 18-15. Cutler-Hammer push-button station with a special Stop push button.

FIG. 18-16. Square D Company water-proof push-button station.

the controller, and therefore it is desirable to have a time element in the overload device. This occurs to a limited extent when a special type of enclosed fuse is used.

Another common form of overload protection is a series relay that opens a contact by means of a magnet when the current exceeds a certain value. These relays should have a dashpot to obtain a time element, so that the relay can be given a setting more nearly equal to the full-load current of the motor. Thermal overload relays are now more generally used for motor protection. See Chap. 23 for a description of different types. Where a magnetic contactor is used on only one side of the line, a single-pole relay may be used with this contactor, but it is necessary to use a fuse on the other side of the line. The advantage of a relay is that it can be restored to its normal position very easily. The fuse, however, must be replaced by a new one. If a combined relay and fuse is used, it is usual to select a fuse with a higher rating than the setting of the relay, so that under ordinary conditions of overload the relay will operate and save the fuse.

It takes some time to raise the temperature of a motor to a dangerous point when it is overloaded. If this overload is within the commutating limits of a motor, the additional load will not injure the motor until the temperature has been raised to the danger point. This usually takes from 5 min up to a half hour or more, depending upon the size of the motor and the amount of overload. If the overload is continued indefinitely, it will injure the motor, but short periods of operation are permissible The result has been that operators set the overload protection high enough so as not to operate on short-time peak loads. Therefore, the motor is without any real protection against continuous overloads. Very few fuses, overload relays, circuit breakers, or similar apparatus give complete protection to industrial motors. They operate in case of short circuits or abnormal overloads, but usually they are set too high to open on a small overload, which may be sufficient to injure the motor if continued for a long time. There are time-element overload devices that have time elements of 5 to 30 min, instead of 5 to 30 sec, as is the case with most of this apparatus. The longer the time element can be made, the more desirable it is for the operation of motors.

It is often stated that an overload relay having a long-time element will not operate quickly enough in case of a short circuit or a ground to protect the motor. Standard practice, however, requires the use of fuses or a circuit breaker at the point where the motor circuit leaves the main power wires. The fuses or the circuit breaker at this point must be set to protect the wires leading to the motor. If these wires are made a little larger than for the full-load capacity of the motor, the circuit breaker at this branch point may be set so that it will not operate on normal overloads of the motor, but will protect the motor under abnormal conditions and also afford protection to the wires leading to the controller. The ideal protection, therefore, is feeder protection against short circuit and a time-element overload device on the controller that will protect the motor against continuous overloads, while permitting overloads for short periods of time.

Overload relays are commonly made up in three forms:

1. The first allows the armature to return to the open position immediately after the overload has been removed. The function of such a relay

is to open the line contactor. Connections are made so that the contactor will be retained in the open position until the master switch is manipulated.

2. The overload relay is provided with a catch, which holds the armature in the closed position and requires the energizing of a separate magnet to release the catch and restore the relay to its normal condition.

3. This is the same as 2, except that the catch is released by hand instead of by a magnet. This is objectionable because the operator must place his hand on the device, which is in the neighborhood of live parts.

Arrangement 1 is the most common and is usually preferred, owing to its simplicity and cheapness. Arrangement 2 is usually connected to the master switch, so that the relay is reset by moving the master switch to the center or off position.

APPLICATIONS

The magnetic-contactor controllers described above are those having the most general application. A few of the typical applications are for motors driving line shafting, pumps, machine tools, woodworking machinery; in fact, any apparatus that is motor driven that does not require a special arrangement of circuits.

CHAPTER 19

ALTERNATING-CURRENT CONTROLLERS

Many types of d-c motors have been built and a variety of methods of control have been devised. However, very few a-c motors, other than induction motors, are used in industrial work, and the methods of control in common use are quite simple.

WOUND-SECONDARY MOTORS

When resistors are used for accelerating or controlling the speed of induction motors, they are usually placed in series with the three-phase wound secondary of the motor. The ends of this winding are brought out to three slip rings on the motor shaft, so that resistance may be inserted between each of the three rings. The method of control corresponds very closely to that of a compound-wound motor with only a small amount of series field. In studying this type of control and applying it, the problem is simplified if the operating conditions are considered to be those of the corresponding d-c motor and no attempt is made to analyze the complicated reactions that are taking place in the wound-secondary motor.

This method of control requires the use of a primary switch, which should be separated electrically from the part of the control that is used for changing the resistance of the secondary circuit. Usually the secondary is wound for less than 600 volts, and in standard motors the secondary voltage and current do not change materially for different primary voltages. This fact makes possible the use of the same secondary controller with a number of different primary switches. For a primary potential of 600 volts or less, air-break switches are used. If it is 2,200 volts or more, oil switches are frequently employed, although for certain classes of service air-break magnetic contactors have come into use.

Where the motor operates in one direction only, the primary switch often consists of a circuit breaker, and either a faceplate or drum-type secondary controller is used. If automatic acceleration is required, both primary and secondary control consist of magnetic contactors, as shown in Figs. 19-1 and 19-2.

If the motor is to be reversed at frequent intervals, a drum controller having both primary and secondary switches is generally used for small motors. Large motors usually require magnetic contactors, in which case the same master switches and the same method of overhead protection may be employed as for d-c control. Low-voltage release or low-voltage protection can be obtained in the same way.

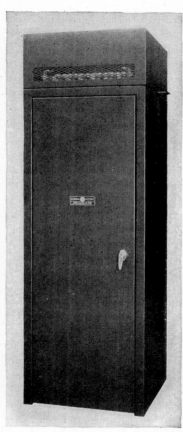

FIG. 19-1. General Electric controller for wound-secondary induction motors four-point 150 amp.

There are several methods for arranging the resistors in the secondary circuit of wound-rotor motors. In each case, sections of resistance are short-circuited by contactors. One method consists of short-circuiting these sections simultaneously on all three legs of the circuit. This keeps the resistance balanced and is theoretically the best method to employ. It requires the use of two contactors or their equivalent for each step of control.

A more economical method consists in short-circuiting the resistor in one leg of the circuit at a time. This requires the use of only one contactor per step and uses the control equipment to much better advantage. Theoretically the unbalancing that results from this method of control is objectionable. A careful analysis of this problem shows that, when the

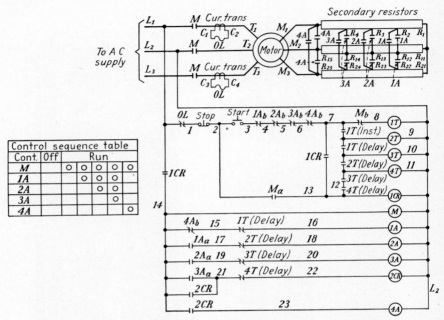

Fig. 19-2.   Nonreversing starter for wound-rotor motor.

Definite time acceleration is provided by the four timing relays $1T$, $2T$, $3T$, and $4T$, which in turn control the secondary contactors $1A$, $2A$, $3A$, and $4A$. All the secondary contactors $1A$, $2A$, $3A$, and $4A$ must be open—hence secondary resistance effective—and their interlocks $1Ab$, $2Ab$, $3Ab$, and $4Ab$ closed to make the start button effective. Operation of the start button energizes timing-relay coils $1T$, $2T$, $3T$, and $4T$ in sequence. Relay $1CR$ closes, line contactor M closes, and the motor starts. Time-delay contacts on $1T$, $2T$, $3T$, and $4T$ prevent the secondary contactors from closing. When line contactor M closes, its interlock Mb deenergizes the coil of timing relay $1T$ which, after a delay, energizes coil $1A$ of the first secondary accelerating contactor. Operation of $1T$ continues timing on $2T$, $3T$, and $4T$ to close accelerating contactors $2A$, $3A$, and $4A$.

unbalancing is properly arranged, the performance of the motor is not materially changed from balanced operation, and a number of other advantages are secured.[1]

In the discussion of this question the inductance and resistance of the secondary winding of the motor will be neglected for the sake of simplic-

[1] An analysis of the problem of unbalanced secondary operation is discussed in detail in a paper by A. A. Gazda, presented before the A.I.E.E. in February, 1917. His theoretical analysis was carefully checked by test, so that the results given represent actual operating conditions.

ity, as their effect is very small on the total results. Figure 19-7 shows a simplified diagram of connections, together with a sequence table. When the motor is first started, the current in each phase of the secondary is equal and no unbalancing occurs. When switch No. 1 is closed, we shall

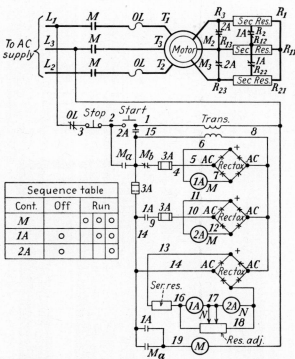

Sequence table			
Cont.	Off	Run	
M		o	o o
1A	o		o o
2A	o		o

Fig. 19-3. Acceleration by magnetic flux decay timing using magnetic timetactors. (*Westinghouse Electric Corporation.*)

The timetactor has two coils, the "pickup" coil and the "neutralizing" coil, both wound on a copper tube to cause a delay in the change of flux in the magnet core. These coils oppose each other.

The pickup coils are energized to start. As the motor accelerates, the pickup circuit of the first relay is open and the magnetic flux in the relay decreases slowly with the aid of the neutralizing coil (see Fig. 18-3). After an interval of time, the relay armature is released and closes the first accelerating contactor. The time can be decreased by increasing the strength of the neutralizing coil. The pickup coil of the second relay is then opened to obtain the second accelerating step. This is repeated for all four relays of Fig. 18-40.

assume, the resistance in one phase is only half the value in the other two. The difference between the maximum and minimum currents in the secondary, however, is only 30 per cent. This is shown in Fig. 19-8. The normal full-load current in the secondary would take an intermittent value between the 100 per cent current in two of the phases and the 130 per cent current in the third phase. The actual full-load current corre-

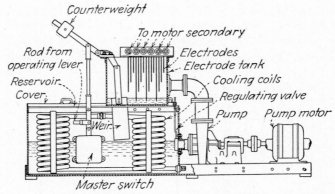

FIG. 19-4.   Liquid controller for large wound-secondary induction motors.

FIG. 19-5.   Front view of a large size of liquid controller.

sponding to this condition would be approximately 111 per cent, which represents an overload in one phase of 17 per cent. Switch No. 2 is now closed, giving a low resistance in two phases and a high resistance in one (see Fig. 19-9). Assuming that the low value of current is 100 per cent, the other two phases will have current of 150 per cent. The equivalent balanced current for this combination is 135 per cent, which represents an overload of approximately 11 per cent in two of the phases.

When switch No. 2 is closed, the currents in the three phases are balanced. Other values of resistance can be used and the analysis be worked out for each combination.

Unbalanced currents in the secondary cause the primary to draw a low-frequency current from the line. This is caused by the single-phase component of the secondary field. B. G. Lamme[1] has explained this very fully for the extreme case in which one phase of the secondary is open circuited.

The heating effect of the unbalanced currents in the secondary of the motor is distributed in proportion to the squares of these currents, the total heating being equal to the sum of the squares of the currents, thus $I_1{}^2 + I_2{}^2 + I_3{}^2$. In other words, the heating in the motor is distributed throughout the motor and the rating

Fig. 19-6. Side view of a large size of liquid controller.

of the motor is not limited by the maximum current in any one phase. These results have been verified by actual test. The secondary loss was found to be only 5 or 10 per cent higher unbalanced than balanced (see Table 19-1).

The rating of a motor of this type is dependent largely upon ventilation. When it is running at a slow speed, the fan action of the rotor is very much less than at full speed. This fan action varies as the square of the speed. The load that the motor carries depends to a considerable extent upon this fan action, and therefore, the temperature of the motor

[1] Lamme, B. G., *Elec. J.*, Vol. 12, p. 394.

TABLE 19-1. OPERATION OF 40-HP THREE-PHASE 60-CYCLE 220-VOLT INDUCTION MOTOR WITH VARIOUS VALUES OF EXTERNAL SECONDARY RESISTANCE

Resistance, ohms per leg			Primary volts			Primary amperes			Equivalent balanced primary amperes (rms)	Secondary amperes			Equivalent balanced secondary amperes (rms)	Speed, rpm	Pound-feet torque	Power factor
0.81	0.81	0.81	220	218	220	114.8	109.2	110.8	111.8	77.2	76.8	76	76.7	415	242	78.6
0.81	0.81	0.39	220	218	220	117.7	110	114	114	64.4	90.1	79.2	78.6	520	242	77.15
0.39	0.39	0.81	220	218	220	117	110	114	113.8	90.6	62.3	79.5	78.4	600	242	77.5
0.39	0.39	0.39	220	218	220	111.7	104	110	108.7	75.2	75.2	74.8	75.15	660	242	79.7
0.13	0.13	0.39	220	218	220	114	108	112	111.4	90.7	55.4	81.7	77.2	768	242	78.4
0.39	0.39	0.13	220	218	220	114	108	111	111.2	63	92.6	72.4	77.1	723	242	78.2

with a given torque will be much higher at a slow speed than at the high speed. The effect of this variation in speed is considerably greater than any effect due to unbalanced currents. In applying these motors, it is,

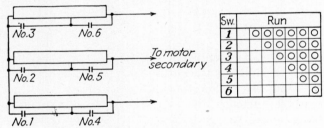

FIG. 19-7. Sequence of switches.

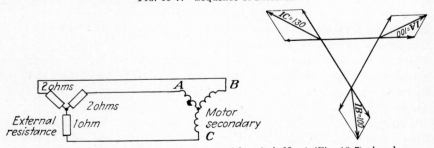

FIG. 19-8. Vector diagram of current with switch No. 1 (Fig. 19-7) closed.

therefore, necessary to limit their torque at slow speeds. This information can be obtained from the data furnished by the motor manufacturers.

Certain applications require a low initial starting torque. This can be very readily obtained by connecting the motor secondary in single phase, leaving one leg of the resistance open circuited. Under these conditions, the motor will exert a starting torque equivalent to approximately two-thirds of the torque that would be obtained with the same amount of resistance in each leg and all three legs in circuit. Since the first notch of the controller gives a relatively low torque, not much work is being done by the motor and it is entirely satisfactory to operate, single phase. This reduces the amount of resistance required. A standard controller can be connected as shown in the diagram in Fig. 19-10 to give a single-phase secondary operation on the first notch. If the resistance furnished with the motor gives half full-load torque with the secondary balanced on the first notch, the controller can be reconnected to start the

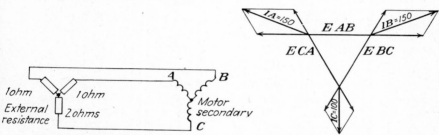

Fig. 19-9. Vector diagram of current with switch No. 2 (Fig. 19-7) closed.

motor single phase and obtain a starting torque of only 33 per cent of full-load torque. This is an easy way to adjust the starting torque where a low value of resistance is required, and it reduces the amount of resistance required for a given installation.

The speed-torque characteristics of a polyphase motor operating with a single-phase secondary winding are explained in Chap. 7 and illustrated in Fig. 7-9.

For motors of 200 hp and larger, the secondary control may consist of a liquid controller (see Fig. 19-4). Each phase of the secondary of the motor is connected to a series of iron plates. These iron plates extend down into a tank, which may be filled with an electrolyte, usually carbonate of soda and water. These plates are of different depths and so arranged that the number of plates, as well as the immersed area, increases as the water level rises. By the proper proportioning of these plates the desired acceleration can be obtained. In Fig. 19-4, the iron plates or electrolytes extend into the upper tank, while underneath is a larger tank used for storing and cooling the electrolyte. A centrifugal pump, driven by a small motor, lifts the electrolyte from the lower into the upper tank. A valve, or weir, in the upper tank can be adjusted to give any desired level and is operated by the same lever that operates the master switch. A master switch controls contactors in the primary of the motor. A movement of the operating lever in either direction first operates the master switch to close the primary circuit of the motor with a small amount of electrolyte in the upper tank. A further movement of the lever increases the height of this electrolyte until full speed of the motor

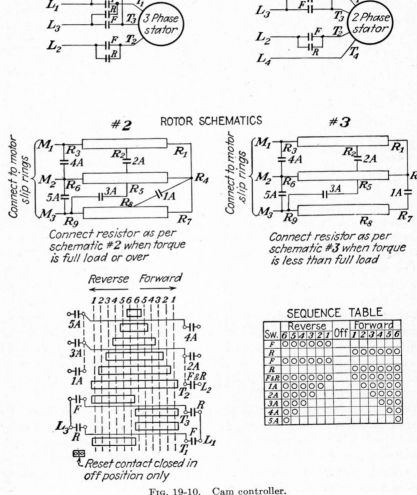

PRIMARY SCHEMATIC 3φ A.C. MOTOR

PRIMARY SCHEMATIC 2φ A.C. MOTOR

ROTOR SCHEMATICS

#2

Connect resistor as per schematic #2 when torque is full load or over

#3

Connect resistor as per schematic #3 when torque is less than full load

Reverse　Forward

Reset contact closed in off position only

SEQUENCE TABLE

Sw.	Reverse						Off	Forward					
	6	5	4	3	2	1		1	2	3	4	5	6
F	O	O	O	O	O	O							
R								O	O	O	O	O	O
F	O	O	O	O	O	O							
R								O	O	O	O	O	O
F&R	O	O	O	O	O	O			O	O	O	O	O	O
1A	O	O	O	O	O				O	O	O	O	O
2A	O	O	O	O						O	O	O	O
3A	O	O	O								O	O	O
4A	O	O										O	O
5A	O												O

FIG. 19-10.　Cam controller.

is obtained.   The pump has only a limited capacity, so that an appreciable time elapses between the movement of the weir and the increase in the height of the electrolyte; this time element can be adjusted so that the minimum period of acceleration is fixed at a safe value.   The weir is large enough to permit the electrolyte to discharge very rapidly, so that, when the lever is thrown quickly from the forward to the reverse direction, the electrolyte will be at approximately its minimum level when the primary switches are reversed.   The continual pumping of the electrolyte

a *b* *c*

FIG. 19-11.   Allen-Bradley full-voltage starter for a small squirrel-cage induction motor. Arranged for mounting in a plastered wall.   In *a*, the starter is mounted within its enclosure; *b*, the starter mechanism is on its mounting bracket; *c*, is the cover plate.

from the lower tank to the upper tank and the discharge through the weir cause a rapid circulation and dissipate the heat energy with a minimum amount of steaming.

The advantages of the liquid controller are (1) its simplicity, (2) its large thermal capacity, which enables it to sustain heavy overloads for short intervals of time, and (3) the absence of definite notches or steps, so that absolutely smooth acceleration is obtained.   In this country there has been little demand for this form of controller in small sizes, partly because of a prejudice against the use of liquid and partly because the other forms of controllers are usually cheaper for small motors.

SQUIRREL-CAGE MOTORS

Full-voltage Starters.   Many squirrel-cage motors are started by connecting the primary to the power supply without external current-limiting means.   Such starters consist of a three-pole magnet contactor (for three phase) operated by a push button.   Thermal overload relays are usually provided as they have enough time delay to remain closed during the starting period and yet be set low enough to protect the motor from con-

FIG. 19-12.   Westinghouse 100-amp Linestarter for a squirrel-cage induction motor. Unit assembly is on steel panel.   No back of panel wiring is necessary for "built-in" applications.

Solderless pressure-type terminals are compact and provide rapid means for making good tinuous overload. The branch-circuit protection takes care of short circuits. The motor current at start will be from four to six times full-load current, but it lasts only 1 or 2 sec. It drops rapidly as the motor speed increases. A momentary drop in voltage may affect the lights, but the drop will not be enough to be noticed where a substantial power supply is available.

Public-service companies limit the size of motor that can be started in this way from their network systems, depending upon the motor location. Motors are available that have reduced starting current at full voltage.

Fractional horsepower motors are started with a manual switch having a thermal overload trip. These motors are usually single phase. Motors of 1 hp and larger are usually three phase.

The current taken by an induction motor in starting can be limited

Fig. 19-13. General Electric magnetic a-c starter, CR7006, N.E.M.A. size 0, open type. Front view oblique from left, with two thermal relays (Fig. 23-6).

by placing resistance in series with the primary and using a short-circuited secondary. This form of secondary is commonly known as a squirrel-cage secondary and the motor is spoken of as a squirrel-cage motor. If resistance is used in series with the primary, the current will be reduced in proportion to the resistance inserted. The torque of the motor, however, will decrease as the square of the voltage across its terminals. This method of starting (see Fig. 19-18) is very simple and inexpensive and is

connections. Dual terminals on line side provide extra connection points for cross wiring between units when required.

No blowout effect is required with deion arc boxes of this design. The arc enters the grids of the arc box by magnetic attraction.

Arc box removed shows heavy-duty silver-alloy bridging-type contacts.

Bridging contacts require no shunts and permit "straight-through" wiring.

Large frictionless knife-edge- or seesaw-type bearing requires no lubrication. Bearing surfaces are hardened for long life.

Long contact springs. No appreciable change in contact pressure as contacts wear.

Disk-type bimetal provides positive snap action of overload relays.

Overload reset push rods are provided.

Quick-break silver contacts on overload relay.

Line and control terminals are all located to facilitate "straight-through" wiring and accessibility.

Electrical interlock with double-break silver contacts is a unit assembly that can be set for either normally open or normally closed operation.

Entire assembly installed in cabinet with three accessible mounting screws.

often used with small motors. There are a few applications for large motors that will require 90 per cent of normal voltage to start, where this form of starter would be more satisfactory than the transformer type. The maximum current is taken at the time the motor starts from rest,

a   *b*

FIG. 19-14. General Electric oil-immersed three-pole magnetic switch for use in corrosive atmospheres or exposed to the weather. This switch is provided with two overload relays (Figs. 23-7 and 23-8) and interlocks for low-voltage protection. It can be used as a full-voltage starter for squirrel-cage motors or as a line switch for any type of control. *a*, Tank lowered; *b*, tank raised in place.

and this current gradually decreases as the motor increases in speed, so that the voltage on the terminals of the motor will gradually increase, as the drop through the resistance is proportional to the current.

Autotransformer Starters. Many squirrel-cage induction motors are started by using a transformer to apply a reduced voltage to the primary of the motor. The advantage of a transformer over a resistor is that the reduced voltage is obtained with little or no loss in power, and therefore the current drawn from the line is less than the current taken by the motor in the ratio of the starting voltage to the line voltage. The connections commonly used for this type of starter are shown in Fig. 19-19. The transformer has only one winding and is usually called an "auto-transformer." The complete device is often called an "autostarter" or a "compensator."

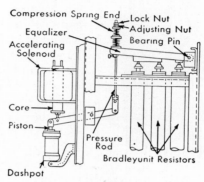

FIG. 19-15. FIG. 19-16.

FIG. 19-15. An oil-immersed push-button station enclosed in a cadmium-plated cast-iron case with wide metal-to-metal flanges between the oil tank and the top cover. The contacts, under oil, are operated by a lever and a shaft that extends through the case in a tight-fitting joint. Thus the station is suitable for use in highly corrosive atmospheres, and it is also weather resistant.

FIG. 19-16. Allen-Bradley accelerating solenoid, dashpot, pressure rod, and equalizing bar arrangement used on large squirrel-cage motor starters (Fig. 19-17).

The relative values of current in the different circuits during starting are shown on the diagram, not including losses in the transformer. These values of current are given merely to bring out the saving in power that results from this method of starting. The starting voltage is assumed to be 65 per cent of normal, which gives approximately 42 per cent of the torque that the motor would exert at standstill, if it were connected to full voltage. This starting torque of the motor at full voltage is usually from 150 to 200 per cent of full-load torque, so, at 65 per cent of line voltage, the starting torque would be from 65 to 85 per cent of full-load torque, which is sufficient to start most loads. Other taps are provided on the transformer so that the starting voltage may be adjusted.

Figure 19-20 shows a vector analysis of the voltage and current in one of the phases of an autotransformer starter assuming 80 per cent of line voltage applied to the motor terminals. The same analysis is given in Fig. 19-21 for a starter using resistance to reduce the voltage of the motor to 80 per cent of normal at the time of starting. These two figures show that, for the same starting conditions, the autotransformer starter takes about one-third of the power from the line and about 80 per cent of the current, when starting from rest. In both cases the wattless current is the same.

If 90 per cent of the line voltage is required to start the motor, there is very little use of employing a transformer for starting purposes. Such a condition usually indicates that the motor is not suitable for the particular application; either a wound-secondary motor should be used or a larger squirrel-cage motor. The starting torque of a squirrel-cage motor can be increased by increasing the secondary resistance. This, however, decreases the efficiency of the motor. Usually the secondary resistance of a squirrel-cage motor is adjusted by using different materials in the rings short-circuiting the secondary windings and is not adjustable after the motor is built. One method of increasing the starting torque of an existing motor is to saw slots in the short-circuiting rings between the connections to the winding bars. Where the motor is used for continuous operation and requires heavy starting torque, it is undesirable to use a high-resistance secondary; therefore the wound-secondary motor is preferable.

Fig. 19-17. Rear view of Allen-Bradley Company automatic two-step resistance starter intended for three-phase service showing the three Bradleyunit resistors. The desired resistance value is obtained by means of an adjusting screw and equalizing bar which operates the pressure plugs at the tops of the tubes (Fig. 16-21). Construction permits removal of the starter from the cabinet as a complete unit.

A commercial starter for small and medium-sized motors is shown in Fig. 19-22. The switch in the lower part of the case is immersed in oil. Above the switch is the transformer, and in front of the transformer is located the overload protection. In the Off position

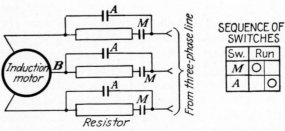

Fig. 19-18.   Connections for starting a squirrel-cage motor by series resistance.

the handle stands central. To start the motor, the handle is moved in the direction that closes the contacts marked *MS* in Fig. 19-19. After the motor has accelerated to approximately full speed, the handle is moved in the opposite direction and the contacts, which are marked *MR*, are closed. The handle is held in this position by a small magnet called the "low-voltage coil," which releases the handle on the failure of voltage and

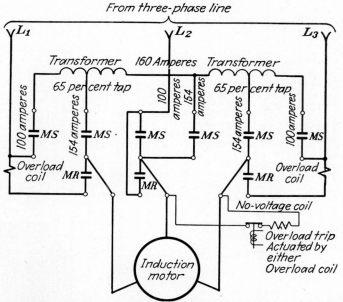

FIG. 19-19. Connections for starting a squirrel-cage motor by an autotransformer starter. In the starting position contacts *MS* are closed. In the running position contacts *MS* are open and contacts *MR* are closed. The amperage given is for the starting position only and is merely relative. The no-voltage coil serves to hold the handle in the running position against the action of a spring that returns it to the Off position if the voltage is interrupted or reduced below a certain value. Either one of the overload coils will interrupt the circuit of this no-voltage coil.

allows it to return to the Off position. A latch is usually provided to prevent the operator from accidentally throwing the handle into the running position first.

In passing from the starting to the running position with this arrangement, it is necessary to open the connections, so that the motor will not be connected to the starting tap on the transformer and at the same time connected to the line, as this would short-circuit a section of the transformer and probably destroy it. In starting large motors, it is often desirable to pass from the starting to the running position without opening the motor circuit. This may be done by using a resistance connected as in Fig. 19-23. This resistance is inserted between the starting tap and the

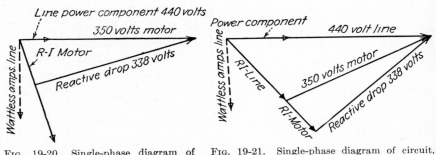

FIG. 19-20. Single-phase diagram of circuit with autotransformer for starting to give 80 per cent of line voltage at the motor terminals, rotor-locked conditions.

Motor characteristics: resistance 0.9 ohm, reactance 3.2 ohms, impedance 3.32 ohms. Wattless current 80 amp, power taken from the line 10 kw, line current 84 amp.

FIG. 19-21. Single-phase diagram of circuit, with resistance for starting, to give 80 per cent of line voltage at the motor terminals, rotor-locked conditions.

Motor resistance characteristics: resistance total 2.68 ohms, reactance 3.20 ohms, impedance 4.18 ohms. Power taken from the line 29.6 kw, wattless current 80 amp, line current 105 amp.

The diagrams show the advantage of using a transformer instead of a resistance for squirrel-cage motor starting. A similar diagram with 65 per cent of line voltage at the motor terminals shows that the power taken from the line is nearly five times that taken with an autotransformer and the current 30 per cent greater. The transformer characteristics are neglected in the above analysis.

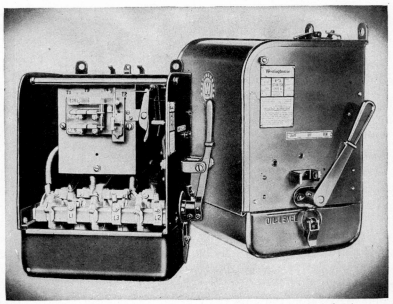

FIG. 19-22.   Westinghouse autotransformer starter for squirrel-cage induction motors.

line to prevent short-circuiting the transformer at the time the connections are changed. In this arrangement the contacts marked 1A represent the starting connections. They are not opened until after contacts 2A are closed.

Where several starting steps are used, the arrangement shown in Fig. 19-24 may be made. This makes use of a small autotransformer, the

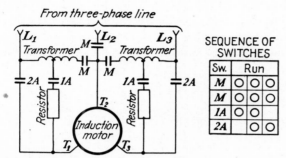

Sw.	Run		
M	O	O	O
M	O	O	O
1A	O	O	
2A		O	O

FIG. 19-23. Connections of autotransformer starter with resistor to obviate opening the circuit when changing from the starting to the running position.

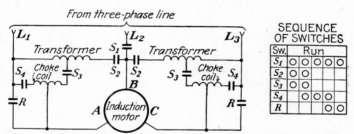

Sw.	Run				
S_1	O	O	O	O	O
S_2	O	O			
S_3	O	O			
S_4			O	O	O
R				O	O

FIG. 19-24. Connections for multipoint starting with an autotransformer to obviate opening the circuit when changing from the starting to the running position.

center of which is connected to the motor load. After the autotransformer is energized, contact S_3 of this auxiliary coil is connected to the starting tap. One-half of the coil then acts as a choke coil and gives the minimum starting voltage. When contact S_4 is closed, an intermediate voltage is obtained. Contact S_3 is then opened and R is closed, which connects the motor directly to the line, giving the final step in starting. This method makes a very simple set of connections for a magnetic-contactor starter where a multipoint starter is required.

A modification of this arrangement is shown in Fig. 19-25. This arrangement is similar to that of Fig. 19-19 but the switches are operated in a different manner. The contacts marked S1, S2, and S3 are first closed. This gives the same connection as closing contacts MS in Fig. 19-19. If contacts S2 are now opened, one end of each autotransformer is disconnected from the line and the motor is left across the line with a part of the transformer winding in series, which acts as a choke coil. Switch R is immediately closed, connecting the motor to the line. This short-circuits a section of the transformer but, since the winding is not energized, no harm results. Switch $S3$ is now opened, disconnecting the motor from the transformer.

Disconnecting the primary of an induction motor from the line when passing from the starting point to the running position makes very little difference with small motors. With large motors, however, in special cases, it may cause surges of current and voltage.[1] These surges are more

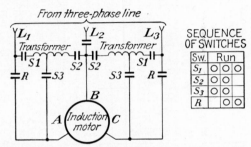

FIG. 19-25.   Modified method of producing multipoint starting with an autotransformer with open-circuit transition.

likely to occur in high-speed than in slow-speed motors. They depend, however, upon the characteristics of the motor and can readily be taken care of by the manufacturer when he furnishes the motor and the starter as a combined unit.

The distribution of current within the windings of an autotransformer starter is somewhat involved, but an approximate analysis omitting minor factors is interesting and explains certain features that are not apparent without such an analysis. We shall first consider the exciting current, or "magnetizing" current, as it is sometimes called. It is composed of two principal items, the magnetizing current, which is a zero power-factor current, and the iron-loss current, which is a 100 per cent power-factor current. These two elements give a resulting current, which is called the "exciting" current and which may have a power factor as high as the power factor of the induction motor when it is connected to the line and the rotor is stationary.

By referring to Fig. 19-26 it will be noted that the exciting current in the longer section of the autotransformer tends to flow in opposition to

[1] This is brought out in Hellmund's paper, Transient Conditions in Asynchronous Induction Machines and Their Relation to Control Problems, *Proc. A.I.E.E.*, February, 1917.

the motor-load current. Since these two currents have power factors that are not far apart, the motor current neutralizes this magnetizing current, and it is possible so to proportion the motor-load current that there will be very little current or I^2R loss in the larger part of the transformer windings. This condition in only approximated, as the motor current is not exactly in phase with the exciting current. It illustrates, however, the fact that the magnetizing current actually reduces the I^2R

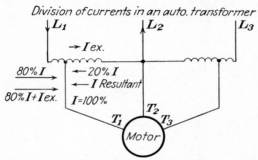

Fig. 19-26. How the exciting current cancels out the load current in the larger part of the autotransformer winding. (I is load current. Iex is excitation current of the transformer.) The load current represented as 100 per cent divides in proportion to the tap ratio. In the case shown with the 80 per cent tap, 20 per cent of the load current tends to flow through the large number of turns and 80 per cent through the small number of turns. The exciting current and the load current in the large number of turns oppose. During starting, when the power factor of these currents is approximately equal, they subtract almost directly. The net resultant current, therefore, in the large number of turns is small and the consequent heating effect even smaller, since the heating varies as the square of the current. These currents add in the small number of turns, but since this is a heavy winding designed to carry load current, the additional heating effect is small. The same effect takes place if the autotransformer is connected on the 65 per cent tap.

loss in the larger part of the transformer windings. The two currents add in the small end of the transformer winding so that, as the starting voltage is decreased, the effect of this magnetizing current becomes more and more apparent. The current taken by the motor, however, decreases with the decreasing voltage, so that one effect offsets the other to a considerable extent.

The distribution of current in an autotransformer during the starting of the motor is further illustrated by Figs. 19-27 and 19-28. We shall assume that the autotransformer starter has been designed for a 30-hp three-phase 440-volt motor and that the rms current of this motor per phase during acceleration is 82 amp when connected to 65 per cent of normal voltage (see Fig. 19-27). We shall also assume that the exciting current of the transformer is 22 amp. The motor current is divided between section a and b of the transformer, as follows: section a, 53 amp and section b, 29 amp. In section a, the two currents add, making a total of 53 plus 22, or 75 amp.   In section *b* of the transformer the currents subtract, making a total of 29 minus 22, or 7 amp.   Since section *b* represents 65 per cent of the total winding, it is seen that the total heating in the transformer is reduced by the exciting current.   If the motor is connected to the 80 per cent tap (Fig. 19-28), the heating in the transformer will be still less, although the motor current is greater.   This is

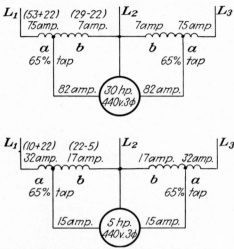

FIG. 19-27. A 30-hp autotransformer starter connected to 65 per cent of the normal voltage.   The distribution of current during the starting period is based on the rms value of the motor current during acceleration.   It is assumed that the exciting current is 22 amp and approximately in phase with the motor current.   This assumption is not strictly correct, as the phase angles of the various components of the current are unsymmetrical and the current values do not add or subtract directly.   The current components also differ in each of the two phases.   The diagram is made approximately correct for purposes of illustration and, therefore, does not take into account the minor differences enumerated above.

because section *a*, which carries the extra current, is only 20 instead of 35 per cent of the total winding space.   This point has been demonstrated by actual tests.

Let us now assume that the 30-hp starter was used for starting a 5-hp motor, three-phase and 440-volt.   The full-load current of this motor is approximately 15 amp when connected to 65 per cent of normal voltage. This motor current is distributed in the transformer windings as follows: section *a*, 10 amp and section *b*, 5 amp.   We assumed above that the exciting current was 22 amp.   The total current in section *a* will, therefore, be 10 plus 22, or a total of 32 amp, as compared with 75 amp for the 30-hp motor.   The current in section *b* will be 22 amp minus 5, or 17 amp total as compared with 7 amp for the 30-hp motor.   The heating effect of the current in section *b* is, therefore, about six times as great for the 5-hp motor as for the 30-hp motor. If the 5-hp motor is connected to the 80 per cent tap, the difference will be still greater.

These two examples show that a large starter used on a small motor may heat up more than it will if used with the motor for which it is designed. The two previous examples are exaggerated and the currents do not cancel to the full extent shown, because of the differences in phase angles, as the examples are simplified to make them easy to follow. In making applications of starters to smaller motors, care must be exercised.

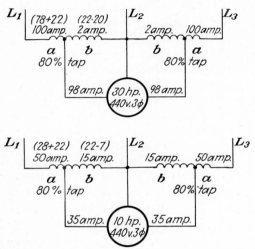

Fig. 19-28. A 30-hp autotransformer starter connected to 80 per cent of the normal voltage. The distribution of current during the starting period based on the rms value of the motor current during acceleration. It is assumed that the exciting current is 22 amp and approximately in phase with the motor current. This assumption is not strictly correct, as the phase angles of the various components of the current are unsymmetrical and the current values do not add or subtract directly. The current components also differ in each of the two phases. The diagram is made for purposes of illustration and is, therefore, only approximately correct and does not take into account the minor differences enumerated above.

It is evident that, if the exciting current were zero or had a very small value, an advantage would be gained by using a large starter with a small motor in the same way that a resistor will heat up less with a small motor than with a large one. This, however, makes a very poor transformer when used with a motor to the full horsepower rating. The exciting current should be made high enough to reduce materially the heating on the 65 or the 80 per cent tap.

From time to time, someone measures the exciting current of an autotransformer starter at no load and is surprised to find it quite large. This is true, and the heating effect will naturally be considerable if it is left on long enough. If this test is carried a little further and the motor is connected to the circuit with its secondary locked in a stationary position and the input current both from the line and in the motor is accurately measured, it will be found that, by decreasing the motor current in the ratio of the transformation and subtracting this from the total input current, the magnetizing current has added in many cases less than 5 per cent to the total current. This is true of the 65 per cent tap. If these tests are now repeated on the 80 per cent tap, the increase in the total current on account of the magnetizing current will be found to be still less.

Another way to analyze the problem is to consider that the magnetizing current taken by the motor is fixed for a given voltage. The autotransformer furnishes this magnetizing current to the motor. If we consider the section of the transformer between the motor terminals, we shall find that the magnetizing current required by the transformer is approximately 180 deg out of phase relation with the magnetizing current taken by the motor. This results in the magnetizing current of the one canceling that of the other. If these magnetizing currents are equal, there will only be a small flow of current in this section of the transformer resulting from a difference of phase relation between the currents.

The section of the transformer winding between the motor terminals and the line and designated as section a in Figs. 19-27 and 19-28 has a magnetizing current flow through its windings that is not neutralized by the magnetizing current of the motor. The two magnetizing currents add vectorially and tend to heat these windings, owing to the I^2R loss. If the resistance of this portion of the winding is kept low, the actual wattage loss is also low, this being only a question of design.

Let us now consider the current taken from the line. This is made up of two components, one the energy component and the other the magnetizing component. If the magnetizing current of the motor subtracts from the magnetizing current of the transformer in section b (the long section), the heating effect in this section is comparatively small. By proper designing of the short section of the transformer winding (section a) so as to keep down the I^2R loss therein, the total loss in the complete transformer can be made quite low. This condition is obtained by having the transformer exciting current approximately equivalent to the exciting current of the motor, and it holds good for only one particular size and design of motor. In the designing of commercial autotransformers, it is necessary to select a certain range of motor sizes and speeds and to select a motor-magnetizing current that represents the average value and then to make the magnetizing current of the transformer equal to this value. The windings of the transformer must be proportioned for the worst condition, which is obtained in section a of the winding when the largest motor is being used and in section b of the transformer winding when the difference between the motor-magnetizing current and the transformer-magnetizing current is a maximum. An additional allowance must also be made for small differences in phase angles.

It will be seen from the above that the exciting current of a properly designed autotransformer for intermittent starting should be much larger than that for power transformers. This excess magnetizing current will overheat section *b* of the transformer winding if it is left on for any considerable length of time without the motor load, because there is no cancellation of current in this section of the transformer winding.

The exciting current varies with the voltage and the frequency. Each time the magnetism in the iron reverses, it generates a voltage in the transformer windings. The product of this magnetism multiplied by the number of turns in the coil multiplied by the frequency must balance the line voltage. Since the number of turns in the coil has a fixed value for a particular design, an increase in voltage at a constant frequency would require a corresponding increase in magnetism in order to balance this increased line voltage. If the voltage remains constant and the frequency decreases, an increase in magnetism would be required to make the product constant. When the iron in the autotransformer is worked pretty hard, as is the case in the starting transformers, an increase in magnetism requires a considerable increase in exciting current, the iron loss going up quite rapidly at this part of the magnetization curve. Therefore, any unusual increase in voltage or decrease in frequency will cause a proportionally larger increase in the exciting current. Standard autotransformers are designed and guaranteed to operate successfully on 10 per cent variation in the line voltage, provided that the frequency remains constant. The converse is also true; *viz.*, if the line voltage remains constant, the frequency may vary 10 per cent. This, however, is a rather unusual condition.

The torque of an induction motor varies as the square of the voltage. It is usual to express the starting characteristic of an induction motor by stating that it has a certain locked torque. This is the torque exerted when the rotor is stationary and normal voltage is applied to the primary windings. This torque is usually expressed in terms of the full-load torque. Thus, a motor having a locked torque of two means that the torque at zero speed is equal to twice full-load torque with normal voltage on the primary. If 70 per cent of voltage were applied to the motor primary, the motor would exert a torque equivalent to 2 multiplied by $(\frac{7}{10})^2$, or 98 per cent of full-load torque. The torque at any other starting voltage can be obtained by expressing this voltage in percentage, squaring it, and multiplying by the locked torque given in per cent of full-load torque.

This starting torque is independent of the method employed for obtaining the reduced voltage. Sometimes the claim is made that a certain motor will start with one style of starter and not with another, the inference being that the starters have different effects on the starting torque of the motor. This is true only if the starters provide different voltages at the motor terminals. The taps on an autotransformer are usually expressed in percentage of full voltage. These percentage ratios are not exact, as it is necessary to compensate for the voltage drop through the transformer. This compensation differs with different motors, owing to the variation in the starting current. It is, therefore, improbable that two different makes of autotransformers would give exactly the same voltage at the motor terminals; this is probably the explanation of the failure of one type to start the motor, while the other was successful. The difference in voltage may seem trivial, but it must be remembered that this difference is squared and that a little extra torque may be all that was required to break the load from the static position and allow the motor to start rotating. As soon as the motor commences to rotate, the friction decreases and the torque of the motor gradually increases, so that the critical period is the instant of starting from rest. Sometimes the torque of a motor varies slightly when starting from rest, depending upon the location of the rotor slots relative to the primary winding. While this variation of starting torque is usually quite small, it may be appreciable in particular motors and, therefore, should be taken into consideration in comparing starters.

The starting voltage can be adjusted by changing the starting connection from one transformer tap to another. When the transformers provide 65 and 80 per cent taps, they give 42 and 64 per cent locked torque of the motor on starting.

Where intermediate values of starting torque are necessary, they can be obtained by connecting one starting lead to the next higher starting tap; for instance, if one side is connected to the 65 per cent tap and the other side to the 80 per cent tap, an intermediate value of starting torque will be obtained with an intermediate value of power input. Connections of this kind unbalance the phase so that more current is taken from one phase than from the other. The amount of this unbalancing, however, is considerably less than the difference in voltages after the motor begins to revolve. In no case is the current taken from either phase greater than would be taken if both leads were connected to the higher voltage. Table 19-2 gives the results of a test made with both balanced and unbalanced connection and shows the torques and voltages at the motor terminals.

The use of two autotransformers in a V connection for starting three-phase motors is sometimes criticized, on the ground that it produces

TABLE 19-2. TEST ON A 100-HP 220-VOLT 60-CYCLE THREE-PHASE MOTOR WITH A
TYPE A AUTOSTARTER, SHOWING VOLTAGES AND STARTING TORQUES OF THE
MOTOR WITH BALANCED AND UNBALANCED TAP CONNECTIONS
Test on 65% tap, motor locked

	Line volts		Volts at motor terminals	Motor torque
	No load	With load		
L_1-L_3	230	199	118.5	
L_2-L_3	229	196	120	278 lb-ft
L_1-L_2	229	194	122	

Test with one winding connected on the 65% tap and the other on the 80% tap

L_1-L_2	229	190	130	
L_2-L_3	229	184	141	340 lb-ft
L_1-L_2	229	193	121	

Test with 80% tap

L_1-L_2	229	188	141	
L_2-L_3	229	185	139	410 lb-ft
L_1-L_2	229	188	141	

These tests show that the transformers in V connection give nearly balanced voltages with unbalanced taps. The starting torque obtained with unbalanced taps is approximately the average of the two torques that would be obtained with either balanced connection.

TABLE 19-3. COMPARATIVE TEST ON A THREE-PHASE 60-CYCLE SIX-POLE SQUIRREL-
CAGE MOTOR SHOWING STARTING TORQUE WITH AUTOTRANSFORMERS IN OPEN V
AND IN Y, 100% OF RATED VOLTAGE APPLIED TO TRANSFORMER WINDINGS

Motor torque	Three transformers in Y connection	Two transformers in open V connection
At 65% voltage	33.5% of locked torque	33.1% of locked torque
	34.3% of locked torque	34.0% of locked torque
At 80% voltage	52.0% of locked torque	51.7% of locked torque
	52.4% of locked torque	52.2% of locked torque

unbalanced voltages at the motor terminals and, therefore, decreases the starting torque of the motor. The tests in Tables 19-2 and 19-3 show that there is very little unbalancing and that the amount is negligible. The torque exerted by the motor in starting from rest is practically the same as with the three-transformer arrangement. The variations in the starting torque exerted by different motors of the same design, because of irregularity of manufacture, are considerably greater than the effect of slight unbalancing.

The National Electrical Manufacturers Association has agreed that the standard starting period for "medium duty" manually operated autotransformer starters shall be 15 sec. This is simply an arbitrary designation and means nothing unless a careful study is made of the effects of starting on the transformer. It does not mean that, if the starting period exceeds 15 sec for one start, the transformer will be injured.

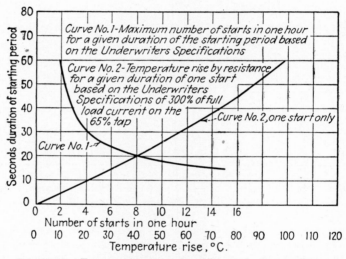

Fig. 19-29.   Temperature rise under different starting conditions.

See the National Electrical Manufactures standards for other applications.

It should not be assumed that a commercial starter can be applied where it is necessary to start as frequently as is indicated by this test. Standard starters may be used for accelerating motors where the starting period is approximately 15 sec, and not over six or eight starts are made without allowing the transformers to cool down to the room temperature. Several starts of a longer period, even as long as 30 sec, can be made if the transformer is cold and the starts are not repeated too often.   The curve in Fig. 19-29 indicates the relative increase in temperature under different starting conditions.

Many starters can be used on other voltages and frequencies than those for which they are rated; but, in making such interchanges, it should be remembered that we have three elements to consider:

1. The autotransformer.
2. The low-voltage coil.
3. The overload relay.

The low-voltage coil is independent of the size of the motor, but it is sensitive to changes in voltage or frequency, as the excess voltage will cause it to overheat and on a low voltage it will fail to hold. When there is a decrease in voltage together with a decrease in frequency, these will counterbalance each other. For instance, a 550-volt 60-cycle coil operates successfully on a 460-volt 50-cycle circuit.

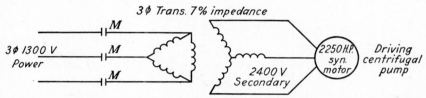

FIG. 19-30. Diagram of pump motor control, Queen Lane Pumping Station, Philadelphia, Pa. Vector diagram Fig. 19-31. This impedance starter eliminates the two secondary switches required for reduced voltage starting.

The autotransformers should not be used on voltages more than 10 per cent in excess of the normal rating, but they may be used for any voltage of less value, provided that the current of the motor does not exceed the normal value for that particular transformer. For instance, the 30-hp 440-volt autostarter can be used with a 15-hp 220-volt motor by changing the low-voltage coil. It is obvious that, if the current value is kept the same, the overload relay will not be affected. If the frequency is decreased, the voltage should also be decreased; for example, the 550-volt 60-cycle transformer can be used on a 440-volt 50-cycle circuit for a motor that is smaller than the rating of the transformer proportionally to the decrease in voltage.

If the frequency is above normal, as in the case of a 25-cycle starter being used on a 40-cycle circuit, the transformer will still be satisfactory; and if the size of the motor is kept the same, the same starter can be used by changing the low-voltage coil. The low-voltage magnet is provided with a brass shading coil for 60-cycle and a copper shading coil for 25-cycle circuits, so that a change in frequency over this range may require a change in the shading coil if the best results are to be obtained.

Automatic acceleration for a-c controllers at present is usually limited to the series-relay method or a time-element method. The time-element method is very satisfactory where the timing device can be relied upon. For rapid acceleration and reversing service, the series-relay method is very good.

Impedance Starters.   Impedance in series with the primary windings of an induction motor when it is started from rest has its maximum effect in limiting the initial starting current as shown by Fig. 19-31.   Let A represent the value of this impedance in phase with OY, which has 90-deg lag from the voltage line OX.   The line OM is the phase angle of the motor current at starting.   The distance OY is the amount of impedance effective in limiting the starting current of the motor.   As the motor accelerates, its power factor increases and the effect of the impedance A decreases to the valve C when the motor is synchronized.   Assume a starting current of four times full-load current.   As the speed increases,

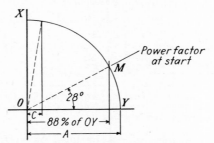

Fɪɢ. 19-31. Vector diagram of impedance starter.

the current decreases and the power factor increases, so the voltage drop due to impedance becomes very small.   This indicates that reactance has much less effect on voltage drop in the motor circuit at full speed.   If resistance is inserted in the primary circuit to limit the starting current, its effect will be just the opposite.   It will be least effective in starting and most effective at full speed.   This is why primary resistor starters are less desirable for induction motors.

When the transformer load is a single synchronous motor, the effect of its impedance in limiting the motor starting current is as follows:

Assume: Locked amperes = 5 × full-load current
          Locked torque = 60 per cent of full-load torque
          Locked power factor = 28 per cent
          Transformer impedance = 7 per cent

At 28 per cent, power factor in starting the effective impedance of the transformer is the cosine of 28 deg or 88 per cent.

88 per cent of 7 per cent = 6 per cent approximately

The voltage at the motor terminals when starting from rest is

100 per cent − (5 × full-load current × 6 per cent impedance)

= 100 per cent − 30 per cent = 70 per cent of full voltage

Starting current = 5 × full load × 70 per cent

= 3.5 per cent of full-load current

Starting torque = 60 per cent of full-load torque × $(70)^2$

= about 30 per cent of full-load torque

This starting torque will be sufficient to start a fan or centrifugal pump. When this motor is only half the transformer load, the transformer imped-ance will have only one-half of the above effect.

The first use of this method of starting synchronous motors was prob-ably the senior author's design of the control equipment for some 2,250-hp 2,200-volt three-phase synchronous motors driving centrifugal pumps in the Queen Lane pumping station in Philadelphia in 1946.

Impedance coils can be inserted in the primary circuit to the motor instead of resistors, as shown in Fig. 19-18, and short-circuited when the motor reaches full speed. This method is desirable for larger motors.

Power service is increasing in capacity very rapidly, which permits larger motors to be started at full voltage. Synchronous motors are replacing the larger size of induction motors. They start like squirrel-cage induction motors and have means for synchronizing when they reach full speed. They correct the power factor, which reduces the cost of power.

CHAPTER 20

SYNCHRONOUS-MOTOR CONTROL

Synchronous motors are used because they can correct the power factor, as well as drive machinery. The synchronous generator is one of the oldest forms of electric machinery and is fully described in textbooks and well understood by electrical engineers. The synchronous-motor construction is identical with and has the same characteristics as the generator, except that the operation is reversed. Alternating-current electric power is supplied to the primary of the synchronous motor and converted into mechanical work by the rotation of the motor. Power-factor correction is obtained by adjusting the strength of the d-c field. A separate source of power is required for furnishing the d-c supply to the field.

METHODS OF STARTING SYNCHRONOUS MOTORS

More care is required in starting a synchronous motor than an induction motor because the former must be brought into synchronism with the a-c supply circuit. During the starting period it is usually necessary to manipulate the field and other circuits and it is, therefore, safer and better to use an automatic controller than a manual controller.

The torque required for starting the motor from rest and bringing it up to synchronous speed is obtained by means of damper windings, which function in the same manner as the secondary of a squirrel-cage induction motor. The primary is connected to the source of supply at full voltage or at a reduced voltage by means of an autotransformer. The primary winding develops a rotating magnetic field, which induces a current in the damper windings. The reaction between these windings exerts a torque that accelerates the motor. The damper windings are useful for obtaining stable operation of the motor after it has been synchronized; they eliminate hunting, or a tendency for the speed of the motor to oscillate above or below synchronism.

The starting torque of these motors is approximately the same as that of a standard induction motor having the same number of poles. It is practicable to build synchronous motors for much lower speeds than induction motors. Increasing the number of poles of synchronous motors increases the size for given horsepower ratings but does not introduce any

326

serious difficulties in the electrical design. On the other hand, a large number of poles in the primary of an induction motor causes excessive leakage and poor power factor. For this reason, low-speed motors are usually of the synchronous type. The starting torque of the low-speed synchronous motor is low, on account of the large number of poles required to give low-speed operation. Four- or six-pole synchronous motors will exert considerable torque at starting.

The torque limitations of a synchronous motor occur as the motor approaches synchronous speed. An induction motor operates at several per cent below synchronism, the difference in speed, or the slip, of the motor generating a sufficient voltage in the secondary to circulate the current necessary to develop the torque required by the load. When the synchronous motor reaches 2 or 3 per cent of synchronous speed, the torque necessary for pulling the motor into synchronism is obtained by energizing the d-c field magnets. These magnets react on the primary and develop an oscillating torque. This torque is positive during most of the cycle, the period of negative torque being short. The closer the motor is to synchronous speed, the longer is the period of positive torque. This oscillating torque swings the rotor into synchronism and locks it in at this speed.

If full field strength is applied when the motor is running at too low a speed, the proportion of negative torque will be much larger and may be sufficient to prevent the motor from accelerating to full speed. When a direct-connected exciter is used, it may be practicable to close the circuit of the field windings through this exciter when the synchronous motor starts from rest, if the starting load is light, as the d-c machine is self-excited and does not build up its normal voltage until the motor has approached full speed.

The method of handling the field circuit of the synchronous motor differs for motors of different designs. In order to obtain the best results, it is necessary to cooperate with the motor designer and select the arrangement of field circuits that will give the best results.

When the primary, or stator, is connected to the line and the secondary, or rotor, is stationary, a 60-cycle rotating magnetic field is set up in the rotor. This causes current to flow in the grids or damper windings on each pole face, which exerts a torque to start the motor and accelerate it in the same manner as an induction motor. It also induces a voltage in the field windings, which should have the circuit closed through a resistor to prevent the development of an excessive voltage in these windings. At start, as in an induction motor, the current will be heavy, the power factor and the impedance low, and the rotor frequency the same as the primary. The current decreases, the impedance and the power factor increase, and the secondary frequency decreases with increase in speed. At 90 per cent of speed, the current drops rapidly and the impedance increases inversely as the current. The secondary frequency decreases to zero at synchronous speed.

The motor pulls into synchronism when unlike poles of the primary and field windings are opposite each other; therefore, the least power dis-

turbance is caused if the d-c field is built up as the unlike poles approach each other. The change in field frequency, primary current, or primary impedance is used by different manufacturers to initiate the closing of the field circuit. It is desirable to accelerate the motor to its maximum speed as an induction motor before energizing the field in order to keep down the momentary primary-current increase that occurs at this time. This maximum speed depends upon the motor load, which will be different from time to time. The controller should delay closing the field circuit until the motor has accelerated as far as possible (probably 2 or 3 per cent of synchronous speed) but should connect the field as soon as the motor has reached a balancing speed. Automatic means for doing this at the right speed and when unlike poles are approaching will be described.

The smaller motors, particularly the slow-speed ones, can be started with a light load at full line voltage

Fig. 20-1. Westinghouse synchronous motor controller, using the definite time method of acceleration.

and with very simple means for closing the field circuit. When the line disturbances must be kept to a minimum, an exact method for energizing the field and for obtaining reduced voltage starting or starting on a part winding of the motor must be used. A relay responsive to primary current can be used to transfer the primary windings from the starting control to the device for establishing running connections, as the current drops rapidly above about 90 per cent of speed.

The reduced-voltage methods for starting induction motors explained in Chap. 19 can be used, or the part-winding method (see Fig. 20-8) can be applied to motors having this type of winding. Some of the methods for automatically energizing the d-c field windings will now be described.

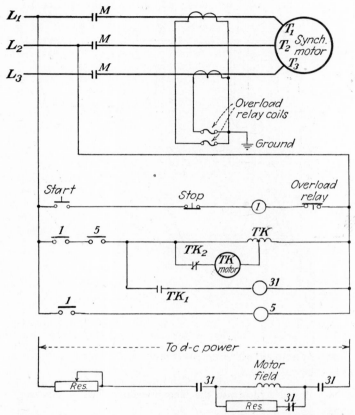

FIG. 20-2. The time-delay synchronous motor controller. The Start button closes switch No. 1, which closes switch No. 5 and starts the synchronous motor TK. After a fixed time, TK_1 closes, which closes switch No. 31 and energizes the d-c motor field. TK_2 then opens and stops motor TK. Power-factor relay and instruments have been omitted from the diagram to make the motor connections easier to follow.

The Field-frequency Method. When the motor is at rest and the field circuit is closed upon itself through a resistor, the rotating field set up by the primary of the motor will cause an alternating current to flow in the closed field circuit, owing to transformer action. When the rotor is at rest, the frequency in the field circuit will be the same as the line frequency. As the motor increases in speed, the frequency of the field circuit decreases but the maximum current remains substantially constant.   As soon as the rotor reaches 2 or 3 per cent of synchronous speed, the current in the field circuit drops very abruptly, as is shown in Fig. 20-3 and can be used to operate automatic means for changing the motor connections from starting to running.

The Electric Machinery Manufacturing Company[1] uses a polarized field-frequency relay (see Fig. 20-3), which operates on the drop in field

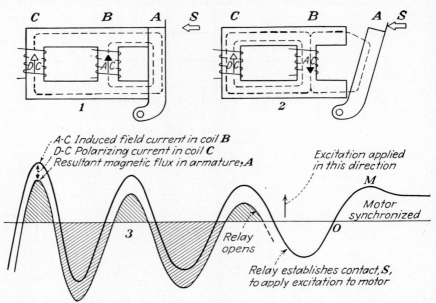

Fig. 20-3.   Operation of the field-frequency relay used by the Electric Machinery Manufacturing Company for accelerating synchronous motors (see Fig. 20-4 for wiring diagram).

current when synchronism is nearly reached.   They describe the operation of this relay as follows:

In Fig. 20-3, 1 and 2 illustrate the magnetic fluxes in the polarized field-frequency relay.

In 1, when the induced field current in coil B flows in one direction, the flux of this coil opposes the flux d-c coil C to force the combined strong resultant flux through the armature A of the relay.   This condition is that which occurs during the lower shaded loops of 3.   In 2, when the induced field current in coil B is reversed, the flux of coil B combines with that of coil C so that the resultant flux through relay armature A is relatively weak, as shown by the smaller upper shaded loops of 3.

The effect of the d-c polarizing coil C of the relay, therefore, is to make the

[1] Recently both General Electric Company and Westinghouse Electric Corporation have developed similar systems of control, as the patents on this system have expired. The older systems are retained in this book, as they cover many existing installations.

magnetic flux in the relay armature A unsymmetrical with respect to the zero line of the induced-field-current wave. Thus the relay armature cannot open in the portion of the induced-field-current wave spanned by the large lower loops of relay-armature flux. The relay armature will open only in the portion of the induced-field-current wave spanned by the small upper loops of relay armature flux.

The induced field current in relay coil B decreases in amplitude as the motor reaches synchronizing speed, and an upper shaded loop of relay armature flux is reached as is shown in 3, where the relay armature A will no longer stay closed. The relay then drops open to establish contact S to apply excitation to the motor field at the point indicated on the induced-field-current wave.

The time of opening of the relay depends partly on the retarding pull of the relay flux. When set to open at lower synchronizing speeds (92 to 94 per cent) an air gap between the armature and the core causes the relay to open more quickly than when set to open at higher speeds with less relay air gap. Hence the field contactor always closes at the same favorable point on the induced-field-current wave.

The excitation is applied in the direction shown by the arrow, opposite in polarity to that of the induced field current at the point of application. This is done to compensate for the time required to build up excitation caused by the magnetic inertia of the motor-field winding. The inertia is such that the d-c excitation does not become appreciably effective until the induced current has reversed at O, in 3, to the same polarity as the direct current. The excitation continues to build up, synchronizing the motor at M, which represents the approximate normal relative positions of the rotor and stator poles of the motor when running in synchronism.

During starting, a current, induced in the field winding of the synchronous motor (Fig. 20-4) and declining in frequency as the motor accelerates, flows through the field-discharge resistor, the reactor, and coil B of the polarized field-frequency relay. The magnetic core of the relay has a d-c coil on leg C, an induced-field-current coil on leg B, and a pivoted armature A with contact S. Coil C connected to the source of d-c excitation establishes a constant magnetic flux in the relay core that polarizes the relay. Superimposed on the magnetic flux in the relay core, caused by d-c coil C, is the alternating magnetic flux produced by the alternating induced-field current flowing in coil B. The armature A thus carries the sum of the two fluxes produced by coils B and C on one-half cycle of alternating induced-field current, and a much smaller amount of flux on the other half cycle.

At the moment of starting the motor, the relay armature A snaps to the closed position shown in Fig. 20-4, opening the contact S. Up to the synchronizing speed of the motor the flux through the armature of the relay is enough to keep the armature closed. The reason for this is that the reactor across which coil B is shunted has a relatively high voltage drop, whereas the reactance of relay coil C is relatively low. Hence at all except very low frequencies of the induced-field current enough current will flow through relay coil C to hold the relay armature closed. As the motor accelerates, however, the induced field current declines in frequency and an increasingly larger portion of it is diverted from the relay by the reactor until at 93 to 98 per cent synchronizing speed, depending on the synchronizing speed the relay is set for, the reactor shunts enough current from coil C to permit the relay armature to open.

Since the relay in Fig. 20-4 is polarized by coil B, the relay armature opens only when the magnetic fluxes of coils B and C are of certain relative strength and in opposition.   The design of the relay is such that this opening will take place to establish contact S, and thus close the field contactor to apply excitation at the favorable point for synchronizing.

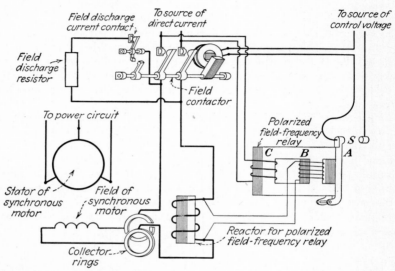

Fig. 20-4.   Wiring connections of the field circuit for the polarized field-frequency relay of Fig. 20-3 (see text for description).

Another method of accomplishing this is to provide a double-throw contactor having two magnets.   The upper magnet is energized from direct current and tends to close the upper set of contacts; the lower magnet has its windings in series with the field.   The contactor normally has the lower contacts closed and the lower magnet circuit connected in the motor field.   In starting, the voltage inducted in the field windings maintains the lower contacts closed by means of the magnet.   When the motor nearly reaches synchronous speed, the lower magnet is almost deenergized, owing to the induced voltage in the field windings approaching zero.   This permits the magnet at the top of the contactor to overcome the pull of the lower magnet and to open the lower contacts and close the upper contacts, in this way initiating the necessary connections for changing the controller from the starting to the running position, but does not ensure that the connection will be made at the most advantageous instant.   It is suitable for small motors.

The Speed-and-time Method. The control for energizing the field has been combined by Westinghouse in an automatic motor-driven relay. An element responsive to the drop in primary current, when the motor is nearly at synchronizing speed, starts the relay motor. At this speed the

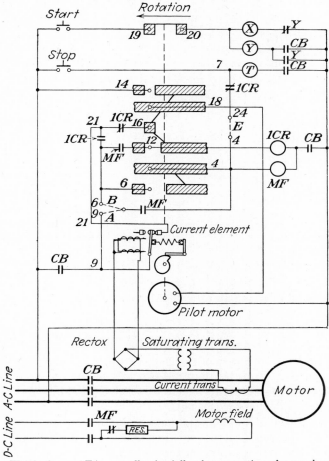

FIG. 20-5. Westinghouse STA controller for full-voltage starting of a synchronous motor (see text for description, p. 334).

rectified primary current taken from a current transformer is represented by a wavy line, shown in Fig. 20-6. The low part of this curve occurs when primary and secondary poles are opposite each other. The coil of a spring-closed contact member is connected in this rectified-current circuit. There is low tension in the spring when the relay motor starts, but the spring tension is gradually increased by cam action as the relay motor operates. After a few seconds the spring tension overcomes the magnet, when the current curve is in one of its valleys. The relay contacts then close and energize the motor fields at a favorable time to build up the field, as unlike poles approach each other. The relay continues to operate until it has returned to its initial position, ready for another start. The few seconds required to build up tension in the spring allow sufficient time for the synchronous motor to reach its maximum speed before its fields are energized.

In Fig. 20-5 with the motor running or shut down, the position of the STA elements will be as shown; *i.e.*, fingers 4, 16, 18, 19, 20 will be "made," 6, 12, 14 will be "open," and spring tension on the current element will be maximum. The contacts 19 and 20 guarantee that the

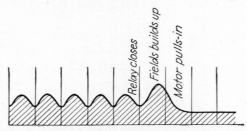

FIG. 20-6.   Rectified primary current during the acceleration of a synchronous motor showing where relay applies the d-c field.

primary breaker cannot be closed unless the elements are in the position shown (the Off position) since these contacts interrupt the circuit to the *X* and *Y* closing relays in all other positions.   Jumper *B* is closed; *A* and *E* open.

To start, push the Start button that energizes relays *X* and *Y* and closes the primary breaker. Instantly, the current element picks up to break contact 9-21 as the result of current inrush to the motor. When the inrush current drops to about 50 per cent of the initial inrush value (90 per cent speed), current element contact 9-21 closes and completes a circuit to the pilot motor through 1*CR* contact 21-16 and drum fingers 16 and 18. After a short initial movement, finger 14 "makes" and connects the pilot motor across the line so that the movement continues. The second circuit to make is finger 12, causing relay 1*CR* to pick up. At approximately the same time, the current element calibrating cam releases the spring tension, so that contact 9-21 again opens. After 9-21 has opened, finger 6 makes. As the spring tension is gradually restored, 9-21 will close to complete a circuit to field contactor *MF* through 1*CR* contact 21-6. Once *MF* has closed, a holding circuit is established, either through jumper *A* to the line or through jumper *B*, *MF* contact 6-12, and fingers 12-14 to the line. These holding circuits by-pass current element contact 9-21 until the drum returns to the Off position, so that transient operations of the current element attendant to application of excitation do not trip *MF*.

With jumpers *A* and *E* in place and *B* removed, the motor will shut down if current element contact 9-21 opens as a result of pull-out. The opening of 9-21 trips relay 1*CR* and the contact 7-24 closes, energizing the circuit-breaker trip coil. With jumper *B* in place and *A* and *E* removed, the motor will resynchronize in the event of pull-out. The opening of 9-21 trips both 1*CR* and *MF*, but the breaker does not trip since the jumper *E* is not in place. The 1*CR* contact 21-16 closes to start the STA unit through a sequence when 9-21 recloses, the same as occurs when the motor reaches 90 per cent speed during a normal start.

The saturating transformer is not always included. It will be used when there is a possibility of obtaining heavy short-circuit currents in the case of a fault and where the switching equipment must withstand the same without injury. The saturating transformer prevents possible destruction of the Rectox.

Another speed-time device is the General Electric slip-cycle imped-ance relay, type SCI. The relay has a rotating element with a contact arm, which is caused to swing back and forth as a result of the torque produced by a combination of voltage and current coils as a function of the motor impedance. This causes the contact to open and close. As the synchronous motor accelerates, there is an increase in the stator impedance, as shown by the decrease in the line current.

There is also a cyclic variation of impedance at a frequency equal to twice the slip frequency. This frequency is low when the motor is close to full speed and the intervals during which the relay contact remains closed will increase. This contact energizes a time-delay relay that closes its contacts when the interval becomes long enough. The timing is adjusted so that the interval that closes this second contact occurs at the motor speed at which its field should be connected to d-c power. This is the period *A* in Fig. 20-7. The time-delay relay energizes the field-circuit relay, which has sufficient time delay to close the field circuit at *C* in Fig. 20-7. This is the point where unlike stator and rotor poles are approaching each other and will lock together to synchronize the motor during interval *CD*.

RESYNCHRONIZING AND PULL-OUT PROTECTION

Either momentary low voltage or severe overload conditions may cause a synchronous motor to pull out of synchronism. Under these conditions the motor stalls and some protective features must be auto-matically provided. If the pull-out has occurred because of low voltage and the voltage recovers quickly, or if the pull-out has been caused by overload conditions that disappear promptly, the motor may be operated temporarily as an induction motor with field excitation removed, to reaccelerate and resynchronize. The inconvenience of a complete shutdown is, therefore, avoided. Under many conditions it is not possible or desirable for the motor to resynchronize, and power must be disconnected to prevent damage to the motor.

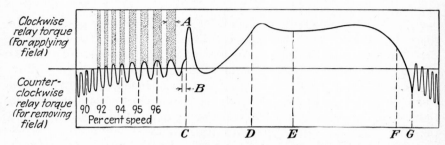

FIG. 20-7. Action of SCI control during pull-in and pull-out in a General Electric Company system. (1) *Impedance changes.* As the motor accelerates, the stator impedance changes as follows: (*a*) average impedance increases; (*b*) frequency of cyclic variations decreases. (2) *Relay responds.* As acceleration continues, SCI relay torque responds as follows: (*a*) relay torque reverses momentarily; (*b*) relay contacts oscillates with torque reversals; (*c*) frequency of reversals decreases; (*d*) time interval of relay-torque reversal increases, as shown, by rapidly widening shaded areas. (3) *Speed is selected.* When the speed-selective interval increases to the present value *A*, the associated timing relay operates, thus indicating that the correct synchronizing speed has been reached. (4) *Angle is selected.* After present angle-selective time interval *B* has elapsed in next cycle, the field is applied at *C* with a favorable angular relation between the rotor and the magnetic field of the stator. (5) *Motor pulls in.* During the interval *C-D* the motor pulls in. The field-applying circuit is maintained during the synchronizing interval while the rotor attains its normal synchronous relation. (6) *Synchronous operation.* The motor carries normal load in synchronism from *D* to *E*. The relay torque reflects rotor oscillations that are quickly damped out by squirrel-cage winding. (7) *Overload pull-out.* A heavy overload is applied at *E* and the motor pulls out of step at *F*, where the motor impedance and relay torque are changing rapidly. (8) *Field is removed.* As the relay torque reverses, the field contactor is deenergized and the field is removed an instant later at *G* to permit resynchronizing. (By a simple reconnection of control, the motor can be shut down at the same instant the field is removed.)

The control connections of a synchronous-motor controller can be arranged to permit either resynchronizing or removal of power when a pull-out occurs. The relays that operate to accomplish these results are the same field frequency, current, slip-cycle impedance, or power-factor relays that control the synchronizing when a normal start from rest is made.

REDUCED-VOLTAGE STARTERS

Low-line voltage interferes with the magnetic contactor performance during starting and increases the time required to accelerate the motor to full speed.

Some automatic starters that start with the d-c field energized have a small contactor, which short-circuits the motor field rheostat or exciter field rheostat when the motor is being synchronized. This operation overexcites the field, improves the pull in torque, and reduces the current peaks when the motor is transformed from starting voltage to full line voltage. When an individual exciter is used to provide the motor-field excitation, the added contactor improves the operation of the d-c contactors by having full exciter voltage impressed on the operating coils while the motor accelerates to full speed.

Low-speed synchronous motors can be started by connecting them directly to the line. The starting kilovolt-amperage with full line voltage approximates three times the normal input kilovolt-amperage. This value is no higher than that required for some of the high-speed synchronous motors started with 65 per cent of line voltage, which is the standard starting voltage when autotransformers are used. When full line voltage is applied to a motor, the starting period is decreased approximately 60 per cent (from 1 min to 24 sec).

The line-voltage starter in addition subjects a synchronous motor to fewer current peaks than the reduced-voltage starter of the type that opens the motor circuit at transfer from starting to full voltage, but the starting kilovolt-amperage is higher. High starting kilovolt-amperage is of less importance on large power systems, but the design limitations of the motor in some cases prohibits starting with full line voltage. When conditions permit line-voltage starting, the control equipment is simplified and the number of main contactors or circuit breakers is reduced.

THE EMERGENCY STOP

Certain applications, such as rubber and paper calenders, require means for quickly stopping machinery in case of emergency. One means of accomplishing this is to use a magnetic clutch and a magnetic brake. When the emergency occurs, the operator actuates the emergency switch that disconnects the motor from the machinery by means of the magnetic clutch; at the same time, the brake is applied, bringing the machinery quickly to rest.

Another method consists in the use of dynamic braking. When the operator actuates the emergency switch, the motor is disconnected from the line and the a-c windings are short-circuited through a resistor. The revolving field magnets generate a voltage in the a-c windings, which causes a heavy current to flow, converting the motor into an a-c generator and bringing it quickly to rest. Tests have indicated that with many designs of motors the load can be stopped as quickly with dynamic braking as by the use of a clutch-and-magnet brake. Dynamic braking requires more switching apparatus, but it eliminates the clutch-and-magnet brake.

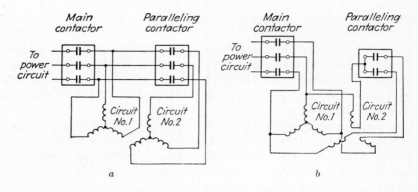

c

Fɪɢ. 20-8. Electric Machinery Manufacturing Company automatic part-winding control for a synchronous motor driving a centrifugal pump. The control is the dead-front, two-step, air-break type. The sequence of operations of this control are given in *c*.

a. The primary connections for the control shown in *c*. It indicates the switching means used for two-step part-winding starting. The main contactor opens both circuits in case of overload on the motor or of short circuit.

b. Alternative connection of the second circuit by means of a two-pole contactor con-

POWER-FACTOR CORRECTION

Synchronous motors, like synchronous generators, can have the field overexcited and deliver a wattless current 90 deg in advance of the load current. This leading wattless current will neutralize an equivalent amount of lagging current and, in this way, improve the power factor of any particular installation.

It is this ability to improve the power factor of the given installation that makes it so desirable to use synchronous motors. In order to furnish this leading current, it is necessary to build a motor larger than would be required to drive the load, and it, therefore, adds to the expense of the installation to improve the power factor.

If the installation is a factory or any other large user of power having a considerable number of induction motors the amount of lagging current that would be necessary for neutralizing is considerable. Unless the loads to which the synchronous motors are attached are in large units, it may be cheaper to use induction motors for all the mechanical drives and to supply one synchronous machine running light, commonly known as "floating" on the system. The entire output of this machine can then be used for power-factor correction.

---

nected in the start of the second circuit. This contactor can be located near the motor if that is desirable. The main contactor opens both circuits.

c. Pressing the Run button (1) closes the main contactor (2) connecting the motor to the line on part winding. Closing of main contactor sets timing relay (3) in operation. As soon as the motor is energized, the contact of field-control frequency relay (4) opens. The motor accelerates on part winding. When a predetermined time has elapsed, timing relay operates to close paralleling contactor (5). The second circuit of the motor is then connected to the line, and the motor is then on full winding. When the motor reaches the correct speed for synchronizing, the field-control frequency relay closes its contact, closing field contactor (6). Closing of the field contactor applies excitation, obtained from the direct-connected exciter on the motor, to the field of the motor, and the motor pulls into synchronism. Overload protection while the motor is on part winding is provided by part-winding protective relay (7). Overload protection while the motor is on full winding but not yet in synchronism is provided by out-of-step protective relay (8). Overload protection after the motor is in synchronism is provided by overload relay (9). These relays all operate to open the main contactor (2), which opens both circuits of the motor. Other equipment on the control: (10) d-c ammeter; (11) a-c ammeter; (12) exciter field rheostat; (13) safety lock-out; (14) pilot light to indicate d-c excitation is available; (15) Stop button.

CHAPTER 21

ELECTRON-TUBE CONTROL

OPERATION AND FUNCTIONS

The electron tube can be considered a one-way switch that is closed by heating the cathode. Negatively charged electrons are emitted from the surface of the heated cathode and travel at a tremendous speed to the anode, forming a current-carrying path (see Fig. 21-1). Note that,

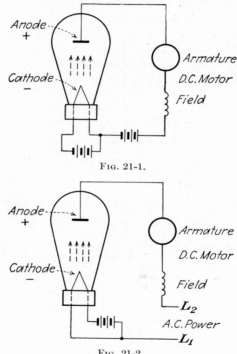

FIG. 21-1.

FIG. 21-2.

while the electron flow is from ($-$) to ($+$), the current flow in the tube is conventionally from ($+$) to ($-$). It will not flow in the reverse direction.

When we substitute a-c power for the battery (see Fig. 21-2), we get an intermittent pulsating source of d-c power through the motor, as only one-half of the power is used. When we add a second tube and add the other half of the a-c power wave, we can obtain full-wave rectification, a source of pulsating direct current sufficiently smooth for motor-armature operation (see Fig. 21-3). When a shunt motor is used, two more tubes are required to energize its field.

Grid Control. The armature voltage can be controlled by inserting a grid between the anode and the cathode and connecting it to a relatively low voltage; when this voltage is negative, it has a pronounced effect in

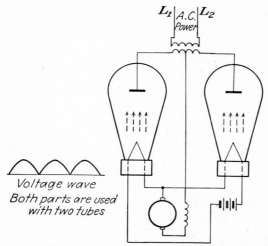

FIG. 21-3. The use of two tubes to give rectified d-c power.

reducing the number of charged negative electrons reaching the anode. When the grid is positive, the number of electrons reaching the anode is increased.

By control of the grid voltage, the voltage at the motor terminals can be changed from zero to the maximum in an infinite number of steps. The grid requires very little power, and its voltage can be controlled by a small dial like that of a radio. A shunt-motor field can obtain power from a similar pair of tubes, and the field current can be changed in the same way by applying different voltages to the grid. The tube furnishes a source of variable voltage power with very little power loss.

Functions. The tube control has three important functions:

1. Converting a-c power into pulsating d-c power.
2. Providing an adjustable-speed control over a wide range by adjusting the applied voltage on the armature and field coils, and by means of circuit refinements maintaining the selected speed constant from no load to full load.

3. Providing adjustable-current limit during acceleration and operation.

Conversion of Power.   The control functions of starting, reversing, dynamic brake, overload, and low-voltage protection can be taken care of by contactors in such a way that the contactor is not required to open or close the circuit under power conditions.   Standard push buttons and other master switches can be used at the control position.   In practice, the adjustable-voltage rectifier usually consists of two thyratron tubes for the armature circuit and two for the motor field.

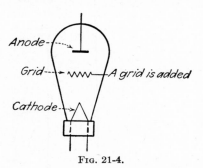

Anode-
Grid---
A grid is added
Cathode-

FIG. 21-4.

The average voltage delivered by the tubes is controlled by the phase relation of their grid voltage, which is obtained from the a-c circuit through a transformer.   When the grid voltage is effectively in phase with the anode voltage, the tube will be turned full on, and when the two voltages are effectively 180 deg out of phase, the tube will be turned off completely and no current will flow.   By means of varying the phase relation between these limits the tube can be turned on to any desirable degree.

Adjustable-speed Control.   The phase-shift method is the most common way of varying the output voltage of the thyratron tube.   The phase shift can be obtained by a combination of a resistor and a condenser or a resistor and inductance (see Fig. 21-5).   The phase shift can be adjusted by hand or by mechanical means, much as tension in a strip of material being fabricated or a loop of fabric can intercept a light ray (see Fig. 21-12) to control the motor speed.   These controls can apply to either the armature or the field voltage, or to both.

Another way to shift the grid-voltage wave is shown in Fig. 21-6. When the variable reactance is changed, it changes the phase angle of P, which controls the secondary windings S_1 and S_2.

The curves shown in Fig. 21-5 give the grid-voltage wave in its normal position.   The diagram shows a method of shifting the phase angle by applying d-c voltage to the grid transformer and adjusting its amount and direction by a potentiometer control.

The speed regulation of the motor from an uncompensated tube power source will be worse than from standard d-c power, both because the voltage drop in the armature circuit due to the inductive reactance will

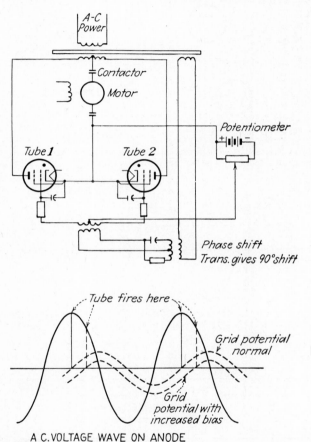

A C. VOLTAGE WAVE ON ANODE

FIG. 21-5. Simple form of motor control. Curve shows voltage change with grid-bias adjustment.

be greater and because the counter emf of the motor will have to drop further with a pulsating power source to provide voltage enough to balance the drop through the armature. This latter effect can be seen by referring to Figs. 21-7 and 21-8. The area ER represents approximately the voltage required to overcome the IR drop in the armature circuit. When the current increases, this area must increase in the same

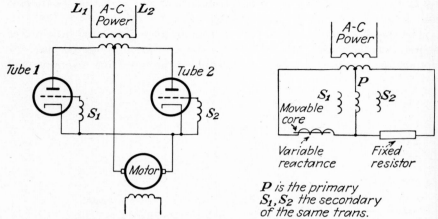

FIG. 21-6. Speed control using a phase shift of grid potential wave by change of phase angle of primary windings P and secondary windings S_1, S_2.

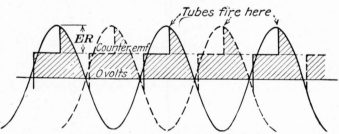

FIG. 21-7. A d-c motor operating from a tube rectifier. The shaded area ER measures the approximate voltage available to overcome the IR drop in the armature circuit. More load will increase this area.

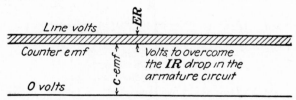

FIG. 21-8. A d-c motor operating from d-c power ER is much less as the area is continuous.

proportion. Now refer to Fig. 21-8, which shows a standard d-c voltage supply, where the area ER represents the voltage required to overcome the IR drop. If the current is doubled, the counter emf line in Fig. 21-7 must drop more than that in Fig. 21-8, to compensate for the increased IR drop. The drop in the counter emf line represents the drop in speed with increasing load and is greater for the pulsating, rectified d-c power than for normal d-c power.

This additional voltage drop can be compensated for and the motor speed can be kept constant if the phase shift of the grid voltage is automatically adjusted to a change in the motor load. This can be done by connecting the grid circuit of a small tube in shunt to a part of a resistor that is across the armature terminals and by connecting the tube in the

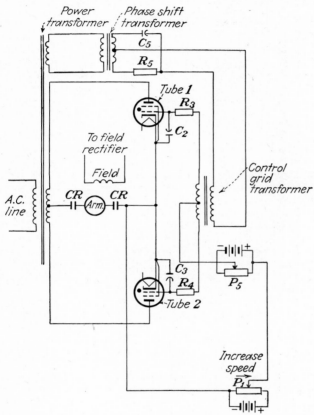

FIG. 21-9. An elementary rectifier circuit for a d-c motor without any regulating means.

circuit of the grid of the power tube in such a way as to increase the voltage delivered to the motor as the load increases. So far, we have assumed a constant field from constant line voltage. The arrangement is a voltage regulator applied to the motor terminals. The speed can be adjusted over a wide range by setting the grid circuit to regulate the voltage of the motor for the desired speed (see Fig. 21-10[1]).

[1] Figures 21-9 to 21-11 are taken from a paper presented by K. P. Puchlowski before the A.I.E.E. on "Electronic Control of D.c. Motors" (*Trans. A.I.E.E.*, Vol. 62,

The voltage-regulator setting must also be automatically changed to increase the voltage when the load increases in order to compensate for the additional voltage drop in the armature circuit and to reduce the voltage when the load decreases.   This change in voltage over the regulator setting is necessary to maintain constant speed.   When a motor is

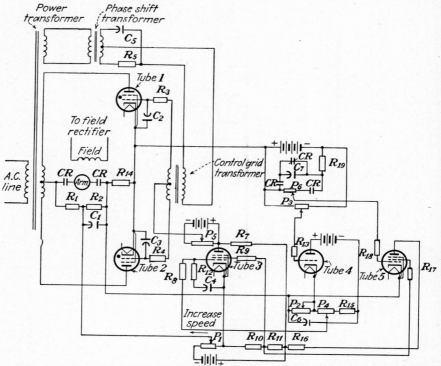

FIG. 21-10.   Complete diagram for a d-c motor controller with regulating means.   Tubes 1 and 2 rectify the a-c power; tube 3 provides armature-voltage regulation, which controls the speed; tube 4 provides IR drop compensation; tube 5 provides current-limit control for acceleration and safe operating loads (see Fig. 21-11).

connected to a standard d-c system, it often has a small reverse-series field coil to weaken the field strength with increasing load.   This tends to increase the speed in proportion to the drop in counter emf, and one change cancels the other to maintain constant motor speed.   With tube power, a second control tube performs the functions of the reverse-series field.   Its grid is connected so that the grid voltage changes in exact proportion to the load.   The control tube is connected in the grid circuit of

p. 870, 1943).   In this paper the reasons for various control tubes are explained in detail with curves showing the motor performance under different conditions.

the power tubes in order to increase their delivered voltage in proportion to the load and reduce this voltage when the load decreases. This control tube holds the motor speed more nearly constant than does the reverse-series field in a conventional motor (see Fig. 21-10).

Adjustable-current Limit. Since power tubes can be injured by severe overloads, a third control tube is added to hold the current constant during acceleration and to limit the overload current during operation.

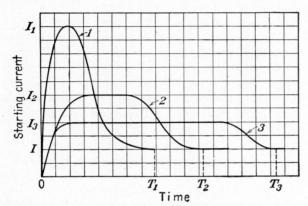

FIG. 21-11. Curves showing the effect of automatic current limitation during the acceleration of the motor. Curve 1 shows the current inrush in a motor operating from a d-c line; curves 2 and 3 show the motor current limited automatically by the electronic control to three and two times the full load, respectively. Should an operating load stop the motor, the thermal-overload relay will open the circuit.

The grid of this tube is also connected so that its voltage will be in direct proportion to the armature current. The tube is inserted in the regulator tube grid circuit to decrease the output voltage of the rectifier when the current approaches the maximum for which this third control tube is set. This gives a flat current curve during acceleration (see Fig. 21-11).

Parts of the Electron-tube Controller. The electron-tube control now consists of the following parts:

1. Two power tubes, to convert the a-c power to a source of pulsating d-c power (see Fig. 21-9).

2. The first control tube, to maintain the armature voltage of the motor constant and provide means for adjusting this voltage to give a preset speed (see Fig. 21-10).

3. The second control tube, to increase the power voltage in proportion to the load, to compensate for the *IR* drop in the armature circuit (see Fig. 21-10).

4. The third control tube, to limit the current in the armature circuit to a preset value (see Fig. 21-10).

The shunt field of the motor receives power from one or two more power tubes. The field strength can be changed to give speed adjustment by controlling the grid voltage of these tubes.

A voltage-regulating tube can be added, if necessary, to maintain a constant preset voltage across the field coils. When field control is used to obtain higher motor speeds, a movement of the control from high to low speed causes the motor voltage to rise above the applied voltage. In the conventional d-c system, this causes a reverse current, which reduces the motor speed quickly to the new setting of the controller. When tubes are used as a source of power, a reverse current will not flow and there is a tendency for the armature voltage to build up to an undesirable value. This can be prevented either by using an overvoltage relay of the magnetic type or by using another tube. When the mechanical load is heavy and positive, the voltage will usually remain at a safe limit without an additional relay. This condition should be checked when the application is being made.

DEVELOPMENT FOR INDUSTRIAL USE

Tube control of power has been developing slowly for industrial applications, as larger tubes are required for power circuits and they have been expensive. A tube controller looks more like an instrument and does not get credit for its actual ruggedness. The control scheme is new to most of the users, who prefer the type with which they are familiar and that their repairmen know how to maintain. First the gas engine and now the Diesel engine have had to face this same problem, but it gradually diminishes with use.

Variable-voltage control using a motor-generator set to convert a-c power into adjustable voltage d-c power (see Chap. 11) has been slowly introduced—first, for mine hoists and then for reversing mill motors; later, for automatic elevators, skip hoists, reversing planer drive, and other applications. Variable-voltage control, however obtained, is the most logical way to adjust the speed of d-c motors and, in time, will be extensively used. The electron tube can replace the motor-generator set as a source of adjustable voltage power where regeneration is not required, and it is now used for the smaller motors. It can be used to control a generator field where the power exceeds the capacity of commercial tubes or where regeneration is necessary. As the cost of tube control decreases, it will find wider use, replacing other types of adjustable-speed control.

An interesting use of tubes for controlling motors is described in the latter part of Chap. 6.

PERFORMANCE AND APPLICATION

Problems to Be Met. The performance of d-c motors receiving power from electron-tube control is not the same as that of those operating on standard d-c power; the principal differences are in heating and in commutation, particularly where field weakening is used to obtain greater speed range.

Heating. The pulsating voltage from tube power causes a considerable ripple current in the armature, in addition to the average current read by a standard d-c meter. If the meter used is an a-c meter, which shows the rms current, the reading will be higher than that shown by the d-c meter. The motor torque is proportional to the average current shown by the d-c meter; therefore, the motor load must be less if the heating is kept constant. The heating is more than the square of the current increase shown by the a-c meter. Tube power may increase the heating 40 per cent in some special cases. The increased heating is not the same for all motors. It is influenced by the inductance in the armature circuit, a factor that is not important when standard d-c power is used. Inductance reduces the ripple current and tends to reduce the difference in heating; this inductance may be in the motor itself, or an external inductance may be connected in the circuit. Slow-speed motors have larger frames and more inductance in their armature circuits. Field circuits have so much inductance that the current is close to a constant value. When the manufacturer furnishes both the motor and the controller for a definite application, the heating factor is considered in designing the equipment.

Single-phase power causes more heating than polyphase power. Usually, the additional heating can be neglected with polyphase tube control.

Commutation. Motors that show no sparking at their commutators on standard d-c power may develop sparking on tube control. This is not very noticeable on small motors, but it becomes important in the larger sizes. It is more of a factor in motors operated on higher speeds by field weakening and limits the speed range obtained in this way. This trouble will not occur if the motor is designed by the manufacturer for tube control.

Frequency. Tube control is usually furnished for 60-cycle power and it will operate successfully on 50 cycles. At reduced frequencies, the inductive effect decreases and more ripple current may develop, so that a different design of motor and control may be necessary for 25-cycle power.

Speed Range. Motors on tube control can be operated on a 20 to 1, even 50 to 1 speed reduction below base speed with very little difficulty, because at this range the principal factor is armature-voltage drop, which is compensated for in the control. At very low speeds, other factors develop; they are friction, brush drop, armature slot, and torque pulsations at a multiple of line frequencies.

Friction can be reduced by using ball or roller bearings, and this should be done where low speeds are necessary.

Brush drop will average plus or minus 2 volts for standard motors and, with a large current, may become several times as great as the counter emf at very low speeds. Brush voltage drop is not constant, and its predominating effect over the counter emf at very low speeds is a difficult problem. This same problem occurs in motor-generator-set control, where there are generator brushes in addition to the motor brushes.

The ripples in torque at low speeds caused by the armature slots can be eliminated with skewed slots, but this may mean a special motor. Skewed slots are common in many a-c motors. Polyphase tube control materially reduces these ripples.

The torque ripples resulting from the pulsating power supply do not constitute a very well-defined factor, but they do exist and must be considered at low speeds.

All but the last item occur when d-c motors are operated at very low speeds from standard d-c power supplied by a variable-voltage generator. Tubes can be used to control this generator field.

Control Limitations. The *IR* compensation voltage assumed a constant resistance in the armature circuit. Heating changes this resistance and has a very definite effect on speed regulation at very low speeds, such as require 5 to 10 volts counter emf. This is true also with motor-generator-set control.

At high speeds with weak field, the armature reaction on the field flux is important. An *IR* compensation voltage that will provide flat speed regulation at base speed may not be satisfactory at these high speeds, in some cases, without changes in the control.

No attempt has been made in the foregoing to show the detail connections to the control tubes, as these connections are different for the various motor sizes and according to the practice of each manufacturer. Many control applications do not require all the control tubes described.

Engineering Skill Required. Some of the problems of tube control just stated show the importance of expert advice or an over-all guarantee from the manufacturer when selecting this control. These limitations have been overcome by careful design in the same way that other control problems have been met. Tube control developed for communications and supervisory functions will be useful in motor control, but it must be applied by engineers who understand this field of application. It will be modified for this purpose and furnishes one of the major fields for motor-control development.

PARTICULAR APPLICATIONS

It has been shown that a very small amount of low-voltage power in the grid circuit can control a large amount of power in the tube circuit; the tubes thus become amplifiers that have many applications.

They can control the field of a large generator where a motor-generator set is used to obtain a variable-voltage system of control and can be used to give time lag, to limit the armature current, and to respond to other tube circuits.

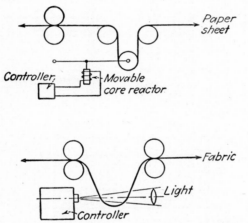

Fɪɢ. 21-12. Speed control between sections of a machine.

In Industry. Electron-tube control can be used to maintain a constant-speed relation between sections of a paper machine, the rolls of a continuous strip or plate mill, a rubber mill, or for any fabric where the process requires maintaining the tension, or loop, in the material between sections of the machine within fixed limits, as in Fig. 21-12.

The electronic speed control of d-c shunt motors as applied to sections of a paper machine is shown in Fig. 21-14. A tachometer-type small d-c pilot generator is driven from each motor shaft and delivers a voltage directly proportional to its speed. This pilot generator is connected in the grid circuit of an electronic tube, which in turn is connected to a tube amplifier that furnishes the field exciting current for this d-c "working" motor. Any slight change in the speed of the working motor will affect the voltage of the tachometer generator, which in turn will change the voltage of the working motor field to correct its speed. This method of speed control is quick acting and responds to a very minute speed change in the working motor.   An adjustment can be made in the tube circuit to change the speed of the working motor.   (Other means than the voltage change of a tachometer generator can be used for regulating the "working" motor speed, such as its frequency.)

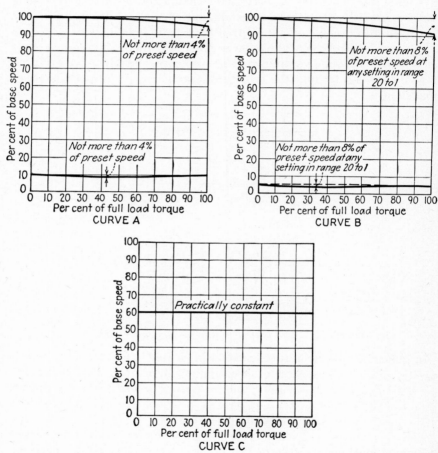

Fig. 21-13.   Speed-regulation curves.   Percentage of base or full field speed in terms of percentage of full-load torque.   Curve *A* for a 10 to 1 speed range, curve *B* for a 20 to 1 speed range, and curve *C* for constant speed at 60 per cent of base speed.

The tachometer principle of speed control is used to keep the various sections of a paper machine at their proper relative speeds so that paper can to travel as high as 2,000 ft per min at the finishing end of the machine.   The quickness of response of electronic tubes has made this speed possible.   Figure 21-14 is a schematic diagram of a paper-machine

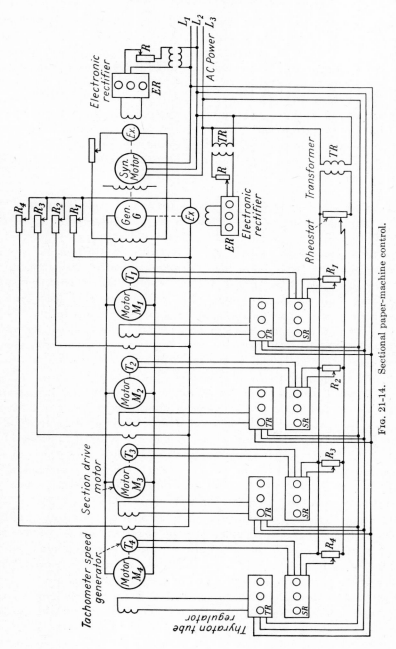

Fig. 21-14. Sectional paper-machine control.

control which illustrates this new method of speed control. This control provides:

1. A constant source of reference voltage common to all motors (the a-c power supply).
2. A means for obtaining a voltage from each section of the machine, proportional to its speed, that can be compared with the reference voltage (the tachometer generator).
3. A means for automatically maintaining the speed of any section so that its control voltage will be the same as the reference voltage (electronic tubes).

Each section of the paper machine is driven by its own d-c motor. The field of this motor is energized through rectifier tubes from a constant-potential a-c power circuit. The control voltages are obtained from tachometer-type small a-c generators driven by the d-c motors operating each paper-mill section. The fields of these generators are supplied from a common source of d-c power through individual adjustable resistors that have high resistance compared with the generator fields and are mounted together so that they have the same room temperature. When each section of this machine is running at its correct speed, its control voltage is adjusted to have the same value as the reference voltage. If the speed of any section changes, the field of its driving motor is automatically adjusted to correct the speed by means of regulators as follows:

The control voltage is balanced against the reference voltage in a circuit connected to the grid of an electronic tube so that any difference between these voltages causes current to flow from an electronic amplifier to alter the voltage in the field of the drive motor and bring its speed back to normal. This speed regulator operates so fast that it is practical to run the paper at 2,000 ft per min at the delivery end. The detail connections are complicated and differ for various applications.

In Communication, Remote Control, etc. They are used in communicating, through radio, with ships, airplanes, tanks, and military stations; night fliers use them to turn on seadrome lights. The amplifying property is used to measure minute vibrations in dynamic balancing and in testing propellers for vibration. It can be used for remote control of motors to open garage doors, operate hydraulic valves, etc.

For Control through a Master Switch. The grid circuit of an electron tube can be connected to a master switch to control the starting, stopping, reversing, and the speed of a motor. The master switch can be a pressure regulator, a float switch, a thermostat, a time clock, a speed regulator—all with split-second timing. The electron tube has made spot welding possible. It gives stepless control and accurate regulation of motor speeds.

For Control by the Light Ray. The electron tube can transform light into electric current by replacing the heat-activated cathode with one made of photosensitive material. Light now replaces heat in causing the emission of electrons. The stronger the light, the greater the current passing through the tube. This photosensitive tube can be connected to the grid circuit of another tube, to amplify its power.

The electric eye is in common use to open a door when a person approaches it and his body intercepts the light ray. This action affects a light-sensitive tube which closes a magnet switch that operates the door-opening motor. After the person passes through the door, the light ray causes the light-sensitive tube to actuate another switch which closes the door. This same device prevents starting an elevator car when there is a person in the doorway and has eliminated many accidents. Most of the elevator accidents to persons occur when they are entering or leaving the car. Another application of the light ray is to stop an elevator car level with the landing. The light ray counts persons or objects passing a fixed point, spots pinholes in metal strips, protects workmen in hazardous locations, and has found many applications.

In Television and the X Ray. Electron tubes perform other functions, such as converting electric power into light, as in the cathode-ray tube used in television reception, and indirectly, as in the X-ray tube and a fluoroscopic acreen.

For High Frequency. Electron-tube control is used to generate high-frequency alternating power, now widely used in radio transmission. High frequency is useful in the heating of metals and insulating materials in many manufacturing processes.

For Amplification. The amplifying function has proved very useful in the more complicated systems of control, as, when it is used, so little power is required for the initiating control. The control relays controlling the grid circuit of tubes can be made very small, the burning of contacts will be eliminated, and very little heat will be developed. This type of control can be sealed up in an airtight container to eliminate dust, corrosive gas, and moisture. The control box will be small, so that it can be readily replaced by a spare unit and taken to the shop for repairs.

Ignitron-tube Rectifiers. These are large power tubes used in place of motor-generator sets to convert from alternating current to direct current for heavy mill equipment and electrolytic plating. They respond to half-cycle power which is controlled by an "ignitron rod" instead of a grid as shown in Fig. 21-5. The firing of this ignitron rod can be controlled by a phase shift similar to Fig. 21-6.

The rectifier can deliver any voltage from zero to its rated value, but it cannot be operated for long periods of time on reduced voltage unless capacity for some reduced-voltage operation is provided for in the tube design.

Six-phase rectifiers are often used to smooth out the d-c voltage curve. The initial cost, including erection, does not exceed the cost of an equivalent motor-generator set. The rectifier has better efficiency and requires less maintenance than the motor-generator set. It is immediately available for use when required.

The ignitron rectifier has found wide use in electrochemical processes in the mining field and for electric railways. Some applications have been made to large motors in steel mills. This rectifier cannot be used for returning power to the line. When a negative load exists, dynamic braking can be used. The energy absorbed during the negative load will probably not exceed one-half of the positive load and will usually be less. This negative load will not often occur over 25 per cent of the time and usually for short intervals, so it should not be difficult to dispose of it.

The power delivered to the load can be regulated for voltage, speed, or current or for both voltage and current by the similar means described for motor-generator power in Chaps. 12 and 13. Development work is under way to extend the use of ignitron rectifiers because of their saving in power and maintenance.

CHAPTER 22

REMOTE AND SUPERVISORY CONTROL

There are several methods of transmitting a rotary motion from the sending station to a remote location by using four wires. The method shown in Fig. 22-1 has a transmitter consisting of a circular resistor connected to the poles of a d-c motor as shown. When the d-c brushes are rotated, they cause a rotating field in the receiving motor, the armature of which follows the rotation of this field. Very little torque is required to rotate the transmitter, and considerable torque can be developed in the receiver. This type of remote control is made by the Allis-Chalmers

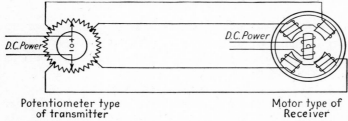

Potentiometer type
of transmitter

Motor type of
Receiver

Fig. 22-1.   Allis Chalmers remote system of indicating and control.

Company, who states that it has an accuracy of plus or minus ½ to 1 per cent and that the rotor of the receiver can develop as much as 360 lb-in. torque. This type of receiver could operate a master switch and also another transmitter connected to a receiver at the sending end, which signals back to the operator the position of the remote master switch.

This system of remote control has been used to start motors and control their speeds; to indicate water levels, static pressures, valve or gate positions; temperature; rudder angles; and many other things.

SELSYN SYSTEM OF REMOTE INDICATING

Remote indications can also be obtained by use of a three-wire circuit connecting two small induction motors called "selsyns." The General Electric Company describes this system as follows: Selsyns are similar to three-phase induction motors but have two definite field poles, the windings of which are connected to a single-phase, a-c source of excitation. Two of these units are used in a simple selsyn system. One is operated at the sending point as a generator and is called the transmitter; the other is operated at the receiving point as a motor and is known as the receiver. The secondary windings of the transmitter are connected to those of the receiver, as shown in Fig. 22-2.

When the primary excitation circuits are closed, an a-c voltage is impressed on the primary of both the transmitter and the receiver. Since the receiver rotor is free to turn, it assumes a position similar to that of the transmitter rotor. As the transmitter is turned (either manually or mechanically), the receiver rotor follows at the same speed and in the same direction.

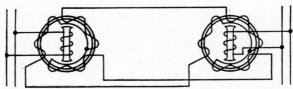

Fig. 22-2.   General Electric Co. connection diagram showing interconnected stator windings and rotor windings connected to the source of excitation for remote control.

This self-synchronous action is caused by the single-phase current in the primary inducing voltages in the three legs of each secondary. These three voltages are not equal in magnitude and vary with the position of the rotor. When the two rotors are in exactly corresponding positions, the voltages induced in the transmitter secondary are equal and opposite to those induced in the receiver secondary; *i.e.*, they are balanced; therefore no current flows in the secondary windings. If, however, the transmitter rotor is moved from the original position, the induced voltages are no longer equal and opposite and current flows in the secondary windings. This current flow sets up a torque which tends to return the rotors to the synchronous position. This position corresponds to the new position of the transmitter. Thus, if the transmitter rotor is moved, whether mechanically (by gears, for example) or manually by operator (for a signaling or control operation), the receiver immediately assumes a similar position. The systems of remote control just described require separate wires for each device indicated or controlled. The units are not large or expensive, and the system is used where only a few units are required at any one location not very far from the central station. When it is necessary to control and supervise a group of units located a considerable distance from the central station, the supervisory system is used.

SUPERVISORY CONTROL

This is a system which controls and supervises the operation of a group of units at locations remote from a central point by means of two No. 16

wires of the telephone type. It performs the same functions that would require a separate wire for each operation and indication.

The supervisory system operates like a dial telephone. The operator closes a small switch corresponding to the unit he wishes to control. This switch automatically signals the unit and connects its control panel to the central control panel in the same man-ner that dialing your telephone connects you to the person you wish to talk to. The supervisory control *always* signals correctly and the unit always signals back unless the line is "busy" or "out of order."

After connections have been established, the operator can initiate the starting of the unit, such as a pump motor, or stopping it or changing its speed. Valves can be opened or closed or any normal control function can be performed at the remote station as easily as if the operator were at that remote station. After each operation the remote station sig-nals back to notify the operator of the com-pletion of the operation. At the same time an ammeter or other instrument can indicate to the operator the load on the motor or the position of a gate valve. Supervisory con-trol functions by sending pulses of direct current from a 48-volt storage battery to the remote station where relays respond to the code message and initiate the desired opera-tions. The same coded messages can be used for a number of controllers, each of them having its own call number. In this way a limited number of code pulses can serve a

FIG. 22-3. Float-operated transmitter.

large number of units. The current and voltage requirements are well within the limits set by telephone companies for leased wire service. These two wires can also be used for telephone communications which consist of a-c waves that transmit speech and are not affected by the d-c pulses used for supervisory control.

Pipe lines transmitting oil, gas, etc., have pumping stations at intervals. The starting, stopping, and speed of the motor-driven pumps can be remotely controlled, pressure in the pipe recorded, and any accidental stopping of a pump reported automatically to a central office many miles away by a single pair of telephone wires, which can also be used for telephone conversations.   The use of a separate, two-wire circuit, such as a leased telephone line, is the least complicated and most desirable for transmitting these pulses of d-c power.   It is probable that only one pair of wires is required for motor control and communications.

FIG. 22-4.   Selsyn transmitter for Fig. 22-5.

FIG. 22-5.   Chart recorder.

Another method (Fig. 22-10) makes use of one frequency of a carrier-current system, altering the pulses of this current to send and receive signals and to operate equipment.   This method is necessary where the total distance or wide spacing of the transmission-line poles makes it expensive to install a telephone circuit.   The wireless transmission of microwaves can also be used and has been selected for some applications.

Carrier-current channels are used in place of separate metallic circuits, where questions of reliability of line circuits and economy dictate its use. The controlling factor in whether or not carrier current is used is often the distance between the stations in question, due to the cost of the carrier-current terminal equipment compared with the cost of installing a

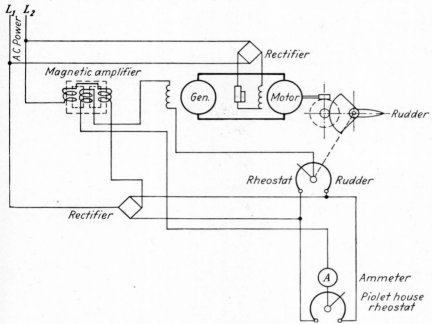

FIG. 22-6. Remote rudder control.

The rudder rheostat follows the pilothouse rheostat to give zero voltage to the generator field and stop the rudder motor. The magnetic amplifier greatly increases the change in generator field as the rudder nears the zero position. This materially increases the accuracy of the rudder position related to the control position in the pilothouse. Reversing the pilothouse rheostat reverses the generator field, which reverses the motor.

This same control can be used for remote positioning of valves, dampers in air ducts, and other objects of similar character.

The ammeter A shows the response, and when the pointer returns to zero, it indicates that the operation has been completed.

telephone-type line. Carrier-current terminal equipment usually consists of a transmitter receiver, a high-voltage coupling capacitor, and a resonant choke coil.

SUMMARY OF OPERATION

1. Equipment requires only a single "channel" and a number of remote stations may be operated over the same channel.

2. The entire equipment is normally at rest.

3. Selective telemetering indications of current, voltage, kilowatts,

The supervisory relays are assembled in dust-proof, cast-metal cases. The covers are provided with glass fronts so that the relays may be inspected without removing the covers.

The escutcheons also may be spread out and connected by mimic, miniature metal or painted bus to form a single line diagram of remote station power circuits.

Non-locking, push-type master control key, protected from accidental operation by finger-guard.

Master release key, for releasing alarm lamp and bell, protected from accidental operation by finger guard.

Line test jacks. The line wire circuits between stations may be tested when desired by plugging in a test meter.

The dispatching equipment is mounted on a modern steel panel 16 inches wide by 90 inches high.

Supervisory Control Relay

Coverplate over drilling and cutout for future supervisory relay case where expansion of remote station requires additions to the supervisory control.

A master indicating lamp (and alarm bell on rear of panel) operate whenever a breaker trips by any other means than control from the dispatcher's office.

White selection lamp indicates when proper selection has been made of desired apparatus.

Disagreement lamp indicates when apparatus unit is in a position opposite to setting of control key.

Large red lamp indicates closed position of apparatus unit.

Twist-type control key selects desired operation of apparatus unit.

Large green lamp indicates open position of apparatus unit.

Selection key selects remote apparatus unit assigned to escutcheon.

Fig. 22-7 and 22-8. Typical dispatching-office control arrangement.

Fig. 22-7. Entire dispatcher's equipment.

The supervisory relays are assembled in dustproof, cast-metal cases. The covers are provided with glass fronts so that the relays may be inspected without removing the covers.

Cover plate over drilling and cutout for future supervisory relay case where expansion of remote station requires additions to the supervisory control.

A master indicating lamp and alarm bell on rear of panel operates whenever a breaker trips by any other means than control from the dispatcher's office.

The escutcheons also may be spread out and connected by mimic, miniature metal or painted bus to form a single-line diagram of remote-station power circuits.

Nonlocking, push-type master control key, protected from accidental operation by finger guard.

Master release key, for releasing alarm lamp and bell, protected from accidental operation by finger guard.

Line test jacks. The line wire circuits between stations may be tested when desired by plugging in a test meter.

The dispatching equipment is mounted on a modern steel panel 16 in. wide by 90 in. high.

Fig. 22-8. Key and lamp escutcheon.

White selection lamp indicates when proper selection of desired apparatus has been made.

Disagreement lamp indicates when apparatus unit is in a position opposite to setting of control key.

Large red lamp indicates closed position of apparatus unit.

Twist-type control key selects desired operation of apparatus unit.

Large green lamp indicates open position of apparatus unit.

Selection key selects remote apparatus unit assigned to escutcheon.

water level, etc., can be obtained regardless of the type of channel employed.   The same channel as is used by the Visicode equipment can, in all cases, be used for the selective metering indications.

4. Breakers can be synchronized by the use of Visicode, either by means of indications received on a special synchroscope or by means of a remotely controlled automatic synchronizer.

FIG. 22-9.   Typical remote-station panels.

5. Any type of electrically controlled apparatus unit can be remotely controlled and supervised.

6. Continuous, individual lamp indications are provided for supervising the position of each remote apparatus unit.

7. "Raise–Lower" control combined with simultaneous telemetering indications permits accurate voltage, speed, and load control for generators; opening and closing of gates and valves in hydro stations; controlling voltage of feeder regulators; etc.   No additional channel is required.

8. The operation of Visicode supervisory control equipment is extremely fast.   The codes are sent and received at approximately fourteen impulses per second.

9. The control is positive and inherently antipumping. Each selection is automatically checked before it is possible to proceed with any control operations. Trip-free or antipumping breaker control relays are not required for any circuit breakers controlled.

10. Coded operation control provides protection against the possibility of false operation of any apparatus unit due to foreign voltages on line

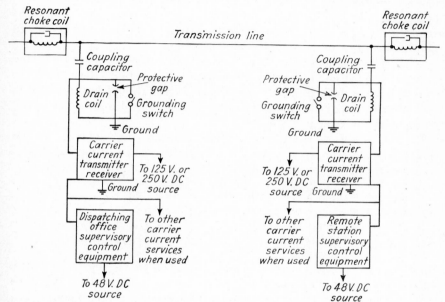

Fig. 22-10.   Diagrammatic showing the arrangement of supervisory control and carrier-current equipment on a transmission line.

wires, such as might be caused by induction from nearby high-tension lines or by lightning.

11. The dispatcher's control operates in a manner similar to that in which an operator in the remote station itself would control the apparatus by means of the usual local control.

12. The equipment is composed of extremely simple, mechanically uniform telephone relays. No polarized relays are used.

13. A carrier-current channel over which this equipment will operate can also be used for other functions, such as relaying and communication.

14. This equipment can be designed to provide "three-way" supervision of apparatus units. Thus, the red and green lamps can be used to indicate the two extreme positions of travel of a device, and neither lamp lighted can be made to indicate the device in the in-between position.

15. Line supervision is provided when the supervisory control equipment operates over a metallic circuit.

16. After selection of a unit any number of operations may be made on the device controlled without the necessity of reselection.

Supervisory control has been used extensively in the power-distribution field since its first application in 1921. More recently it has been applied in the industrial field, where it is found to be very useful for long-distance control and for shorter distances where the supervisory equipment costs less than installing individual control wires. This equipment comes in self-contained unit cabinets like a switchboard; the design follows telephone practice.

When the control engineer applies this system for motor control, each installation must be furnished with the regular operating safety guards to protect persons from injury. A transfer switch should be provided in sight of the motor to connect the controller to a local master switch for testing and adjustment.

When supervisory control is used to transmit an "order" from an operator to a remote-control station and verify its execution; the operation requires four steps to complete the "order:"

1. The selection of the control unit to be operated.
2. A check signal giving proof of correct selection.
3. The operation of the equipment.
4. A check signal showing the completion of this operation.

These operations and check responses are accomplished by codes of d-c pulses transmitted at the approximate rate of 15 per second. The pulses are all of the same length and type and are counted by sets of relays. The selection and control operation depends upon the number of pulses. Variations in the length or spacing of the pulses are not used.

The "master station" has a push button and three signal lamps, red, green, and white, for each control unit. When the button is pressed, the code signal is transmitted to that particular unit, which returns a code signal to light the white lamp. After the selection has been made, a key is pressed, which causes the motor to start or to begin some other operation. When this operation is completed, a signal is transmitted back and illuminates the red lamp. The control is then automatically disconnected from the master station, and the white lamp extinguished. The master station is now ready for other use. Should the motor be automatically disconnected from the power supply by its overload relay or other device, this unit sends a signal to the master station that extinguishes the red lamp, lights the green lamp, and sounds an alarm bell. The control station is then automatically disconnected from the master station. Other operations and signals are obtained in the same way.

CHAPTER 23

PROTECTIVE DEVICES

The National Electrical Code specifies the required branch-circuit protection for motor feeders and the minimum size of wire permitted. This overload protection is intended primarily to prevent damage to the branch feeders that would cause a fire hazard. It also affords short-circuit protection to the motor and the control, but it does not protect them for operating overloads. This latter protection is part of the controller.

OVERLOAD PROTECTION

The overload protective device in a motor circuit must be capable of rupturing the short-circuit kilovolt-amperage which can be delivered to that circuit. In most cases the feeder circuit breaker normally used for that purpose will be sufficient. This is usually true for the smaller installations or where the feeder breaker is located some distance from the transformer substation and has other overload protection ahead of it. A careful check should be made to find out if suitable protection is provided. The Electrical Manufacturers Association has adopted recommendations for the relative size of circuit breakers where two or more breakers are in series.

The best practical way to limit the short-circuit kilovolt-amperage on a motor feeder when necessary is to install reactor coils in the circuit. This method of protection is presented in a paper before the A.I.E.E. by H. D. Short.[1] He states that a 2,200-volt three-phase 60-cycle feeder with 200-hp load can have its short-circuit kilovolt-amperage reduced to 25,000 with any size of power system, by using three reactors with not over 1.57 watts loss per horsepower per coil, or a total of 315 watts. The opening of the 200-amp feeder breaker will disconnect these coils. A 200-hp single motor can have these coils located in the starter (Fig. 23-1), so that they will be disconnected from the power source when the motor is stopped. The increasing size of substations serving large industrial plants requires a check to be made of the magnitude of short circuits.

In addition to overload protection, industrial controllers are commonly provided with such protective devices as low-voltage release, etc. Some of these devices are designed to protect the motor against abuse;

[1] *Elec. Eng.*, April, 1950.

Fɪɢ. 23-1.   Alternating-current motor starter with reactor coils.   (*Electric Controller and Manufacturing Company.*)

others are for the protection of the operator or the machinery driven by the motor.   The more common devices are for protection against the following conditions:

1. Overload.
2. Low voltage.
3. Phase reversal.
4. Phase failure.
5. Shunt-field failure.

Fuses.   The oldest form of overload protection is the fuse, consisting of a strip of metal in the main circuit that is melted, or fused, when the current exceeds a predetermined value.   The earlier forms of fuse consisted of an open link.   A better and more accurate fuse was obtained by enclosing the fusible link so as to give it a more definite time element and prevent the particles of molten metal from dropping on surrounding objects.   Fuses are easy to obtain in the ordinary sizes, as they are carried by most supply houses. Small fuses are inexpensive where only occasional overloads are experienced. Where the motor is worked hard, with the result of repeated blowing of the fuse, the cost of fuse renewals, even for small motors, becomes excessive, and it is cheaper to use some form of overload device that does not require renewal. A switch should be provided for disconnecting the fuses from the line before they are renewed. Even the best designs of fuse are not very accurate, so that it is necessary to overfuse a motor somewhat to be sure of having a fuse of sufficient capacity. The inherent time element in a fuse is a distinct advantage on a motor load, as the fuse will not respond to momentary variations in load, although it will act promptly on excessive overloads.

Fuses are now available that have a heater element in parallel with the fusible link, to increase the time of opening on normal overloads but give quick opening on a fault condition. The fusible link alone does not develop sufficient heat to melt it on normal overloads. The opening depends upon the transfer of heat to the link from the heater, which requires more time than would the direct heating of the link.

High-voltage fuses (2,200 volts and over) are made with a boric acid filler, which extinguishes the arc. These fuses have some time element inherent in their design.

Fuses used in polyphase motor circuits will cause single-phase operation if one fuse opens and, therefore, may cause a motor to burn out. Instead of fuses, three-pole circuit breakers should be used where possible for these motors. When conditions make it necessary to use a fused switch, the heater type of fuse affords better protection.

Circuit Breakers. The circuit breaker is a switch provided with an overload trip, which may consist of a magnet with a movable core. The attraction of the core of the magnet trips the circuit breaker and opens the circuit. Usually the current at which the circuit breaker trips is adjusted by changing the air gap between the core and its pole face. The overload trip can be provided with a dashpot for giving it a time element. This should always be done for motor loads. The overload trip of the current breaker may be a bimetal element with a heater in series with the circuit. The heater causes the bimetal to bend and trip the latch holding the breaker closed on overload. The heater element is selected for the proper tripping current. Most circuit breakers are reset or closed by hand, although magnetic reset can be provided. No new parts are required for reestablishing the circuit after the circuit breaker has opened. The continual rupturing of the circuit gradually wears away the arcing tips of the circuit breaker so that these must be renewed occasionally.

Overload Relay. The overload relay is a small device that opens the circuit to the operating coil of a magnetic contactor or to the low-voltage coil of a circuit breaker.　The relay closely resembles the overload mechanism of a circuit breaker, with the addition of the small contacts referred to above.　The relays of the magnetic type (see Fig. 23-2) should be provided with dashpots, to give an inverse time element when they are used with motors.　When the overload relay is used in connection with magnetic contactors, arrangements can be made for reestablishing the electric

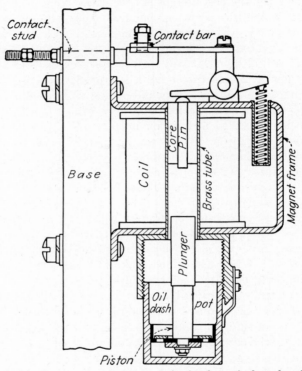

Fig. 23-2.　Sectional view of a dashpot overload relay—single pole.　Two adjacent magnets can be used in each of two power lines arranged so that either magnet will open the contact which in turn opens the line contactor (see Fig. 23-3).

circuit from a push button or a master switch.　When the relay trips its pilot circuit, this circuit may be maintained open by a mechanical latch on the relay or it may be opened through an electrical interlock on the magnet contactor.　If a mechanical latch is used on the relay, this latch may be released either by hand or by another small magnet.　The two methods are known respectively as "hand reset" and "magnet reset." Where the circuit through the relay contacts is opened on an interlock attached to the main contactor or through another relay, the device is known as "electrically reset."　The hand reset on the relay is not recom-

FIG. 23-3. Two-magnet overload relay with dashpot time delay (see Fig. 23-2 for sectional view).

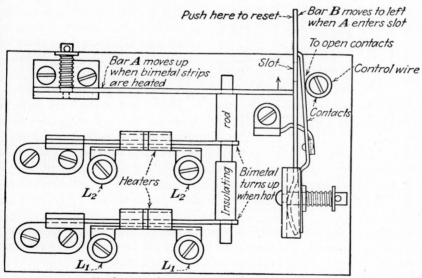

FIG. 23-4. Westinghouse thermal overload relay with two overload elements of the bimetal type with heaters.

mended for most applications, as it is not desirable for the operator to place his hand near the live parts on the control panel.

Time-element Overload Tripping. The ideal overload motor protection is a device that will permit the motor to carry safe overloads for short periods, but will open the circuit when the motor begins to overheat. The device must open the circuit quickly if a fault occurs. The device should have a time-delay element that closely follows the motor temperature. This is best done by mounting the overload relay on the motor in a way that makes its tripping element follow the motor temperature. Item 14, Section I, in Table 23-1 shows this type of relay. Additional protection is required to guard against short circuits or grounding, usually the circuit breaker protecting the feeder. The thermal relay (Table 23-1, Items 5, 6, and 9 to 13) affords reasonable protection for motors operating on short-time loads, such as those of cranes, hoists, elevators, and machine tools. In many cases, the dashpot relay will be satisfactory.

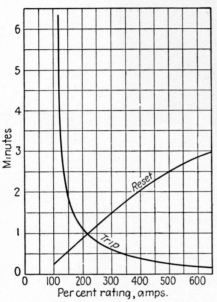

Fɪɢ. 23-5.   The time required to trip the relay contacts (Fig. 23-4) and the time required for the bimetal elements to reset.

The nature of the work done in most of the motor applications places a limit on the normal overload. When an accidental condition occurs, the increase in load is so much above normal that it operates the overload device even when it is set high enough to carry the short-time peak loads. The correct selection of the motor size permits the use of an ordinary time-delay overload device.

Thermocouples are inserted in the winding of large motors and generators and connected to switchboard instruments to indicate the winding temperature so that the load can be properly regulated.

Overload devices with two coils or heaters usually afford reasonable protection for two- and three-phase motors and feeder circuits, but a coil in each phase is required for some conditions, as is set forth in the National Electrical Code, which should be consulted if there is any doubt as to two-coil devices being adequate.

a

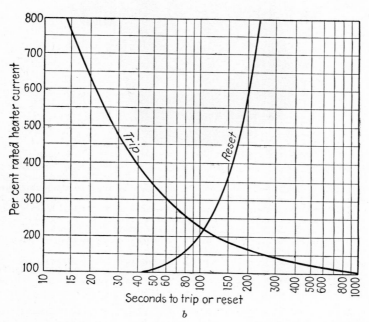

b

Fig. 23-6. General Electric thermal overload relay of the bimetal type with separate heater. This isothermic overload relay gives overload protection to the motor and the machine. It can be set for either manual or automatic reset. *a*. The photograph of the relay, with the cover removed, shows heater, thermostatic strip, and control-circuit contact. The heater unit, carrying the motor current, causes the thermostatic strip to deflect upward and open the contacts with a snap action. This relay is used with 2-hp starters. *b*. The time required to trip the relay in *a* and the time required to reset the contacts.

Figure 23-2 shows a commercial form of overload relay having a dashpot to give it an inverse time-element feature. Another form of relay has a copper disk rotating between the poles of permanent magnets to provide a definite time element. The dashpot type of relay is usually designed to

Fɪɢ. 23-7.   General Electric oil-immersed induction-type overload relay for motors only—single coil.   On heavy currents that overheat the motor quickly, the relay operates quickly; on currents slightly above normal that require some time to overheat the motor, the relay action is delayed.   The advantage of this relay over a magnetic dashpot relay is its ability to "remember" previous intermittent overloads because of its thermal storage capacity. This means that the heating element of the relay can be brought up to tripping temperature by being successively subjected to small increments of overload, which would not in themselves trip out the starter but which would eventually create dangerous temperatures within the motor.

a, Bimetallic strip that deflects when heated, opening contacts.   *b*, Heavy steel core that provides rigid support and accurate operation under all conditions.   *c*, Rating determined by coil selected.   *d*, Coil easily removed by simply unscrewing retaining cap.   *e*, Bimetallic strip firmly attached to sleeve so that heat generated by current in sleeve is transmitted directly to deflecting strip.   *f*, Copper sleeve that acts as secondary of short-circuited transformer to conduct current proportional to that in motor.   *g*, Plunger pin that trips snap-action mechanism when overload occurs.

give an inverse time element on increasing loads. Sometimes it is operated from series transformers with saturated cores in order to limit the pull on abnormal overloads. This latter form of relay is known as a fixed time-element relay. It is the preferable form to use in connection with a

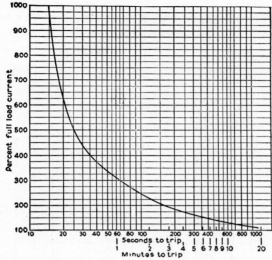

FIG. 23-8. The time required to trip the relay of Fig. 23-7. Note that this type of relay has a much longer time delay than the bimetal type. The tripping curve shows how closely the temperature characteristic matches that of a motor.

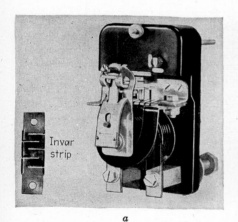

a   *b*

FIG. 23-9. Westinghouse invar-type single-pole overload relay. This type TI-2 overload relay has both thermal time delay for moderate sustained overloads and instantaneous trip for abnormal loads. The time-delay feature makes use of invar, a metal that is magnetic at ordinary temperature but loses its magnetism at 240°C. The current passes through the coil and the invar strip shown just above the coil, thence to the other lower stud. Part of the magnetic flux passes through this invar strip and locks the armature in the open position until the current heats the invar strip to 240°C. This gives the time-delay overload feature. On very heavy overloads the magnetic pull on the armature is sufficient to break the invar lock-out pull and instantly close the armature opening the control circuit.

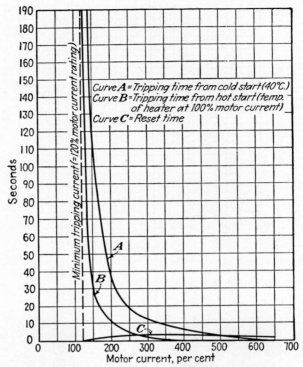

FIG. 23-10.   The performance of relays in Fig. 23-9.

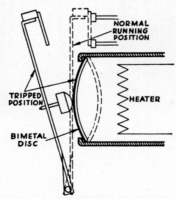

FIG. 23-11.   Westinghouse bimetal disk overload relay.   Heat causes the disk to snap from the dotted position to the one shown in solid lines.   The contacts have quick make-and-break action.

controller that is connected to a large power-supply line and is provided with a separate feeder circuit breaker for taking care of short circuits.

Some operators are under the impression that it is desirable to adjust the time element of dashpot overload relays. This adjustment would be desirable if a long time element were obtained. Commercial forms of

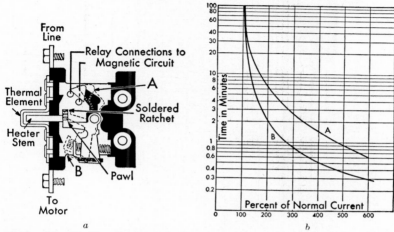

FIG. 23-12. Allen-Bradley Company thermal overload relay solder-pot type with separate heater. The resisto-therm overload relay operates on the soldered-ratchet principle. The heart of the relay consists of a heater stem that is almost completely surrounded by a resistance coil or resistance strip carrying the main motor current. The other end of the heater stem has a ratchet wheel soldered to it. This ratchet wheel engages a pawl that holds the relay contacts closed against spring tension. A sustained overload on the motor heats up the resistance unit, which, in turn, heats the stem and finally melts the solder. Once the solder is melted, the ratchet wheel is free to turn and the contacts are forced open by spring action. This opens the coil circuit of the switch and disconnects the motor from the line. The time required to open the motor circuit is very short in case of heavy overloads and much longer with light overloads. Only a few seconds are required for the solder to cool and hold the ratchet wheel firmly in place, allowing the relay to be reset by pressing a Reset button. The relay can be reset any number of times without affecting the accuracy or the reliability of the protection provided.

a, A shows contacts in open position. Pressing the Reset button transmits pressure to point *B* and thus recloses the relay. *b,* Current-time characteristic of the resisto-therm relay. Curve *A* is the average motor-heating curve. Curve *B* illustrates the tripping time of the resisto-therm relay.

relays do not afford a time element that compares in length to the time required to heat up even small motors. It is desirable, therefore, to obtain as long a time element as possible with the dashpot relay, and any adjustment provided should be set to give the maximum time element. But if too long a time element is attempted with the dashpot relay, there is a tendency for it to stick under adverse conditions. It is necessary, therefore, to adjust this time element so that the maximum time given will ensure satisfactory operation.

All motor circuits should be protected by feeder circuit breakers or

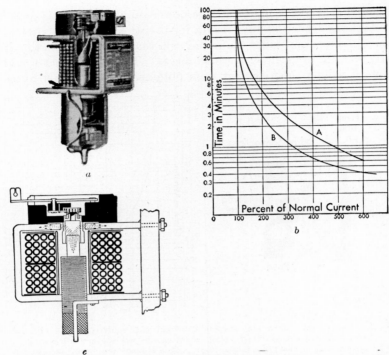

FIG. 23-13.   *a.* Allen-Bradley Company inducto-therm relay for a-c motors only.   The inducto-therm relay utilizes the heating effect created by a current induced in a copper heater tube.
    The relay operates on the soldered-ratchet principle.   Its contacts are held in a closed position by a reset lever, which engages a soldered ratchet wheel.   An overload current through the magnetizing coil of the relay increases the induced current in the copper heater tube in direct proportion to the overload current, which, if the overload remains on long enough, will melt the solder, release the ratchet wheel, and trip the relay.   The contacts must be reclosed manually by pushing the reset lever to the right as soon as the copper tube cools sufficiently to solidify the solder.   The accuracy of the relay depends only upon the melting point of the utectic solder, which is a definite value and remains constant.
    The tripping value of the relay is adjustable over a wide range of current ratings by simply changing the position of the threaded iron ore within the magnetizing coil.   By the lowering of the core, the magnetic flux becomes weakened and a greater overload current is required to melt the solder.
    This relay can have a plunger and dashpot added to trip the retaining latch and provide inverse-time overload protection against abnormal loads such as locked rotor.
    b. Time-temperature curve of relay in *a.*   Curve *A* is the average motor-heating curve. Curve *B* represents the tripping time of the overload relay.   *c,* Diagram of *a* showing the frame, coil, threaded core, heater tube, ratchet wheel, and magnetic flux.

fuses.   If the feeder circuit is connected to a very large transformer or to a power circuit having large capacity back of it, the feeder circuit breaker should be of ample capacity to take care of the power ahead of it in case of a short circuit to the feeder or the apparatus connected to this feeder. This circuit breaker must have a smaller time element on its trip than that obtained with the overload relay on the controller panel.

The thermal overload relay has two elements, a heater in series with the circuit to be protected and a heat-responsive element. The heater is selected to suit the ampere rating of the circuit, and the time delay is the time required to transmit the heat to the tripping device. The trip

FIG. 23-14. Square D Company thermal-overload relay of the bimetal type with one-half of the insulating block removed to show its operation. To the left is the control switch that is tripped by the bimetal element pressing against a pin. The dark U-shaped piece is the bimetal that is heated by the bright U-shaped "heater" projecting inside the bimetal. The heater is selected for the correct load. The screw at the right adjusts the tripping from 85 to 115 per cent of the heater rating. The element projecting out at the top is for resetting the relay by hand when it trips or for changing it for automatic reset.

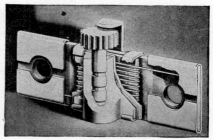

FIG. 23-15. The Square D Company melting alloy overload relay.

operates only when the heat exceeds a fixed value. A bimetal strip is generally used as the heat-responsive element. It bends or deflects when heated and trips the control-circuit contact open when it is heated enough. Figure 23-4 shows how such a relay works. The curve indicates its tripping time on various loads.

Figures 23-7 to 23-9 and 23-13 show relays that combine time delay for

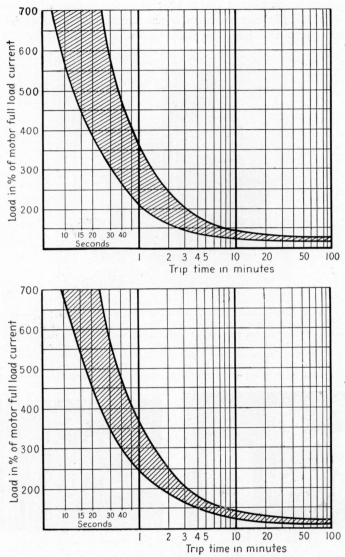

Fig. 23-16. Time-temperature curves of Square D Company relays.   *a*, The tripping characteristic of a melting alloy relay.   *b*, The tripping characteristics of a bimetal relay with separate heater.

normal overloads and instantaneous trip on short circuit. Figure 23-11 is a type of bimetal-disk overload relay.

LOW-VOLTAGE PROTECTION OR RELEASE

Devices of low-voltage protection or release are arranged for disconnecting the motor from the line on the failure of voltage. The National Electrical Manufacturers Association recognizes two forms of this protection:

Low-voltage Release. This provides for disconnecting the motor from the line on the failure of voltage but permits the motor to start automatically when line voltage is reestablished. Such a device is the magnetic-contactor control with automatic acceleration. It is used for pumps, fans, and similar applications, which should restart automatically when the voltage is restored to the line.

Low-voltage Protection. This device disconnects the motor from the line on the failure of voltage and prevents the motor from being started again on reestablishment of line voltage. In order to start the motor, the operator must push a button or operate a lever. This latter is a very necessary precaution where the motor is used for driving machine tools or woodworking machinery, printing presses, or in fact, any device that might cause injury to a person working on the machine.

These devices are sometimes known as "undervoltage" instead of "low voltage," both terms having the same significance. Usually they do not respond to a small drop in voltage.

PHASE-REVERSAL PROTECTION

The device for phase-reversal protection operates to disconnect the motor from the line in case one of the phases of the polyphase circuit has been reversed. Such reversals sometimes occur when repairmen are installing service transformers or making other repairs. The effect of such a reversal is to cause the motor to operate in the opposite direction. For some applications such a reversal will not cause any damage, but where the motor drives an elevator or hoist, a serious accident may result. Some public-service corporations supplying electric power to users require the installation of a reverse-phase relay device on all elevator motors to protect themselves from liability resulting from such an accident. There are a number of these devices now in the market. Some of them consist of a small relay having two parts, corresponding to the stationary and the movable element of a motor or wattmeter (see Fig. 23-17). Power supplied to these parts causes rotation in a definite direction. The torque thus established maintains a contact in the closed position and represents normal operation. If either phase is reversed, the torque of the relay is also reversed, which opens the contact and disconnects the control and the motor from the line.

Another form of relay is shown in Fig. 23-18. This relay is made up of standard contactors. The operating coil is supplied through two circuits, as shown. One of these circuits has a resistance in series with it; the other an inductance. The resistance and the inductance cause a displacement between the two phases, so that, when their effect is added, the relay is maintained closed. If either phase is reversed, the phase angle is changed, causing the two circuits to oppose each other, reducing the magnetic action on the coil, and opening the relay. In the case of the two-phase arrangement, the contactor is provided with two separate coils, one in each phase.

Some devices of this character have been designed to close a circuit on reversal of phase, rather than to open it. Such devices have special applications in connection with power circuits, but they are undesirable for industrial control, as the failure of the contacts to make a good electrical connection or the breaking of one of the wires would prevent such a device from operating. Where the contact is closed for normal operation, the breaking of a wire or the failure of the contact would disconnect the controller from the line and automatically stop the motor, which is a safer arrangement.

PHASE-FAILURE PROTECTION

Sometimes one line of a polyphase circuit may be opened accidentally. If the motor has not started, it will fail to do so and may be injured by being left connected to the line. This can easily happen in a mechanically operated elevator control, where the failure of the motor to start might cause the operator to leave the controller in the running position. By the use of a low-voltage device across two phases of the three-phase circuit, or one relay for each phase of the two-phase circuit, the motor can be protected from such an accident. The relays are connected in such a way that the main switch will not close until both relays are closed. This arrangement is often combined with a phase-reversal relay device to give protection from both phase reversal and phase failure (see Figs. 23-17 and 23-18).

If a motor is rotating and one phase is opened, the motor will continue to operate single phase if the torque does not exceed the single-phase torque of the motor. Such operation, however, causes the whole load to be carried by one phase of the motor and may seriously overheat these windings. If the overload protection is set at a low enough value, it will protect the active phase from an excessive overload. Unfortunately, such overload devices are frequently set too high to afford proper protection. While the motor is operating, voltage is maintained across all three terminals of a three-phase motor or across both phases of a two-phase motor, owing to the active phase-generating voltage in the inactive circuit. The voltage generated in the inactive circuit is very little less than the normal voltage, so that any phase-failure device depending upon a drop in voltage for operating it will not respond when connected to a rotating motor.

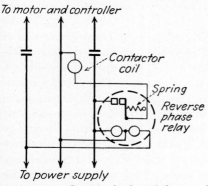

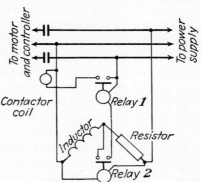

FIG. 23-17. Combined phase-failure and phase-reversal relay of the wattmeter or motor type. The coil for the contactor in the motor circuit is connected through the contact in the relay. This contact is held open by a spring and is closed as a result of the torque exerted by two coils connected to two of the three phases. These coils set up a motor action that forces the contacts together against the spring pressure when the phase relation is correct. If any of the three phases is reversed, the torque on the wattmeter movement is reversed and the contact opens. If the voltage fails in either phase, the torque is reduced to zero and the spring opens the contacts.

FIG. 23-18. Combined phase-failure and phase-reversal relay for a three-phase circuit. This consists of two small relays the contacts of which are closed by electromagnets. Relay 2 is connected across one phase of the circuit and remains closed as long as that phase is energized. The coil of relay 1 is connected between the three phases of the circuit, one end of the coil having an inductor in one branch and a resistor in the other branch. This combination brings the current in the two branches of the circuit so that its effect upon the coil of relay 1 is added when the phase relation is correct. On a reversal of phase relation, the currents in the two legs of the circuit through the coil of relay 1 oppose each other and the relay drops open. On failure of voltage in any one of the three phases, relay 1 is opened either directly or through the opening of relay 2. The contactor coil for the control is in circuit with the contacts of relay 1, so that the opening of this relay disconnects the motor from the line.

Fortunately, many installations, such as elevators, hoists, etc., operate for only a short time without coming to rest, so that a phase-failure device will operate the first time the motor is brought to rest and prevent its restarting.

SHUNT-FIELD FAILURE

Shunt-wound d-c motors may operate at an abnormal speed and destroy themselves by centrifugal action if the shunt field becomes disconnected from the line. While this kind of accident is of very rare occurrence, guarding against it in some particular cases is thought advisable. The usual method of guarding against this form of accident is to provide a relay and place its magnet winding in series with the shunt-field circuit of the motor. When this relay is energized, it closes the pilot circuit to the controller. If the shunt-field circuit should open, this relay will open the pilot circuit to the controller, which in turn disconnects the motor from the line.

One serious objection to the use of this relay is the transformer action that takes place in the motor as a result of sudden changes of load. This action is particularly noticeable when the motor is compound wound. A rapid change in load causes a change in the field flux. This exerts a transformer action on the shunt-field windings and may be sufficient momentarily to reverse the current in these windings. This does not mean that the flux in the field circuit of the motor is reduced to zero. It simply means that the rate of change of the flux is sufficient to generate a counter voltage in the shunt-field windings large enough to cause a momentary pause in the current through these windings. This is not very hard to do, as the shunt field usually has a very large number of turns, which, multiplied by a small change in flux, will cause a considerable voltage. A reaction of this kind in the shunt-field circuit of the motor may cause the relay to drop out and disconnect the motor from the line. The connections to the controller are such that, when the relay does open the circuit, the motor will not start again automatically. It requires action on the part of the operator to reset this relay.

A number of devices have been used to delay the action of this relay in order to prevent an interruption of service. One method consists in adding considerable inertia to the moving parts of the relay by means of a pivoted weight or similar device. Another method is to use a heavy tube of copper around the magnet core. This copper tube acts as the short-circuited secondary of a transformer and delays any change in magnetism in the relay. Usually one or the other of these devices will prove satisfactory, although in aggravated cases additional precautions must be taken.

Engineers, as a rule, do not consider it necessary to use shunt-field protective relay except with large motors that may run light under certain conditions of load. Safety devices of any character should be avoided where they are unnecessary, as they add complication to a control equipment and require additional inspection and care to maintain it in an operative condition. It is seldom that any safety devices are used other than overload and low voltage. Wherever a safety device is used, it should be tested at frequent intervals to ensure its proper operation in case of accident.

TABLE 23-1. RELAY CLASSIFICATION*
I. Overload protection

Type and application	Mechanical construction	Principle of operation
1. *Fuse.* A fuse is used when overload and short-circuit protection cost must be minimized. When applying fuses, maximum ratings should approximate 150 % full-load current of d.c. and a.c. wound-rotor motors, and 250 to 300 % of full-load current of squirrel-cage motors	Non-Renewable Cartridge Type of Fuse / Renewable Link Knife-Blade Type of Fuse	Properly applied fuse carries 110 % full-load current indefinitely. At 150 % full-load current, fuse link melts and breaks circuit in specified time in accordance with rating.
2. *Instantaneous Magnetic Relay.* Protects against high overloads. Usually calibrated to trip instantaneously at a current above motor peak starting current. Interrupting capacity of line contactor determines maximum current that can be interrupted safely.		Current through coil produces force tending to lift armature and to break contacts. Weights or springs opposing armature movement determine current value at which relay instantly trips.
3. *Time-delay Magnetic Relay.* Protects running motor against sustained currents only slightly above full-load current. Dashpot or other damping means prevents tripping on peak starting current or momentary high overloads.		Addition of dashpot to No. 2 relay prevents tripping on starting or momentary high currents. Delay period is inversely proportional to sustained overload current. De-energization of power circuit after relay operation permits instant return of armature. Relay may be designed for closing or resetting contacts automatically, manually, or electrically. Number of turns and current capacity of coil determine specific rating.

* This table was prepared by R. B. Immel, design engineer, and was published in *Product Engineering.* See this publication for more details.

TABLE 23-1. RELAY CLASSIFICATION (*Continued*)

I. Overload protection

Type and application	Mechanical construction	Principle of operation
4. *Deion Boric Acid Power Fuse.* Used with low interrupting capacity switches on a.c. circuits to obtain high interrupting capacity. Installation of single circuit breaker of equal capacity and disconnecting means usually costs 20 to 50% more. Fuse is usually arranged to serve also as a means of disconnection. Links are renewable in ratings of 7.5, 15, 23, and 34.5 kv. with interrupting capacities of 0.45, 0.75, 1.0 and 1.2 million kva., respectively.	Spring Pin prevents twisting fuse link Plunger Boric acid Fibre tube Auxiliary fuse wire Strain element Main fuse Ferrule Gap Disk	At certain current value, main fuse link burns out and releases plunger, which pulls a.c. arc through boric acid in center of tube. Auxiliary fuse wire interrupts small arc. Larger arc is extinguished by deionizing action of water vapor, which is produced by reaction between arc and boric acid, when deionization of air medium exceeds rate of ionization by the arc.
5. *Thermal Overload Relay.* Protects against sustained overload currents at 115 to 125% full-load motor current to values slightly exceeding locked rotor current. Usually ideal for running protection because thermal lag prevents tripping on starting or momentary high currents. Two separate relays or a combination relay with two or more current elements are usually employed on three-phase a.c. circuits to protect all phases and prevent the motor operating on single phase. Relay must have fuse or circuit-breaker protection against short circuits.	SINGLE POLE BIMETALLIC DISK TYPE THERMAL OVERLOAD RELAY Moving contact Stationary contact Insulation base Heater Normal bimetallic disk position Tripped bimetallic position TWO-POLE THERMAL RELAY Insulated operating rod Stationary contact Moving contact Heater Normal bimetal position Contact snap spring Contact snap spring tripped position Bimetal tripped position	Heat expands one side of bimetallic disk or strip more than the other, thus causing warping or deflection, which will make or break a contact. Since deflection of flat strip is slow, a quick-acting contact mechanism is usually employed to prevent burning of contacts. Disk-type elements reverse convexity suddenly. Tripping time is inversely proportional to sustained overload current. Cooling rate of bimetal determines times for reset. Relays may have automatic or manual reset.
6. *Thermal-melting Alloy Relay.* Gives inverse time limit protection against sustained overload. Usually designed for manual reset since there is no automatic force available for resetting.	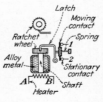 Latch Moving contact Ratchet wheel Spring Alloy metal Stationary contact Shaft Heater	Ratchet wheel and shaft, to which torque is applied through spring latch, are restrained from rotating by low-melting alloy in bearing box. Melting of alloy at predetermined temperature produced by heating coil when sustained overload current occurs, permits contacts to open. Resetting awaits refreezing of alloy. All friction is overcome by use of a strong operating spring.

TABLE 23-1. RELAY CLASSIFICATION (*Continued*)
I. Overload protection

Type and application	Mechanical construction	Principle of operation
7. *Instantaneous Magnetic-trip Circuit Breaker.* Air circuit breakers have higher interrupting current capacity than most contactors. They may be considered a combination of overload relay and circuit-opening device. They are often made for a multiplicity of main circuits and may be equipped with various operating and tripping mechanisms.	OPEN POSITION *Arcing tips* A · *Stationary contacts* *Moving contacts* *Manual operating handle* *Trip pin* *Iron frame* *Coil* *Spring* · *Adjustable armature stop* *Armature*	Magnetically actuated tripping pin opens toggle-held arcing contact and main current-carrying contacts at specified overload current.
8. *Time-delay Magnetic-trip Circuit Breaker.* Air circuit breakers with dashpot damping are applied widely on d.c. and low-voltage a.c. circuits. Dashpot permits closer setting for tripping current because momentary or starting current peaks will not trip breaker. Oil circuit breakers, whose mechanisms and arc-quenching principles differ from those shown, are usually applied to high-voltage and high-power a.c. circuits.	CLOSED POSITION A · *Toggle links* *Latch* B *Fluid* *Piston* *Dashpot*	Addition of dashpot on circuit breaker delays tripping time in inverse proportion to sustained overload current. Illustrated breaker-mechanism contacts cannot be held closed manually on high currents, as the tripping device will operate regardless of whether breaker handle is held or is free. This mechanism is called "trip free."
9. *Thermal and Magnetic-trip Circuit Breaker.* Combined inverse time-delay thermal and instantaneous magnetic-trip protection is obtained by a relatively simple, low-cost, and small-sized circuit breaker for low-voltage a.c. and d.c. circuits. Frequently applied to line-starter and similar apparatus for overload and short-circuit protection and disconnect-switch service. Capable of interrupting 5,000 to 10,000 amp. Single- and multiple-pole assemblies are available.	OPEN POSITION *Operating handle* *Springs* · *Bimetal* *Shunt* *Contact-bearing* A · B *Stationary contact* · *Armature latch* *Arcing grids* · *Moving latch* CLOSED POSITION A	Contacts are closed by handle, which is connected to moving contact by a biasing spring. Thermal overload protection is provided by bimetal element, which moves trip latch when sufficiently heated. Instantaneous magnetic trip for predetermined high currents is provided by series coil and electromagnet. When latch is made ineffective by thermal or magnetic action, contact arm bearing moves to such a position that the contact is opened by biasing spring.

TABLE 23-1. RELAY CLASSIFICATION (*Continued*)

I. Overload protection

Type and application	Mechanical construction	Principle of operation
10. *Thermal and Magnetic Relay.* Used to protect d.c. motors against overload. Delay of thermal element before opening of control contacts is inversely proportional to current for low and medium overloads of 120 % or more of full-load motor current. Magnetic element trips contacts instantaneously on high overload currents of 200 % or higher.	Moving contact / Insulated operating rod / Iron frame / Stationary contact / Vertical armature for inst. trip / Springs / Coil / Horizontal armature for thermal trip / Iron core / Invar heater 1—2 RELAY TRIPPED THERMALLY B 1—2 RELAY TRIPPED MAGNETICALLY B	Thermally actuated armature is normally held by spring and magnetic attraction of invar heater carrying motor current. Heater magnetism is lost at about 465°F. and armature is attracted to magnetized frame, thus opening control contacts. Separate magnetically actuated armature operates instantly on higher current. Thermal relay must be adjusted to operate at 12 to 20 % above motor current. Magnetic trip may be adjusted to operate at 200 to 600 % full-load current.
11. *Transformer-type Thermal Relay.* Current element withstands more severe overload and short-circuit currents than some other thermal relays. Can be applied only to a.c. circuits; therefore, usually built with two poles. Trips at specified value of primary ampere turns. The construction shown automatically compensates for ambient temperature.	Spring Moving contact / Latch / Bimetal / Iron punchings / A B Primary winding / Secondary winding	Bimetal element is deflected upward by heat produced by secondary transformer current, which is determined by number of turns and current capacity of primary coil. Illustrated relay is compensated for ambient temperature changes by upper bimetal element, which neutralizes deflections of heated element caused by ambient temperature.
12. *Inductive Thermal Relay.* Especially suitable for oil immersion. With automatic reset it should be used only for protecting low-voltage protection circuits. For two-wire control circuits, only the manual reset or an auto-reset relay plus a reset relay should be used, the latter serving to "lock out" the control when an overload occurs.	Insulated housing / Bimetal / Stationary contact / Spring / A Moving contact / B contact / Copper tube / Coil / Iron core	Copper tube inside coils and around an iron core acts as a short-circuited secondary of transformer. Heat generated in tube, which is proportional to coil current and number of turns, is transmitted to bimetal element, causing it to deflect and open control contacts when damaging overloads occur.

TABLE 23-1. RELAY CLASSIFICATION (*Continued*)

I. Overload protection

Type and application	Mechanical construction	Principle of operation
13. *Inductive Melting-alloy Relay.* Applicable only to a.c. circuits and usually has manual reset. Differs from No. 6 only in method of heating alloy metal. Relay is adjustable within certain limits for each coil.	Ratchet wheel, Moving contact, Alloy metal, Stationary contact, Copper tube, Spring, 1, 2, A, B, Adjustable core, Coil, Iron frame	Heat from inductively heated copper tube is transmitted to low-melting alloy around shaft of ratchet wheel. Melting of alloy at predetermined temperature produced by sustained overload current in coil permits spring to rotate ratchet wheel and open contacts. Heat generated in tube may be varied by changing position of core, thus varying the magnetic flux in the tube.
14. *Thermostatic Disk.* Protects against overheating of motors when caused by such conditions as too-frequent starting, sustained or frequent overloads, high ambient temperature, ventilation failure or abnormal voltage. Additional overload apparatus must be used if protection is required against stalling and phase failure. Bimetallic disk is usually mounted on frame of squirrel-cage motor and on winding of synchronous wound rotor or d.c. motors. It may open power circuit by means of a contactor or close an alarm circuit.	Thermostatic disk applied to squirrel cage motor. Bimetallic disk, Moving contact, 1, 2, Insulation, Motor frame, Stationary contact. Thermostatic disk applied to windings of d-c, wound rotor, or synchronous motor. Steel housing, 1, 2, Copper heat conducting strip, Motor winding	Principle explained for No. 5. Actual motor heat rather than that produced by heating coil actuates bimetallic disk. Resetting awaits cooling of motor frame or winding.

II. Overload relay accessories

1. *Saturating Inductive Shunt.* Connected in parallel with heater of a.c. thermal overload relay to increase tripping time during starting of high inertia loads and to protect heater from high overload current. Less expensive than a current transformer.	 Iron punching Winding A B	When thermal overload relay heater carries rated current, potential drop across heater is below saturation voltage of reactor and very small current is diverted from heater. Reactor saturates at high overcurrents and a large current is shunted through it. Winding current capacity and number of turns determine rating.

TABLE 23-1. RELAY CLASSIFICATION (*Continued*)

II. Overload relay accessories

Type and application	Mechanical construction	Principle of operation
2. *Saturating Current Transformer.* Used to extend operating range of a.c. thermal overload relay heater, to increase tripping time, and to protect heater against high overload current.	*(diagram: Primary winding A B, Iron frame, Secondary winding E F)*	When primary current is low, secondary or heater is directly proportional to ratio of primary to secondary winding turns. High primary current saturates iron core and ratio of secondary to primary current diminishes.

III. Overvoltage

1. *Instantaneous Relay.* Applied to circuits and equipment where an increase in voltage over normal or rated voltage may damage electrical apparatus or affect output of driven machinery.	*(diagram: Moving contact, Insulated operating rod, Stationary contact, Coil, Iron frame, Non-magnetic armature guide, Armature, Adjustable armature stop)*	At normal voltages magnetic attraction between armature and frame is insufficient to lift armature and open control contacts. At a voltage determined by armature stop setting, armature is lifted to break contact circuit. This voltage depends directly upon the distance between armature and frame core.
2. *Inverse Time-delay Relay.* Operates only on sustained peak voltages and will not interrupt service on momentary overvoltages. Voltage relays may be used to interlock a.c. and d.c. power supplies when both are used on the same controller. The induction type of relay is for a.c. application only.	*(diagram: Moving contact, Stationary contact, Operating pin, Aluminum disk, Permanent magnet, Punching)*	Operates on induction principle for a.c. service only. Main potential coil is below aluminum disk. Upper two windings are energized by auxiliary coil on main pole. Interaction of magnetic fields from these coils produces torque to rotate disk and operate contacts when voltage is high. Field of permanent magnets delays disk rotation.

IV. Undervoltage

1. *Instantaneous Relay.* Applied to a.c. or d.c. controllers to prevent motors from operating on reduced voltage, which may affect motor speed or torque characteristics. May be adjusted to release armature, or to "drop out" at a voltage near the "pickup" voltage, at which magnetic force closes armature.	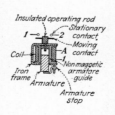 *(diagram: Insulated operating rod, Stationary contact, Moving contact, Coil, Iron frame, Non-magnetic armature guide, Armature, Armature stop)*	Operation is similar to instantaneous overvoltage relay but has make instead of break control contacts. Since dropout voltage is almost the same as pickup voltage, relay may be used to prevent starting or operating on a predetermined undervoltage.

TABLE 23-1. RELAY CLASSIFICATION (*Continued*)

IV. Undervoltage

Type and application	Mechanical construction	Principle of operation
2. *Inverse Time-delay Induction Relay.* This relay guards against sustained undervoltages. Where circuit breakers or latched-in contactors are used, it will deenergize control circuit before voltage becomes too low to operate tripping solenoids of circuit breaker. Control circuits may be arranged so that it is impossible to start a motor unless voltage is correct.	Operating pin Spring Moving contact / Aluminum disk Stationary contact / Permanent magnet / Punching	Operation is similar to overvoltage type except for control contact. By means of slide-wire resistor, disk torque may be adjusted to close control contacts at a predetermined voltage and to release them when voltage drops. Rotation of disk through field of permanent magnets provides inverse time characteristics

V. Polarity control

Type and application	Mechanical construction	Principle of operation
1. *Directional Relay.* In many electrochemical processes, a reversal of current may cause damage even if the current is small or of short duration. This relay operates on voltage and can prevent energization of a load circuit if its polarity is incorrect. The relay may also be used to shut down a generator if polarity is incorrect.	1—2 / 1 Coil Permanent magnet armature 3 / 2 / 1 Coil polarity correct to attract armature 3	Direction of current flow in coil either assists or neutralizes flux from permanent magnet. Armature is held in either attracted or repelled position depending upon coil polarity.
2. *Current and Voltage Relay.* An ordinary voltage or current relay, upon which two coils may be installed, may be used for current-reversal protection. Applied to a battery charging circuit, it prevents battery discharge through generator if generator stops accidentally.	Stationary contacts Moving contact / Iron frame 3 / 4 / Armature / Current or potential coils	Ampere turns produced by potential coil are sufficient to operate relay. Ampere turns produced by charging current through current coil also assist in holding relay closed. If generator voltage becomes lower than battery voltage, current reverses and tends to drive generator. Reversal of current in series coil neutralizes magnetic effect of potential coil and allows relay to open.

TABLE 23-1. RELAY CLASSIFICATION (*Continued*)
VI. Field protection

Type and application	Mechanical construction	Principle of operation
1. *Field-failure Current Relay.* Prevents starting or running of a d.c. motor with open field circuit, since coil or coils are connected in series with motor field. On adjustable-speed motors, coils must be selected so that relay will operate on minimum field current and coils will not overheat on maximum field current.		Current passing through field, which is in series with coils, operates relay so that control circuit is effective. If field current fails, relay is deenergized and control circuit opens.
2. *Differential Voltage Relay.* A field-failure current relay will not provide protection when all or part of the field is shorted out because short-circuit current may still cause the current relay to hold circuit closed. A voltage relay used as differential relay protects against short circuit and field loss resulting from winding failure.		Voltage coils are connected across identical sections of field in such manner that magnetic force from one coil neutralizes that from the other. Armature will not move while this condition exists. If this balance is destroyed by winding failure or short circuit, relay operates to stop motor.
3. *Ratio Differential Relay.* Protects against internal faults on a.c. apparatus by balancing current entering the apparatus against the current leaving it. Each phase has a relay. Leakage of current from one phase to another or to ground can be detected and the apparatus disconnected before serious damage occurs. Relays operate only on unbalance in the machine itself; not on system faults.		A field proportional to currents in sum coils reacts with field proportional to their difference. Resultant field tends to rotate disk. Quadrature flux is supplied to upper poles by transformer windings on each of lower poles. Current through sum coils tends to hold contacts closed. A current that is proportional to load current through difference coil will open contacts. Current through difference coil is the difference between input and output currents.

TABLE 23-1. RELAY CLASSIFICATION (*Continued*)

VI. Field protection

Type and application	Mechanical construction	Principle of operation
4. *Winding Temperature Relay.* Protects against excess heat in windings of a.c. motors. Before relay operates to stop a motor, (1) winding temperature must exceed calibrated value, (2) line current must be above normal, and (3) these two conditions must exist for a predetermined time. Relay will not operate on transient overload.	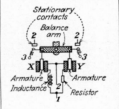	Operates on Wheatstone-bridge principle. Two fixed resistances in relay serve as two arms of bridge, while two copper exploring coils embedded in winding serve for other two arms. At normal operating temperature, no current flows in upper winding. If motor winding becomes overheated, bridge balance is destroyed and current flows in relay upper winding. Field thus produced by upper winding reacts with that of lower winding and produces a torque to rotate disk to stop motor.

VII. Frequency control

Frequency Relay. Prevents operation of induction or synchronous motor on higher or lower than normal frequency, which is proportional to motor speed.		As long as frequency for which relay is set remains constant, balance arm does not move. A change in frequency changes impedance of inductance coil and destroys magnetic balance, since any frequency change has relatively little effect on resistor circuit.

VIII. Phase reversal or failure of bearings

Phase-reversal and Phase-failure Relay. Prevents (1) change in direction of a.c. motor rotation and (2) operation on single phase. Reversal of phase rotation in a polyphase system reverses motor rotation. Failure of one phase would compel a motor to operate on single phase, with probable excess current and resultant overheating.		Operates on same principle as two-phase induction motor. Eddy currents induced into aluminum disk react with rotating field to produce a torque. Disk tends to rotate and holds contacts closed if line-phase rotation is correct. If a line phase opens when motor is running, spring force opens relay contact because single phase develops no torque. If phases become reversed, disk rotates to stop motor. If phase rotation is altered, a motor being started will run only an instant until relay operates.

TABLE 23-1.   RELAY CLASSIFICATION (*Continued*)
IX. Power factor

Type and application	Mechanical construction	Principle of operation
Power-factor Relay. Opens circuit and stops motor or re-synchronizes synchronous motor when power factor of a.c. circuit drops below predetermined value. Principal application is to synchronous-motor controllers. Provision must be made on controller to make relay ineffective during starting period, as power factor is very low.	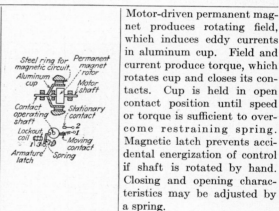	When voltage and current are in phase, their magnetic fields produce no torque to rotate aluminum disk. Torque from the two fields is proportional to their product times the sine of the angle between them. Relay may be calibrated to operate at 60% lagging power factor.

X. Zero speed relay

Zero Speed or Plugging Switch. Used with reversing line starter to stop a.c. motor quickly after pushing. Stop button. When rated speed of coasting motor is "plugged" down to about 40 r.p.m. by application of a voltage of such phase rotation as to produce an opposing torque, control switch opens and opposing voltage is removed. A typical device with the construction illustrated requires about ½₀ hp. when driven at 1,800 r.p.m.	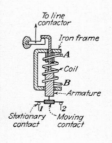	Motor-driven permanent magnet produces rotating field, which induces eddy currents in aluminum cup. Field and current produce torque, which rotates cup and closes its contacts. Cup is held in open contact position until speed or torque is sufficient to overcome restraining spring. Magnetic latch prevents accidental energization of control if shaft is rotated by hand. Closing and opening characteristics may be adjusted by a spring.

XI. Reverse-switch relay

Current Relay. Prevents closing of opposite-direction contacts as long as arc exists on the opened contacts of motor-reversing controller. On high-voltage a.c. circuits, such as 2,300 volts or higher, the arcs are more difficult to extinguish when the line contactor opens. Should opposite-direction contactor be closed while arc remains on other contactor, a short circuit will occur.	To line contactor Iron frame *A* Coil *B* Armature 1 2 Stationary contact Moving contact	Armature and moving contact mechanisms are mechanically connected to line contactor so that armature is lifted and relay contacts are opened each time contactor is operated. When contactor opens, relay armature is released and is mechanically free to fall but is held up magnetically as long as any current flows. Arc must be extinguished before relay contacts reclose.

TABLE 23-1. RELAY CLASSIFICATION (*Continued*)

XII. Flashover protection

Type and application	Mechanical construction	Principle of operation
Voltage Relay. Disconnects motor from line if flashover occurs from commutator or slip rings to ground. Usually operates instantaneously and fast enough to prevent operation of the system-protective relays and to avoid any great damage to motor.	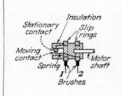	Flashovers usually occur between insulated circuits and frame of machine. Relay operates to deenergize motor power circuit when its voltage coil, which is connected to ground and machine frame, carries current from flashover.

XIII. Overspeed switch

Centrifugal Switch. Prevents overspeed of motor or may be used as a governor. Actuates control equipment to maintain constant speed of rotation. Often used to maintain constant speed on universal or series motors applied to busines machines.	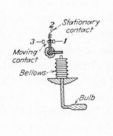	Contacts remain closed as long as spring pressure exceeds centrifugal force when device is rotated. Speed at which contacts open may be adjusted by spring or by varying mass of moving contact. Slip rings connect rotating mechanism to circuit.

XIV. Thermal protection of bearings

Thermostatic Relay. Protects bearings, resistors, cables, transformers, etc. against overheating. Thermostatic bulb may be located in material or in contact with material to be protected. Where equipment has supervision, relay usually actuates a signal to prevent unnecessary shut downs. Where supervision is not maintained, relay may be used to stop motors.		When temperature of material to be protected rises, liquid in contacting bulb volatilizes and creates pressure, which expands bellows operating toggle mechanism.

CHAPTER 24

NATIONAL CODES, INSTALLATION, AND MAINTENANCE

Two codes have been issued covering the installation of electric equipment; one has to do with fire protection, and the other with safety to persons. Because control apparatus is the medium through which persons operate electric equipment and also because of its function of arc rupturing, this class of apparatus requires particular attention from the standpoints of both fire and safety. Some knowledge of these rules is necessary for a proper understanding of the controller problem.

FIRE PROTECTION

The National Board of Fire Underwriters has issued a set of rules known as the National Electric Code. The rules of this code comprise a set of regulations that must be followed when making electric installations if such installations are to be approved by the fire insurance companies. These rules are the result of many years of experience and a large amount of research work. The National Board of Fire Underwriters maintains laboratories for research and testing. Apparatus tested by the board and meeting its requirements is listed in a publication of approved apparatus. The rules and publications can be obtained on application to the respective issuing bodies.

These rules have done great good in this country toward eliminating hazardous and flimsy construction in the design of electric apparatus and have afforded one of the incentives to maintain a high standard in electric apparatus. Any national set of rules exacts the same requirements from every manufacturer and purchaser. When properly formulated, it is fair to all and a benefit to the industry. Electrical engineers connected with manufacturing companies and customers' engineers responsible for applications have cooperated with the Underwriters in the formation of these rules, so that they represent the best combined thought in this country on the subject.

RULES FOR THE SAFETY OF PERSONS

The question of safety may be considered with reference to three classes:

1. The qualified person. This includes inspectors, repairmen, and electricians charged with the installation and maintenance of electrical apparatus.

2. Operators.

3. Other persons. This classification includes the general public and all workmen or employees in an industrial establishment who are not directly charged with either the maintenance or the operation of any particular electric equipment.

The question naturally arises as to who is a qualified person. At present, any manufacturer or owner may employ and authorize a person or persons to install, inspect, and maintain electric equipment. It is probable that, should an accident occur, the employer would be called upon to show that he had exercised care in the selection of such employees. In the future, legislation may require such persons to pass an examination and be licensed for this work.

Injury from electric apparatus may result in a number of ways, the more common being as follows:

1. Touching live parts.
2. Arc or flash.
3. Touching hot parts.
4. Explosion of fuses.
5. Gas or dust explosions.
6. Injury from moving parts of a controller.
7. Phase reversal.
8. Unexpected starting.
9. Overspeed.
10. Lack of emergency stop.
11. Overtravel.
12. Failure of power.
13. Overload.

Most of these hazards are avoided by the proper design and installations of the electric equipment.

The two hazards that most often result in accident are touching live parts and arc or flash. The arc or flash may injure a person by direct burning or by exposing his eyes to the rays of the arc. They are familiar to most electrical engineers.

There are three general methods of guarding against the first six hazards mentioned. These are

1. Enclosure.
2. Isolation.
3. Guards.

The use of enclosures for all electric apparatus is rapidly extending. In industrial plants, the controller and switching mechanism will often be found protected by cabinets or other suitable means. The authors believe that we shall soon use covers over the commutators and brushes of motors. All electrical connections should be made by means of conduit. These enclosures, of course, add something to the first cost of the equipment, but when they are properly designed, the cost is not out of proportion to the results obtained. Even where state or local laws do not require this protection, we must never forget that our industrial workers are human beings of varying ages and that many of them have the instinctive curiosity of youth and are inclined to investigate any apparatus that they do not understand.

Apparatus may be isolated so that it is accessible to qualified persons only, by one of the three following methods.

1. Installed in a separate room with a locked door.
2. Installed on a balcony, gallery, or platform so elevated and arranged as to exclude other persons.
3. Elevated at least 8 ft above the floor line or working platform.

The first method is used for large motors, generators, and switchboards where the expense of a separate room accessible only to authorized persons is justified. The other two methods are used for small motors and controllers installed about a manufacturing plant.

Electric apparatus may be guarded by partitions, screens, fences, or rails, so arranged that only qualified persons may have access to the space within reach of this apparatus. This is a convenient method of protecting large switchboards or control panels, as well as large motors and generators, where a separate room cannot readily be provided.

The National Electrical Safety Code gives a very full and complete discussion of the various forms of hazard and the protection against such hazard. This code does not go into sufficient detail for working purposes. It is, therefore, necessary to supplement this work with more detailed description and rules.

Grounding. In most cases the enclosure of the controllers or the frame of the machine should be grounded. This requirement is obvious to those versed in the art. The exception to grounding is where the apparatus is accessible only to qualified persons and where insulating mats, platforms, or floors are provided surrounding the apparatus. In such cases no grounded parts should be within reach of the person working on this electric equipment.

Disconnecting Means. It is recognized that all electric equipment requires inspection, adjustment, and some repairs, such as renewals of brushes, contacts, etc. In order that it may be safe for a qualified person to perform this work, provision should be made for entirely disconnecting the apparatus from the source of electrical supply.

Where this disconnecting means is not within sight of the person working on the apparatus, means should be provided for locking it in the open position. This is usually done by a padlock. This requirement is also necessary where the apparatus driven by the motor is undergoing repairs or adjustments. Accidents have resulted from the unexpected starting of a conveyor or other machinery when a workman was repairing it.

The unexpected starting of a motor frequently results in accident. This can usually be guarded against by the proper design of control equipment. Low-voltage protection can be provided to prevent unexpected restarting after a failure of power. The controller handle either may be removable or may be provided with a latch or lock in the Off position. The controller handle may catch in the clothes of a person working around this apparatus, or it may become entangled in other apparatus that is being drawn by on trucks, etc., and the motor be started unexpectedly. A latch will prevent this.

All control apparatus should be so arranged that the circuit to the motor will be opened and remain open in case a pilot wire or a contact should fail. The only safe arrangement of a protective circuit is to permit operation only while the circuit is intact. The breaking of a wire or failure of power from some other cause should stop the motors.

Working Space. In installing electrical apparatus, suitable working space should be provided and maintained about the equipment. Where a motor or a controller is mounted above the floor level, a suitable platform or other means of access should be provided. Although this is only a common-sense requirement, it is often overlooked.

Location of Controller. It is desirable to have the controller located so that the motor and driven machinery will be in sight of the operator during the starting period. Where an arrangement of this kind is possible, the operator can observe the apparatus during the starting period and, if an accident should occur, he can stop the motor promptly. Where the operator cannot be located so as to observe all the machinery during starting, additional precautions should be taken to protect persons who may be in or about the machinery at that time. For instance, Stop buttons may be located at various convenient points that will enable some other person to stop the machinery promptly in case of accident. Another precaution would be to arrange the controller handle or the disconnecting means so that it can be locked in the open position by any person who might have occasion to work on the machinery and would be in danger if it were accidentally started.

Resistors. Resistors are used for the purpose of starting and regulating the speed of motors. Their function is to absorb electric energy and dissipate it as heat. In order that they may function properly, they must be provided with a reasonable amount of ventilation. This means that large units should not be located in a corner of the room remote from windows or in any other restricted position. This is particularly true of resistors used for regulating the speed of motors. Unless the motor is very large or is started very frequently, the energy stored in the resistor during the starting period is small and the ventilation in the case of resistors used for starting only is not so important.

Resistors should not be mounted close to combustible material. When the resistor is mounted on the wall, an air space should be left between it and the wall. In general, it is safe to consider the resistor a mild form of stove or other heating apparatus and to take the same precautions in its installation that would ordinarily be taken in locating a stove or small heater.

MAINTENANCE OF ELECTRIC CONTROLLERS

A systematic program for inspection and maintenance should be established and closely supervised.

When the maintenance of electric controllers is neglected, expensive repairs and high losses in production will eventually occur. If, however, maintenance on controllers is given reasonable attention, the loss of production and cost of repairs will not be serious.

The following considerations are important for good maintenance.

1. The first and most important requisite of good maintenance is safety to personnel. Safety is accomplished by enclosing, guarding, or remotely locating apparatus in order to avoid personal contact and by always disconnecting all power before touching or repairing any apparatus.

2. The initial installation should be well made. All parts should have ample capacity. Installation work and wiring connections should be well done. Tests should be made to prove the adequacy of the equipment and installation before final acceptance is granted by ultimate user.

3. An adequate supply of correct renewal parts should be available for prompt use when replacements are necessary. Renewal parts should be obtained from the manufacturer of the original equipment in order to ensure that the parts are correctly made.

4. A systematic and regular plan of inspection should be arranged to keep all equipment in good operating condition. Such a plan provides Preventive Maintenance.

Preventive Maintenance. Some suggestions for good preventive maintenance are given below:

1. Personnel should be capable and alert.

2. Regular inspections of equipment should be made.

3. Inspections should be made frequently enough to prevent serious trouble. Experience will soon indicate installations upon which the service is most severe. Such installations will require most frequent inspections.

4. Inspectors should be trained and prepared to make easy and quick repairs when the need is first observed if it is possible to do so. If extensive repairs are required, the inspector should make a report and initiate plans for completing the repair work at the first opportunity.

5. Some form of record is useful to indicate which installations are most troublesome and what repairs are most frequently needed, to plan for repairs with minimum interruption of service when a major maintenance job must be done, and to know whether or not maintenance costs are excessive.

Any record that keeps the desired information in good form is satisfactory. It should be a convenient record that is easily maintained. The personnel should soon know what type of record will best serve their needs. A suggested record form is shown in Fig. 24-1. Since controllers and motors are closely associated, this record includes information for both controllers and motors.

ENCLOSURES

Enclosures Protect Personnel and Controllers. Most controllers are enclosed by some kind of metal enclosure. This may be done to protect personnel from live parts, or it may be desirable because of local conditions. The most common enclosure is a sheet-metal one that encloses all live parts. It may be ventilated or nonventilated.

Dusty Atmospheres. For cement dust, coat dust, and locations where dirty atmospheric conditions exist, dusttight enclosures will reduce the maintenance on controller parts. These enclosures require gaskets and are so made that no dust or dirt can enter them.

Wet Locations. Weather-resistant, driptight, watertight, and submersible-type enclosures are necessary where the corresponding service conditions are factors in maintenance requirements.

Hazardous Locations. For hazardous locations such as mines, refineries, cleaning plants, or wherever explosive atmospheres are present, the enclosures are of heavy construction. They are so designed that they will withstand explosions of the gases within the enclosure, without damage to the enclosure and without permitting any flames to emerge from it to cause general fires and explosions.

Oil-immersed controllers are also used to prevent explosions in dangerous locations.

Corrosive Atmospheres.   Where acid fumes or other highly corrosive atmospheres exist, maintenance work will be minimized if the controller

CONTROLLERS

NO. _____ LOCATION _____

MANUFACTURER _____ CLASS _____

HP _____ VOLTAGE _____ PHASE _____ CYCLE _____

STYLE NO. _____ SERIAL NO. _____

OPERATING COIL STYLE NO. _____

TRANSFORMER STYLE NO. _____

RESISTOR STYLE NO. _____

STYLE NO. OF CONTACTS   STATIONARY _____

                         MOVING _____

MOTOR

NO._____ LOCATION _____

MANUFACTURER _____ TYPE _____

HP _____ VOLTAGE _____ PHASE_____ CYCLE _____ SPEED _____RPM

SERIAL NO. _____ STYLE NO. _____ FRAME NO. _____

STYLE OF MOTOR BEARINGS –FRONT _____ REAR _____

PULLEY DIA. _____ FACE _____ BORE _____ KEY WAY _____

STYLE NO. BRUSHES _____ BRUSHES _____ PER SET._

CONTROLLER HISTORY

MOTOR HISTORY

Fig. 24-1.   Controller and motor histories.

parts are immersed in oil and the enclosure is protected by a suitable finish.

CLEAN CONTROLLERS REQUIRE LESS MAINTENANCE

Very few industrial controllers operate in clean places.   Oil and moisture are often present as liquids or as vapors in the air.   Dust, lint, or other materials are present as natural results of the operating conditions. These materials—dust, dirt, oil, and moisture—separately or in combination with one another all create maintenance work. They reduce insulating distance across otherwise clean and dry surfaces. They collect dust and dirt that may cause sluggish mechanical action of electrical devices.

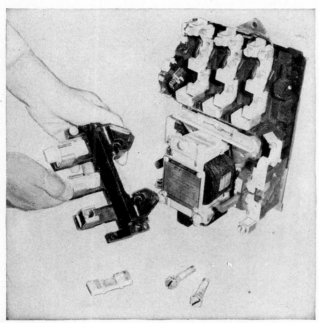

Fig. 24-2. Designs should permit contacts to be replaced easily, quickly, and with few tools.

Accumulations of dust and dirt should regularly be removed either by vacuum or by blowing with compressed air. Excessive air pressures should be avoided because sharp, small particles may be driven into some insulating materials. Special attention may be required to remove metallic dust with magnetic properties, which readily collects and adheres to the magnetized parts of the controller. Dirt, oil, and moisture are sometimes most easily removed by wiping the surfaces with cloths and suitable solvents.

Moisture due to condensation may collect within an enclosure. Drainage holes are sometimes helpful in relieving this condition. Heaters are often used to prevent moisture by condensation. The heaters are most essential when the controller is idle. When it is in operation, the coils and resistors within the enclosure will usually provide enough heat to prevent condensation.

ACCESSIBILITY

For inspection and easy repair work all parts should be made as accessible as possible. Control devices should be designed so that visual inspections can be made while the units are in service. It should be possible to renew contacts, coils, springs, and other important parts

Fig. 24-3. Coils should be easily replaced. On this design a coil is easily replaced by removing two screws for coil connections and three mounting screws.

quickly and with few tools. Installations should be arranged so that all units are accessible for maintenance work.

CONTACTS

Controllers consist of an assortment of suitable parts or devices. These devices open and close electrical circuits when the contacts are operated by either manual or magnetic means. Every time contacts open or close, they are subject to mechanical wear and electrical burning. Contact parts, therefore, are items that may require considerable maintenance, depending upon the operating conditions. The mechanical wear of contacts that operate every second may be more serious than the electrical burning.

Contact Materials. Contacts are generally made of copper or silver. Certain other materials may be used for very special applications, but such materials should not be used without approval of the manufacturer. These materials usually have higher resistance and less current-carrying ability than copper or silver. Large contacts for heavy currents are almost always made of copper. Silver sections or inserts may be used at the place where final contact is made in order to improve current-carrying ability or reduce heating. Silver contacts are generally used on the small current-carrying contacts of relays, electrical interlocks, push buttons, thermostats, pressure switches, and similar devices.

Contact Surfaces. Contacts should be kept clean. This is especially true of copper contacts, because the discoloration that soon appears on clean copper is not a good electrical conductor. It therefore increases the contact resistance and is often the cause of serious heating of contacts. When contacts are renewed, it is important to clean the new contact, if it is discolored, and the surface against which it is mounted.

The slight rubbing action and burning that occur during normal good operation will generally keep the contact surfaces clean enough for efficient service. Contacts that seldom open or close, however, will readily accumulate the thin discolored surface that may cause heating.

The dense discoloration that soon appears on clean silver is a relatively good electrical conductor. It is not so necessary, therefore, to keep silver contacts clean except for appearance.

Burned Contacts. When excessive currents are closed or opened or when contact motion is sluggish, the contact surfaces may be severely burned. If this burning causes deep pits or craters or a very roughly burned surface, both the stationary and moving contacts should be renewed.

It is not essential or even desirable to have contact surfaces entirely smooth. Slightly roughened surfaces that appear during normal good operation, if clean, provide better contact area than smooth surfaces. Therefore contacts with surfaces comparable to very coarse sandpaper may be considered in good condition.

Contacts that are dirty or excessively rough should be cleaned and smoothed with sandpaper. A fine file may be used, but care should be used to maintain the true surface shape or contour of the original contact. The designer has often spent much time and effort to determine the best contact shape. Changing the original shape by careless filing will leave high points or edges that may overheat. Emery paper should not be used to clean contacts. It is an electrical conductor. Furthermore, some particles become embedded in the contact surfaces and cause unnecessary wear.

Worn Contacts and Contact Pressures.   As contacts wear, the material in them gradually disappears because of both mechanical wear and electrical burning.   During the wearing process the contact pressures decrease.   This affects the current-carrying ability of the contacts and, if the pressure is allowed to go too low, will cause overheating of the contacts.   A small contact with suitable pressure will carry current with less heating than a large contact with little or no pressure.   Reasonable provisions are made for the wearing of contacts when the original designs are

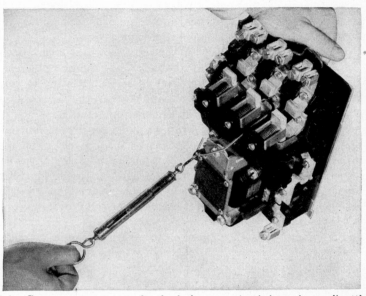

Fig. 24-4.   Contact pressures may be checked on a spring balance by reading the scale when the contacts separate.   The pull should be in a direction perpendicular to the contact surfaces.

made, but replacements will eventually be necessary.   Manufacturers will furnish information on correct contact pressures for their devices. The contact pressures may be reduced because of either worn contacts or damaged contact springs.   If contact springs have been overheated, they may be unable to provide sufficient contact pressure because the material has been weakened by the overheating.   Contact pressures should be checked and maintained within suitable limits.   Always replace both moving and stationary contacts.

Loose Contacts.   Any loose electrical connection will eventually cause trouble.   The bolts or fastening devices that hold contacts in place should always be tight.   Normal expansion and contraction of metals due to temperature changes or excessive vibration will cause bolts or nuts to become loose. Frequent checking for loose contacts is therefore advisable.

Oil-immersed Contacts. The life of oil-immersed contacts is generally shorter than that of contacts operating in air. Frequent inspection of oil-immersed contacts is therefore important.

Welding of Contacts. Very few contacts close without some bounce or rebound when they first come together. This is due to the reaction of the contact springs as they are compressed to provide the final contact pressure. When the contacts bounce, they may separate. At this time the contacts are carrying current, and even though the separation may be very small, an arc is created. This arc may cause sharp projections of burned or roughened contact surfaces to overheat and may weld, or "freeze," the contact surfaces together. Under such conditions the contacts may not open when next expected to do so. Other causes of contact welding are excessive currents when contacts close or open, insufficient contact pressure, sluggish operation either when closing or opening, and momentary closure of contacts without much or any pressure applied.

Silver contacts will weld more readily than copper ones. Well-designed contacts, properly applied, reduce this hazard to a minimum.

CONTACTOR AND RELAY COILS

Coils provide the electromagnetic pull that causes the contacts of relays and contactors to open or close. Series coils generally carry heavy currents and have relatively few turns of rather heavy copper. Shunt coils have many turns of insulated wire. They are generally impregnated in a vacuum or under pressure with insulating compounds and are covered with insulating tapes or materials. The impregnating compounds produce a firm but resilient binding material that prevents cracks when temperature changes occur. The impregnation process eliminates air pockets within the winding and makes the coil a solid mass that is better able to radiate heat and less subject to mechanical injury.

Operating Voltages. Shunt coils for a-c devices are designed to close them at 85 per cent of the rated voltage. Coils for d-c devices will close them at 80 per cent normal voltage. Any coil is expected to withstand 110 per cent rated voltage without overheating.

Open-circuited Coils. A coil with an open circuit will not operate the contactor or relay. The questionable coil should be immediately replaced by one that is known to be satisfactory. The questionable coil can then be checked for open circuits.

Short-circuited Coils. If some turns of a coil become short-circuited, the resistance of the coil will be reduced. More current then passes through the coil. The increased current results in higher operating coil temperatures and frequently causes coil burnouts.

Overvoltage. Coils should be operated at the rated voltage. Overvoltage on coils causes them to operate at a higher temperature, which unnecessarily shortens the coil life. Overvoltage also operates the contactor or relay with unnecessary force and causes more mechanical wear and bounce when closing.

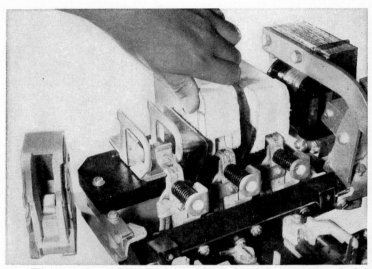

FIG. 24-5. When arc chutes have been removed for inspection or renewaal of contacts, they must be returned to proper position to make arc-rupturing parts most effective.

Undervoltage. Undervoltage on coils causes contactors and relays to operate sluggishly. The contact tips may touch, but the coils may be unable to close the contacts completely against the contact-spring pressure. Under these conditions the contact pressure is below normal and the contacts may overheat and weld together.

Closing and Operating Currents. Because of the magnetic air gap and the characteristics of a-c circuits, the coil current of an a-c contactor is much higher while the contactor is closing and the air gap is larger than after the contactor has closed and the air gap is zero. Since the closing time is short, a-c coils are designed to withstand the closed conditions. They will soon overheat if the unit is blocked or if the voltage is too low to close it and the coil remains energized with the large air gap in the magnetic circuit. Freely operating parts will avoid such coil burnouts. Direct-current coils are not subject to these conditions because the coil currents are constant at all times.

ARC-RUPTURING PARTS

When contacts are expected to open circuits carrying currents that are difficult to interrupt, they are equipped with arc-rupturing parts. The arc-rupturing parts generally surround the contacts and must be so made that they are easily moved out of position or removed entirely in order to inspect and replace both moving and stationary contacts. To be effective

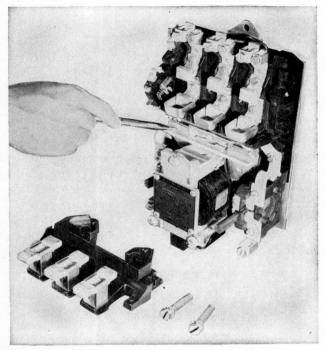

FIG. 24-6. Bearing surfaces of contactors and relays do not require any lubrication

the arc-rupturing parts must be in a definite position with respect to the contacts. Hence the arc-rupturing parts should always be returned to the proper position if removed for any reason.

SHUNTS

The fine strands of flexible shunts sometimes break where the shunt bends. The unbroken strands must then carry the entire current. If many strands break, the unbroken ones become overloaded. They then overheat and eventually burn. Frayed shunts should therefore be promptly replaced by new ones.

BEARINGS

Most bearings require some form of lubrication. Contactor and relay bearings, however, are designed to require no lubrication. If they are lubricated, the accumulation of oil and dirt may cause sluggish mechanical action that impairs the arc-rupturing qualities of the device or causes welding of the contacts.

Except for bearings of master switches, drum controllers, and similar units, no lubrication of controller parts is necessary.

The moving parts of contactors and relays should move freely in bearing surfaces without any evidence of tightness or friction. Periodic inspections to avoid friction in the moving parts is desirable.

Devices sometimes move vertically and therefore have no turning motion. The motion must be guided, and the guiding surfaces are comparable to bearing surfaces. Friction or magnetic sticking at these surfaces should be avoided.

MAGNETIC STICKING

When operating coils are deenergized, some residual magnetism remains in the magnetic circuit. This residual magnetism is sometimes strong enough to hold the device closed after the coil is deenergized. This condition occurs most frequently on small devices upon which contact spring pressures and moving parts are light. Magnetic sticking causes erratic, unsatisfactory, and sometimes dangerous operation. It is avoided by adding a nonmagnetic shim in the magnetic circuit.

DASHPOTS

Air or oil dashpots are used to retard motions. They are machined to close clearances and must be kept clean and free to move. The proper amount and kind of oil should always be kept in oil dashpots. Since the viscosity of oils changes with temperature changes, substitute oils should not be used.

NOISY CONTACTORS AND RELAYS

When the voltage on the coil of an a-c contactor or relay passes through zero, its magnetic pull, or holding power, is zero and the device starts to open. The voltage, however, is soon effective in the opposite direction, and the device is again pulled closed. This operation causes a humming noise in any a-c-operated device and a decided chattering noise in a defective unit. The otherwise objectionable chattering is eliminated and the device is kept closed by the use of a shading coil, usually embedded in the laminated magnetic circuit of the device. The shading coil produces enough out-of-phase-flux to provide holding power to maintain the device closed during the short period when the main flux is zero. Even with shading coils in use, the air-gap surfaces must be free from dirt and well fitted in order to avoid objectionable noise. Broken shading coils are ineffective and, of course, cause noisy operation.

For quiet operation of a-c contactors it is necessary to provide well-fitted surfaces at the air gap. Any dirt in this area introduces a greater

FIG. 24-7. All connections should be tight at all times. They require frequent checking to be sure they are tight. Once tight does not mean that they will remain tight.

air gap when the unit is closed, increases the duty imposed upon the shading coil, and results in noisier operation. To prevent rusting of the fitted surfaces at the air gap, these devices are often shipped with a small amount of grease or oil on them. This lubrication may cause a "seal" that makes them sticky and sluggish in opening when first put into service. These surfaces should therefore be wiped clean before the units are placed in service.

Direct-current coils are not subject to a zero voltage condition. Hence d-c-operated devices are always quiet. For this reason alternating-current-carrying contactors equipped with d-c operating coils will operate quietly.

LOOSE CONNECTIONS

Loose connections of any kind should always be avoided on electrical circuits and apparatus. An open circuit or an unreliable one may cause much lost time and production because it is often very difficult to find.

A loose connection causes a poor contact of high resistance. The copper oxide or discoloration increases the resistance of the contact surface. The higher resistance causes more heating. The increased temperature causes more oxidization and higher resistance. The effect is always cumulative, and the heating increases until the parts overheat, deteriorate, or burn.

A loose connection on a thermally operated device, such as the heater of a thermal overload relay, may, because of the external heat developed near the heater, cause the overload relay to trip and stop a motor when the motor is not overloaded.

Loose connections frequently develop on the terminals of resistors because the alternate heating and cooling of the resistors causes temperature changes great enough to loosen the bolts or nuts that clamp the connections to the resistor terminals. Excessive vibrations may also cause loose connections. The fact that a connection was once tight is no assurance that it will remain tight. Periodic inspections are advisable.

EXCESSIVE TEMPERATURES

Overheated parts always indicate trouble. It is, however, often difficult to know when temperatures are excessive.

Resistors are operated safely at 350° C rise above ambient temperature, but insulated coils are generally restricted to 85° C above ambient. Solid copper contacts are limited to a rise of 65° C, and copper bus work to 50° C rise.

Much-discolored copper parts have been or are too hot. When doubt arises, temperatures should be measured by thermometer or other means. It is not adequate to rely on the touch of the hand, because safe operating temperatures of many electrical parts are unbearable to the hand. It is best to know what the permissible temperatures are and then measure them.

Thermally operated overload relays should be in approximately the same ambient temperature as the motors they protect. If the relay is in a much higher ambient temperature than the motor, it will trip when the motor is not overloaded. If the relay is in the lower ambient temperature, it may not trip in time to protect the motor. If the ambient temperatures must be different, some compensation for the different temperatures can be made by proper selection of the overload relay heaters or by providing a relay that compensates for temperature differences.

GROUNDS

Grounds are both useful and undesirable. The desirable ones are rather easily maintained because they require only good contact connections. An unexpected ground, however, is a serious personal hazard.

Constant vigilance is required to prevent and eliminate undesirable grounds. They cause operating troubles, erratic and dangerous operating

Fig. 24-8. When in doubt about temperatures, secure a thermometer bulb against the hot part. Cover the thermometer bulb with putty or similar material, and leave it there until the temperature has risen to the maximum value. Be sure that no material is between the thermometer bulb and the hot surface.

circuits. Because of them motors may start unexpectedly, motors may not stop when they should, overload and other protective features may be made ineffective.

Grounds often occur in push-button boxes or similar confined spaces where stray strands of wire may make contact at incorrect places. They occur when wires become chafed owing to vibration on rough edges such as conduit entrances. Conduits sometimes become wet from condensation or other reasons, and the insulation on the wires becomes water-soaked and of low insulating value. Conduits should therefore be installed so that moisture within them will always drain away. It may sometimes be necessary to remove the wires, clean the conduits, and install new wiring. Clean and dry conditions always reduce maintenance.

The following points are important for good maintenance:

1. Do everything possible for the safety of personnel.

2. Initial installation should be tested and proved satisfactory before it is accepted.

3. An adequate supply of correct renewal parts should be available.

4. A systematic program of inspection and maintenance work should be instituted.

5. Enclosures should be chosen for the operating conditions.

6. Controllers should be clean and dry.

7. Contacts that are worn very thin or badly burned and pitted should be replaced. Replace contacts by pairs. Maintain correct contact pressures.

8. Contacts should be kept clean. Do not change contact shape by rough filing or grinding.

9. Contacts and all connections should be kept tight.

10. Contactor or relay bearings should not be oiled, but these units should be kept clean and with no friction in the moving parts.

11. Coils should be operated at rated voltage. Both overvoltage and undervoltage conditions are undesirable.

12. Arc-rupturing parts should be kept in good condition and in correct operating positions.

13. Frayed and worn shunts should be replaced.

14. All dashpots should be kept clean. Be sure that oil dashpots have correct oil in them.

15. Conditions that cause excessive temperatures should be corrected. Measure the temperature if in doubt about overheating.

16. Circuits should be tested periodically for undesirable grounds. If objectionable grounds exist they should be eliminated promptly.

CHAPTER 25

PAST AND FUTURE CONTROL DEVELOPMENTS

The control of electric motors is a fascinating subject requiring imagination as well as ingenuity and skill. The controller supplies the operating features not inherent in the motor; together they have made possible the universal use of the electric drive. The control engineer must examine the requirements of each application and check the performance curves of the motor in order to determine what added features are necessary for a successful drive. He must be an experienced application engineer as well as a motor control designer. The controller must automatically stop the motor if an accidental condition arises in order to protect persons and property from damage.

Control practice has developed greatly during the 50 years from 1900; some of the important items are the following:

1. Improvement due to a better understanding of arc rupturing, methods of control, and mechanical design.
2. Better design and performance of electric motors.
3. New systems and methods of control.
4. The use of adjustable-voltage control.
5. The electronic tube and magnetic amplifier.
6. The multiple or group use of motors and means for controlling them for a single process such as a continuous steel strip mill and machines producing paper.

Controllers were generally used first for series motors operating street railway cars and shunt- or compound-wound motors operating elevators and hoists. The shunt motor was also applied to pumps, fans, machine tools, and line shafting which required only "starters." These were manual controllers. When automatic acceleration was required, the time delay was obtained by a dashpot.

By 1900 other methods of automatic acceleration were developing, controlled by the counter emf of the motor or the current in the motor circuit. After 1900 some of the land marks of control development are:

1905   First successful application of "variable-voltage control" to mine hoists.

1907   First application in this country of a motor to drive the main rolls in a steel mill. Variable-voltage control was used with an automatic slip regulator to permit a flywheel to absorb the peak of the power demand.

1909   Automatic contactor control for operating the locks at the Panama Canal.

1910   Variable-voltage mine hoists were used with automatic terminal stops.

1912   Arc splitters were used for circuit rupturing.

1917   An impedance coil was used to reduce current peaks when accelerating an elevator.

1919   Adjustable-voltage control was used for marine propulsion.

1919   Adjustable-voltage control was applied to a sectional paper-machine drive.

1920   Adjustable-voltage control was applied to planer drive.

1922   Adjustable-voltage control was applied to elevators.

1922   Supervisory control was applied to the operation of remote power stations.

1924   High-speed elevators were automatically stopped at landings.

1925   The deion principle was applied to arcrupturing.

1926   Adjustable-voltage control was applied to main-line locomotives (Ford).

1932   Two passenger elevators were successfully operated in one elevator shaft.

1933   The electronic tube was being applied to many control problems.

1940   About this time the Amplidyne, Rototrol, and Regulux were developed for regulating the speed and load of motors and for other control purposes (see Chap. 12).

1950   The control engineer now has a new tool, the "magnetic amplifier." This is a static device which can be used in place of electronic tubes or dynamoelectric machines for quick and accurate motor control (see Chap. 13).

A new engineering development of this kind stimulates work in its field of application and produces a major step forward. Control engineers have had available the electronic tube and dynamoelectric amplifiers for a long time, but these devices do not have the rugged qualities of control equipment, and their use is limited. Now the saturated-core reactor has been developed into a magnetic amplifier of equal ruggedness to control and should find wide acceptance and broaden the field of motor application.

Prophecy is difficult but fascinating and sometimes useful if it is based upon experience. New developments are continually being made, some of them representing a definite departure from existing practice. All these changes must have careful consideration before they are placed on the market, as existing apparatus represents a large investment in engineering designs, tools, stock parts, printed matter, and the education of users.

The Second World War accelerated the development of new devices and methods of control which are now being made available for commercial use. The electron tube is extending its use as a supervisory means and also for power conversion from a-c to d-c power with voltage control for small adjustable-speed d-c motors. Adjustable frequency can also be obtained for a-c induction motors. Speed regulation of several d-c shunt motors which drive separate sections of a machine or mill is available from tube control and will be extended by the magnetic amplifier as it becomes better understood. Accurate speed control is receiving additional attention for some applications.

The magnetic amplifier is a new means for motor control that is just coming into use to replace tubes and dynamoelectric devices. It is rugged and has no moving parts; it may supersede other devices in the near future (see Chap. 13).

Very little attention has been given to the hydraulic speed changer (similar to the Waterbury gear) for general-purpose applications. This device consists of a series of small adjustable-stroke pumps driven by a constant-speed motor (probably a synchronous motor). The load is driven by a similar device having a constant stroke. Its speed depends upon the volume of oil delivered by the pumps. When the pumps are reversed, the receiving device also reverses.

This type of speed changer provides means for operating and reversing a load and changing its speed, all from a constant-speed synchronous motor, simply by mechanically changing the stroke and direction of the pump. A small pilot motor will effect this change and can have electron-tube or magnetic-amplifier control. The electrical problem is simple; the real work is in producing the "hydraulic gear" at a cost that will give it this market. The hydraulic drive for automobiles may point to another device for this purpose. The "package-unit" idea is being rapidly applied to the assembly of control where several motors are operated from one location. This idea is extending to the different parts of a single control such as the line contactors, the accelerating means, and the supervisory units, so that parts of a controller can be quickly replaced or repaired and the package units kept in stock.

Apparatus and systems used in telephone practice have proved useful in the supervisory part of motor control. This is particularly true where electron tubes are used as part of the control. Radio signals and response have had some use in control and are useful on a coding basis for initiating the control of motors where the installation and maintenance of wire control is difficult or where a portable master switch is used. Communication control requires only a working knowledge of this other type of equipment, and its use will be extended.

More study will be given to power-factor correction and means for reducing the short-time peak loads. This will relate more to control systems than to control units. Existing designs will continue to be simplified, to be made more reliable and more compact, and to be produced at a reduced first cost. Protection to persons is of increasing importance; this will influence control design to improve its protection against arcing and the exposure of live parts.

Improvements in details always continue, with an occasional long step forward accomplished by some departure from existing methods or equipment. Every generation has its pioneers, often in the smaller companies that require novelty to widen their distribution. Motor designs are well stabilized, but the control field continues to offer many possibilities for new methods, greater convenience, better performance, and increased protection to persons and to property.

REFERENCES

For supplementary reading, the following references are suggested:

Fox, Gordon, "Principles of Electric Motors and Control," McGraw-Hill Book Company, Inc., New York, 1924. Sets forth very clearly the information about motor performance that a control engineer should have in order to be able to evaluate the results when a motor circuit is switched in various ways.

Harwood, Paisley, B., "Control of Electric Motors," John Wiley & Sons, Inc., New York, 1936. Gives certain interesting details not included in the present book, and treats the subject from a slightly different point of view.

Heumann, Gerhart W., "Magnetic Control of Industrial Motors," John Wiley & Sons, Inc., 1947.

National Electrical Manufacturers Association. A standard publication on industrial control standards which will be very useful to anyone interested in the subject. Some extracts from it are included in this volume.

Shoults, D. R., and C. J. Rife, "Electric Motors in Industry," Chaps. IX–XI, John Wiley & Sons, Inc., New York.

Windred, G., "Electrical Contacts," Macmillan & Co., Ltd., London, 1940. A detailed discussion of many kinds of contacts with numerous references, largely to European practice.

INDEX

A

Acceleration of motor speed, 69–99
  automatic means; 1
  counter emf, 70–72
  current-limit, 72–74
  elementary example, 1–3
  frequency control, 94–96
  manual vs. automatic, 7
  magnetic-amplifier control, 96–99
  methods, 69–70
  secondary frequency, 94
  series lock-out contactor, 74–77
  series-relay, 72–74
  time-delay, 77–94
    dashpot, 77–80
    magnetic induction, 84–89
    motor drive, 81–83
    tube, 90
Accessibility of control, 404
Accident precautions, clearance around apparatus, 399
  controller in sight of motor and machinery, 399
  disconnecting means, 398–399
  emergency stop button, 399
  enclosure of apparatus, 397–398
  grounding, 398
  guards, 398
  isolation of apparatus, 397
  locking in Off position, 399
  safety rules for, 396–398
  starting unexpectedly, prevention, 399
Accidents causing injury, 397
Adjustable-speed control, for a-c motors, 106–109, 235–249
  analogy to d-c motors, 235–238
  constant-horsepower methods, 236–238
  for d-c motors, 102–103
  increased use in steel-mill applications, curve, 249
  with magnetic amplifier, 109–111, 114–118

Adjustable-speed control, with magnetic clutch, 111–114
  Method I, using rotary converter, constant horsepower, 239
  Method II, using rotary converter, constant torque, 241
  Method III, using three-phase commutator machine, constant horsepower, 241
  Method IV, using three-phase commutator machine, constant torque, 244
  Method V, using frequency changer, constant horsepower, 244
  Method VI, using frequency changer, constant torque, 246
  performance curves, 248
Adjustable-speed motors, 102–103, 106–109, 235–249
Adjustable voltage control with series-wound motor and generator, 190
Air gap in magnetic circuit of operating coil, 408
A-c controllers, 296–325
A-c motor curves of wound-rotor type, 104
Amplidyne, General Electric, 202–205
  applications, power-factor control, 205
  speed matching, 205
  voltage control, 203
  description, 202
Amplification with electronic tubes, 343
Amplifiers for motor control, 191–219, 340–356
  dynamoelectric type, 191–205
  magnetic amplifier type, 206–219
  tube amplifiers, 340–356
Arc, in air, forms oxide scale, 39
  centering, in box, 46
  more quickly extinguished by magnetic blowout, 44
  reestablishing, 44

Arc box, 45–230
Arc furnace control, 201, 212
Arc quenching, deion principle, 50–55
  under oil, 42–43
Arc rupturing, 43–44
Arc-rupturing parts, 409
Arcing horns, 47
Armature, series-resistance, 100
  shunt-resistance, 102
Automatic vs. manual controllers, 7
Autostarter (*see* Autotransformer starters)
Autotransformer starters, 308–323
  closed-circuit transition, 313–314
  distribution of current in windings, 316–317
  multipoint starting, 314
  open-circuit transition, 311–314
    danger of, 311
  underwriters' tests, 322
  use on other voltages and frequencies, 323

B

Battery, storage, to excite fields, 168–170
Bearing thermostat, 395
Bearings of contactors, 410
Blooming-mill control, 201, 211
Blowout, magnetic, 44–47
Brake shoe, 159, 160
  clearance, 160, 162
Brake wheel, 157, 159–160
Brakes, 155–166
  in a-c circuits, 158, 162
  adjustment, 160
  application, 166
  for cranes, 130, 134, 135
  in d-c circuits, 161
  dynamic (*see* Dynamic braking)
  friction, 7, 155–162
  magnet, 155–160
  magnets for, polyphase, 162
    series or shunt coils, 161
    shading coil, 156–161
    size, 158, 159
  mechanical parts, 158
  for synchronous motors, 337
  torque and wheel diameter, curve, 157
  wear adjustment, 160
Bridging transition, 226–229

C

Cam controllers, 9–10, 275–277
  blowout, 277
  contacts, 276
  handles, 277
  restricted arcing space, 277
Cascade connections, 106
Clapper type of contactors, 75–76
Classification of controllers, 7–13
Closing current of a-c contactors, 408
Codes for installation and maintenance, 396
Coil temperature, 55
Coils, connected in parallel, 36
  maintenance of, 407–408
Compensator (*see* Autotransformer starters)
Compression-type controllers, 278–279
Compression-type resistors, 256–257
Condensers connected across coils, 36
Constant speed control, with magnetic amplifiers, 109–111
  with magnetic clutch, magnetic-amplifier control, 114
  tube control, 111–114
Contactor bearings, 410
Contactors, electropneumatic, 229
  magnetic, 11–12, 22–24, 38–56
    air break preferable to oil break, 42
    arc rupturing, 43–50
    clapper type, 75–76
    lock-out type, 74–77
    pressure, 39
    rating, 54
    series-lockout type, **74–77**
    for 2,200 volts, 55
Contacts, carry more current with increased pressure, 39
  copper best material for, 38, 405
  design of, 38–44
  heat radiated by mass of metal, 38
  maintenance, 404–407
    of contactor and relay coils, 407–408
  method of testing pressure, 38
  rolling, 39
  sliding action removes scale, 38
  types of, 39
Control developments, 415–418
Control systems, automatic, 7, 11–13
  autotransformer, 308–323

Control systems, manual, 7–8
  multivoltage, 175
  series-parallel (*see* Series-parallel control)
  variable-voltage (*see* Variable-voltage control)
Controller application in, cranes (*see* Crane control)
  electric railways, 221–234
  machine tools, 150–151
    diagrams, 148–149
  printing presses, 150
  pumps, 141–145
    elevator, 145–147, 150
  steel mills, 175–190, 235–249
Controller functions, 1–7
  automatic starting, stopping, regulating speed of motor, 7
  breaking or retardation (*see* Brakes)
  controlling speed, 5
  motor load limiting, 5
  protecting operator from injury, 7
Controllers, advantages and limitations of types, 8–12
  for a-c motors, 296–325
  cam, 9–10, 275–277
  compression, 278–279
  for cranes (*see* Crane controllers)
  diagram symbols, 30
  Dinkey, 277–278
  for d-c motors, 281–295
  drum (*see* Drum controllers)
  electropneumatic, 229–234
  faceplate, 8, 14–18, 277–278
  field rheostat, 254–255
  liquid, 12, 176–177, 301–305
  magnetic-contactor (*see* Contactors, magnetic)
  maintenance of, 400–404
  manual (*see* Manual controllers)
  for squirrel-cage motors, 67–68, 305–339
  for synchronous motors, 326–339
  types of, 7–13
Corrosive atmospheres, 402
Counter emf acceleration, 70–72
Crane controllers, 121–140
  counter torque or plugging control, 128, 129, 132, 133
  for d-c motors, 121–125

Crane controllers, dynamic braking, with d-c power, 134, 135
    with unbalanced primary voltage, 136, 137
  reactor braking, 138–140
  for wound-secondary induction motors, 126–140
    eddy-current lowering brake, 130
    with magnetic amplifier control, 131
Current-limit acceleration, 72–74

D

Damper windings of synchronous motors, 326
Dashpot for time-delay acceleration, 77–80
Deion arc quencher, 50–54
Developments in control, 415–418
Diagrams, how to make, 25–37
    markings, 27–28, 31, 34
    master switch, 36
    types, control-circuit line, 25, 32
      control construction, 25
      control sequence table, 25, 31
      control wiring, 25, 32–33
      elementary, 25, 31, 35
      external, 25
  how to read, 14–24
Diaphragm pressure regulator, 140–145
Dinkey type controller, 277–278
D-c magnetic-contactor controller, 281–295
Disconnecting means, 398
Drum controllers, 8–9, 18–22, 271–275
  blowout, 274
  contact finger, 9, 273
  drum or cylinder, 271
  finger pressure, 271
  lubrication, 275
  segment, 271
  star wheel, 271
Drum-type master switch, 277, 290
Dynamic braking, 7, 162–166
  for adjustable-speed motors, 163
  aid to friction brake, 163
  for cranes, 126–141, 163
  with series motor, 163
  with shunt motor, 163
  for synchronous motors, 337

Dynamic braking, for variable-voltage control, 162–166
Dynamoelectric amplifiers, 191–205

E

Edge-wound resistor, 251–252
Electron-tube control, 340–352
  for a-c motors, applications, 347
  applications to industry, 348, 351–354
  compensating for *IR* voltage drop, 344
  converting from a-c to d-c power, 340
  current-limit control, 346
  limitations, commutation, frequency, heating, and speed range, 349–350
  other uses, 351
Electropneumatic control, 229–234
  advantages and limitations, 232
  contactor, 229
Elevator control, 197–200
Elevator pumps, 145–147, 150
Emergency stop, 337
Enclosures around control, 401
  for dusty atmospheres, 401
  for fire protection, 398
  for hazardous locations, 401
  for protection to persons, 398, 401
  for wet locations, 401

F

Faceplate controllers, 8, 14–18, 277–278
  diagrams, 14–16
  Dinkey type, 277–278
Fan and pump control, 114
Field control, failure protection, 382–383
  maintenance, 400–401
Field-control regeneration, 168–171
Field-frequency method of starting synchronous motors, 319–331
Field rheostat, 254–255, 287
Fire control, code, 396
  location of resistors, 400
  National Electric Code, 396
Float switch for pumps, 142, 143, 146
Flywheel, determining size, 185
  using with adjustable speed sets, 183
Frequency and voltage applied to a-c motor, secondary, 235–249
Frequency control for acceleration, 94–96
Friction brake, 155–162

Functions of control, 1–7
Fuses as a protective device, 368–369
Future control developments, 415–418
  telephone practice, 417–418
  use of hydraulic gear, 417

G

Generators and motors in series, 185–190
Grid resistor, description, 250–252
  spacing of grids, 258–260
  and heating, 258
Grounding, 398
  of controllers, 398
Grounds, 413
Guarding, of controllers, 398
  of persons, 397

H

Heating, of coils, 55
  of contacts, 54
  of resistors, 258
High frequency with electronic tubes, 355
Hoist control (*see* Crane control)
Hunting in synchronous motors, 326

I

Impedance starting for a-c motors, 324–325
Injury to persons, by accident, 397
  precautions, 397
Inspection records, 402
Installation, rules for, 396–414
Isolation of controllers, 399

L

Light-ray control, 355
Limit-master switch, 153
Liquid controllers and rheostats, 12–13, 301–305
  advantages of, 305
  illustration, 301
Liquid-slip regulator, 176–177
Load of a mine hoist, 184
Location of controllers, 399
Lock-out contactors, 74–76
Low-voltage protection, 291, 381
Low-voltage release, 291

M

Machine tools, 150–151
  diagrams, 148–149
Magneclutch, 115–120
  cross section, 117
  dimensions, 119
  performance curves, 118
Magnet brake, 155–160
Magnetic-amplifier control, 206–220
  accelerating motors, 96–99
    a-c motors, 98
    d-c motors, 97, 99
  arc furnace control, 201, 212
  blooming mill, 201, 211
  constant speed control, 109–111
  definition, 206
  load control, 210
  lowering a crane load with a clutch, 131
  magnetic clutch, 114–118
  motor starters, 206–211
  normal and self-saturating control, 211
  paper machine control, 214, 215
  pressure regulator, 145
  principle of operation, 206
  remote control, 361
  self-saturating amplifier, 210
  skip hoist control, 213
  slip regulator for wound-secondary a-c
    motor, 180
  speed control, 209
  theater dimmer, 208, 211, 213
  transductor, 217–218
  types of core, 207
  variable-voltage control, 208
Magnetic blowout, 44–47
Magnetic clutch, adjustable-speed, 111–
  114
Magnetic-contactor controller, Magnetic
  contactors (*see* Contactors, magnetic)
Magnetic time-delay acceleration, 84–89
Magnets for brakes (*see* Brakes, magnets
  for)
Maintenance, of contacts, 404–408
  of controllers, 400–404
  of equipment, 396–414
  records of, 402
Manual controllers, 271–280
  advantages and limitations, 279
  maintenance in the field, 400–401

Manual controllers, overload protection,
  293, 367
  (*See also* types of controllers, as Cam
    controllers; Drum controllers)
Master switches, drum-type, 277, 290
  float-type, 142, 143, 146
  grounded circuit, 37
  limit-master, 153
  pressure-gauge, 144, 145
  push-button type, 291, 292
  in steel mill, 187
  track-master, 153
  for two panels, sneak circuits, 36–37
Mechanical braking, 155–166
Mine locomotive diagram, 150, 151
Motor-generator system, 175–185
Motor speed-torque curves, 100–108
Motors (*see* types of motors, as Adjustable-speed motors, and specific subjects, as Starting of motors)
Multiple connection of d-c motors and
  generators in series, 185–190
Multivoltage-control systems, 175

N

National codes, 396–414
National Electric Code, 396
Noisy contactors, 410–411

O

Oil-immersed contactors, 42–43, 308, 407
Open-circuit transition, 223
Operating currents in coils, 408
Overhauling of control, 400
Overheating, 412
Overload protection, 293–295
  feeder circuits, 367
  motor circuits, 367
  table, 385
Overload relays, 369–381
  inverse-time-element, 372
  resets, 370
  table of, 385–390
  thermal trip, bimetal, 371–373
    induction, 374–379
    melting alloy, 377
  time-element, 372–381
    adjustment of, 372
Overvoltage, 408

P

Paper-machine control, with magnetic amplifiers, 214, 215
with electronic tubes, 352–354
Phase-failure protection, 382–383
Phase-reversal protection, 381–382
Pilot motor, time-delay acceleration, 81–83
Plugging, 164–166
Pneumatic contactor, 229
Power-factor correction, 205, 339
Precautions against accidents (*see* Accident precautions)
Pressure-gauge master switch, 144, 145
Pressure regulator, 140–145
Printing-press controllers, 150
Protection from, failure of motor field, 382
overload (*see* Overload protection)
phase failure, 382–383
phase reversal, 381–382
voltage failure, 381
Protective devices, 367–395
table, 385–395
(*See also* Relays)
Pull-out protection, 335–336
Pump controllers, 141–145
Pumps, elevator, 145–147, 150
Push buttons, 292

R

Railway control, 221–234
Records of inspection and test, 402
Rectifiers, 218–220
copper oxide, 219
diagram, 220
selenium, 219
Regeneration, 167–174
definition, 167
field-control, 168–171
load as a generator, 167
mechanical brake holds load, 168
overloads, 169–171
series-motor control, 280
voltage-control, 171–174
using a booster and motor generator set, 172
Regulators, amplifiers, 191–205
compounding exciter, 191, 192

Regulators, constant-power input, 183
constant-pressure, 140–145
motor speed-slip regulator, 176–178
Regulex, Allis-Chalmers, 193–202
Rototrol, Westinghouse, 192–193
Regulex amplifiers, 193–202
blooming mill, 201
calender dual, 198
hoist control, 200–201
Relays, current limit, 367
field protection, 383
low-voltage, 381
overload (*see* Overload relays)
phase-failure, 382–383
phase-reversal, 381–382
table, 385–395
Remote control, 357–366
using selsyn system, 357, 358
using supervisory system, 358–366
Resistance, calculations, 263–270
definition of, 250
in series with motor field, 185–190
speed-reduction formula, 263
for starting motors, 265
Resistors, 250–270
boss width of grids, 260–261
calculations, 263–270
care in selecting location to prevent fires, 263, 276
compression type, 256–257
connected in coil circuit, 36
continuous vs. intermittent duty, 266
crane service, 261
definition of, 250
disk type, 267
edge-wound, 251–252
field rheostats, 254–255, 287
grid type, 250–251
heat radiation, 265
limiting temperature, 263
location, 263–269
rating, 264
Ribohm type, 255
service application, 265
speed-reduction formula, 263
time-temperature curves of grids, 258–262
tube type, 253
Vitrohm type, 253–254
wire-wound, 256

Rheostats, definition of, 258
  field-control, 254–255, 287
  liquid type, 151–154, 176–178, 300
  (*See also* Resistors)
Ribohm resistor, 255
Rolling contacts, 40
Rototrol amplifiers, 193–202
  arc furnace, 198
  blooming mill, 197, 201
  elevators, 197–200
  with Wheatstone bridge connections, 193
Rudder control with magnetic amplifier, 361

S

Safety to persons, 396–397
Safety codes, 396–397
Safety devices, 367
Selsyn system, 357–358
Series, motors and generators in, 185–190
Series lock-out contactor, 74–77
Series-parallel control, 221–229
  advantages and limitations, 221–222
  electropneumatic control, 229–234
  method of transition, 222
    bridging, 226
    open-circuit, 223
    shunt, 224–226
Series-relay acceleration, 72–74
Series-wound motors, safe load not less than 25 per cent, 101
Shoe brake, 157
Short circuits, 56
Shunt-field protection, 383–384
Shunt transition, 224–226
Shunts, 409
Silver-plated contacts, 407
Slip regulators, 176–183
  diagrams, 176–179
  liquid type, 177–182
  magnetic-amplifier type, 180
  performance curves, 183
Sneak circuits, 38
Speed control, adjustable-speed magnetic clutch, 111–114
  for a-c motors, adjustable-speed, 106–109
    single-phase secondary resistor, 108
    varying-speed, 104–105

Speed control, constant speed with magnetic amplifier, 109–111, 114–118
  for d-c motors, adjustable-speed, 102–103
    series and shunt resistors, 100–102
    variable-voltage control, 103–104
    varying-speed, 100–102
  magneclutch, 118–120
  (*See also* Adjustable-speed control; Voltage control of d-c motors)
Speed-torque curves, 100–108
Squirrel-cage motors, starting, 67–68
  with autotransformer, 308–325
  with full-voltage starter, 305–307
Starting-current peaks, 58, 59
Starting of motors, characteristics, 57
  mathematical analysis, 65
  number of steps, 57–68
  tests, 57–68
  zero-field strength, 61
Steel mill, controller, 175, 185–190
  master switch, 187
Storage battery to excite fields, 168–170
Supervisory control, 358–366
Switches, cam, 276
  drum, 9
  master (*see* Master switches)
  pressure-regulator, 143
  push-button stations, 292
Synchronizing and pull-out protection, 335–336
Synchronous-motor control, 326–339
  correcting power factor, 339
  emergency stop, 337
  methods of acceleration, 326–329
    field-frequency, 329–332
    slip-cycle impedance, 335
    speed-and-time, 333–335
  reduced-voltage starting, 329, 336–337
  resynchronizing, 335–336
  starting similar to an induction motor, 326
  synchronizing, 328

T

Terminal markings, 30
Time element for overload trip, 372–380
Time-element method of acceleration, 77–94

Torque, maximum or pull-out, 104–105
  starting, obtaining in synchronous
    motors, 326
  varies as the square of the voltage, 105
Track-master switch, 153
Transductor type of magnetic amplifier,
  217–218
Transformer starters, 296–325
Transition in electric-railway control,
  222–229
Two-speed a-c motors, 107

U

Undervoltage protection, 291, 381
Undervoltage release, 291
Undervoltage use, 408

V

Variable-voltage control, in d-c motors,
  103–104
  in dynamic braking, 162–166
  in elevators, 197–200
  in steel mills, 189–190

Varying-speed motors, a-c, 104–106
  d-c, 100–102
Vitrohm resistor, 253–254
Voltage control, with amplifiers, 191–197
  Amplidyne, 202–205
  Rototrol and Regulex, 193–202
  for d-c motors, 175–190
    motor-generator system, 175–185
      flywheels, 179
      method of reversing, 176
    motors and generators in series, 185–
      190
    series-wound exciter, 190
  in steel mills, 189–190
  in regeneration, 171–174
Voltage regulation, 56

W

Water rheostat, 151–154, 176–178, 300
Welding of contacts, 407
Working space, 399
Wound-secondary induction motors, con-
  trollers for, 126–140, 296–305